ROYAL DOULTON BUNNYKINS

THIRD EDITION

A CHARLTON STANDARD CATALOGUE

By
Jean Dale
Louise Irvine

W.K. Cross
Publisher

TORONTO, ONTARIO ❖ PALM HARBOR, FLORIDA

COPYRIGHT NOTICES

ROYAL DOULTON (U.K.) LIMITED:

Canadian Catalogue in Publication Data
The National Library of Canada has Catalogued this publication as follow:

The Charlton standard catalogue of Royal Doulton bunnykins

Annual.
1st ed. ([1999])-
ISSN 1485-1008
ISBN 0-88968-282-8 (3rd edition)

1. Porcelain animals-Catalogs. 2. Royal Doulton figurines-Catalogs.
3. Children's china (Porcelain)-Catalogs. I. Charlton Press II. Title: Bunnykins.

NK4660.C515   738.8'2'029442   C98-900623-9

Printed in Canada
in the Province of Ontario

The Charlton Press

www.charltonpress.com

EDITORIAL

Editors	Jean Dale
Editorial Assistant	Susan Cross
Graphic Technician	Davina Rowan
Colour Technician	Marina Tsourkis
Cover Illustration	Eskimo Bunnykins

ACKNOWLEDGMENTS

The Charlton Press wishes to thank those who have assisted with the third edition of Royal Doulton Bunnykins. Also, we would like to thank Louise Irvine for her work on this edition. Louise is an independent writer and lecturer on Royal Doulton's history and products and is not in anyway connected with the pricing in this guide.

Special Thanks

Our thanks go to the staff of Royal Doulton, who have helped with additional technical information, especially **Fiona Hawthorne**, General Manager, Director and Relationship Manager (U.K.); **Sara Williams**, Product Manager, Royal Doulton, (U.K.); **David Lovatt**, Marketing Communications Design Manager (U.K.); **Josie Hunt** and **Julie Tilestone**, Doulton & Company Doulton Direct (U.K.); **Julie Mountford**, International Collectors Club (U.K.); **Chetna Luhar**, Product Manager, Royal Doulton Collectables (U.K.); **Marion Proctor**, Marketing Manager (Canada); **Janet Drift**, Director of Retail Sales (U.S.A.)

Contributors to the Third Edition

The publisher would also like to thank the following individuals and companies who graciously supplied photographs or information or allowed us access to their collections for photographic purposes:

Collectors and Dealers

Jane Arnold, Cheshire, England; **Joan and Bob Barwick**, Ontario, Canada; **Karen Blaiklock**, England; **Jane Buchanan**, Canada; **Ken Clifton**, Stoke-on-Trent, England; **Cathy Gunn**; **Tom Moran**, Pennsylvania, U.S.A.; **Robert Neilsen**, Roundabout Antiques, Queensland, Australia; **Scott Reichenberg**, North Smithfield, RI, U.S.A.; **Pat Sage**, Unionville, Ontario, Canada; **Leah Selig**, Rabbiting On, Merrylands, NSW, Australia; **Ken Sharpe**, Quebec Canada; **Darrell Twigg**, Wales U.K.

A SPECIAL NOTE TO COLLECTORS

We welcome and appreciate any comments or suggestions in regard to "Royal Doulton Bunnykins," a Charlton Standard catalogue If any errors or omissions come to your attention, please do not hesitate to write to us, or if you would like to participate in pricing or supply previously unavailable data or information, please contact Jean Dale at (416) 488-1418, or E-mail us at **chpress@charltonpress.com**.

DISCLAIMER

While every care has been taken to ensure accuracy in the compilation of the data in this catalogue, the publisher cannot accept responsibility for typographical errors.

The Charlton Press

Editorial Office
P.O. Box 820, Station Willowdale B
North York, Ontario, Canada. M2K 2R1
Telephone: (416) 488-1418 Fax: (416) 488-4656
Telephone: (800) 442-6042 Fax: (800) 442-1542
E-mail chpress@charltonpress.com   www.charltonpress.com

HOW TO USE THIS CATALOGUE

THE LISTINGS

The "Charlton Standard Catalogue of Royal Doulton Bunnykins" is divided into four chapters, the first being devoted to Bunnykins tableware and the fourth, to modern Bunnykins figurines. It is within these two chapters that we will outline how the listings function.

The tableware chapter has the Bunnykins designs listed in alphabetical order, beginning with the ABC Theme and ending with Xmas Menu. Within the design layout is a shape/price table incorporating, on the left side of the table, a vertical listing of the different shapes on which the design appears. To the right of the shape column is the price column indicating a level at which collectors may expect to see that design/shape trade.

Within these columns are two sub-listings that must be understood to make the catalogue the useful tool that it is intended to be.

The Barbara Vernon designs carried her facsimile signature, unless, of course, the shape was too small and the signature was therefore dropped. These signatures were in continuous use until the early 1950s. As a result, a shape that was in production from 1934 to the mid-1950s will appear in the shape column as with signature and without signature. The demand is much greater for shapes with the facsimile signature and this necessitates a two-tier pricing structure.

The second sub-listing is the copy printed in bold type, indicating a design that is current, on a shape that is current, and that is still being produced by Royal Doulton. The lines that are not bold indicate shapes that have been discontinued.

In the pricing tables of the tableware section, we have listed all the shapes that are known to exist with a specific design. There is a good possibility that more shapes exist, and these will be added to the design table in future editions as they become known.

The list of Bunnykins figurines is simple by comparison. Royal Doulton numbered the Bunnykins figurines in chronological order, as they were issued, starting with DB1 and carrying on to the present, which is DB313.

STYLES AND VERSIONS
Tableware

All designs are named by the designer and, within any design, modifications may be needed so that the design may better fit the shape. As designs are changed or modified, it is necessary to bring our classifications to bear on Bunnykins tableware.

Styles: If the same design name is used at various times by different designers, the earlier issue then becomes Style One and the latter, Style Two.

Versions: The design may have one or more elements removed from the main design.

Variations: The design has all elements intact but minor modifications have been made to allow the design to better fit the shape

Figurines

All listings include the modeller, where known, and the name of the animal figurine, designer, height, colour, dates of issue and discontinuation, varieties and series.

Styles: If the same design name is used at various times by different designers, the earlier issue then becomes Style One and the latter, Style Two.

Versions: Versions are modifications in a major style element.

Variations: Variations are modifications in a minor style element. A change in colour is a variation

SIGNATURES

A second word about the facsimile signature of Barbara Vernon is needed. Designs discontinued by 1952 should all carry the Barbara Vernon signature. However, there is the possibility that the signature was cut a way from the transfer when the shape was too small to accommodate it, and the piece was issued without it

While the absence of the signature affects the value of a piece, we consider that the value would be in the range of 75 percent of the catalogue price listed.

SHAPES

Some shapes will not carry a Bunnykins design. For example, the Stratford teacup will carry a design, while the Stratford saucer has a decoration of running rabbits around the edge. In our design/shape listing, we show only the item that carries the Bunnykins design. In this case, the Stratford teacup, which carries a design, will be listed but the saucer will not. It is understood that a saucer comes with the cup.

CONDITION

Condition plays a very important part in the pricing of any collectable, Bunnykins included. An item in "mint" condition (no cracks, scrapes, nicks, marks or wear) will command catalogue price. If the piece shows any of the previous problems then the piece will fall into the "used" category and will sell for 25 to 50 per cent of catalogue value.

PRICING

The impact the internet would have on collectables was not fully anticipated. All the old avenues such as fairs, shows, dealer stores, retail outlets, direct mail and auction houses would come under severe pressure by the lowering of margins which the internet fostered. This would have a direct impact on pricing

When Royal Doulton Bunnykins, 2nd edition, was up for revision in the spring of 2003, the process began of gathering prices to generate the 3rd. Our method of collecting pricing information had to change.

Why! Simply because of the tremendous growth of the internet, and looking deeper, the rapid growth of on-line auctions in which 20th century collectables fit so well. Our auction results multiplied more than a thousand fold.

Dealers' websites have all but replaced direct mail. The direct mail house of five years ago is now the virtual store of 2003. Items, prices can all be changed daily, with little effort or cost.

Land-based auctions still contribute to pricing for they, through their historical connection with the collectors, gather in the scarce and rare pieces. The value of which is helpful in establishing an overall price trend. Seldom does the rare trend higher, without the basic items being carried along in unison.

Now, following this far, you are starting to wonder what has changed from the old model to the new, it is the internet component comprising two parts: on-line auctions and virtual stores, which were not available previously, but must now be inserted into the equation.

(1) Auctions:
A. Land-based auctions. As before, we continually monitor auction results capturing the pricing data produced.

B. Virtual auctions. With the new on-line auctions, both dealers and collectors participate. Prices become a true indication at that moment of the value of the item on a wholesale basis.

(2) Virtual stores: Dealers' virtual stores have replaced our previous direct mail component.

The price gathering process has changed dramatically. The analizing of the data remains the same.

TABLE OF CONTENTS

INTRODUCTION

COLLECTING BUNNYKINS TABLEWARE

Generations of children around the world have been weaned with Bunnykins nursery ware as it has been in continuous production since 1934. Few could have imagined that their favourite baby plate would one day become collectable but that is the fate of many of the Bunnykins designs, particularly the early pieces featuring Barbara Vernon's signature.

Barbara Vernon Designs

Barbara Vernon was a young nun in an English convent school when she first imagined the exploits of the Bunnykins family to entertain the children in her class. Her father was the Manager of the Royal Doulton Pottery in Stoke-on-Trent and he recognised the potential of her rabbit drawings for a range of nursery ware. Sister Mary Barbara, as she was known in the convent, began to send her sketches to the factory where they were adapted for the lithographic printing process by one of the resident designers, Hubert Light. He also created the backstamp from the *Tug of War* scene LF1 and designed the chain of running rabbits which has appeared around the rim of the Bunnykins pieces since their launch in 1934.

A surviving catalogue of 1937 shows that the range grew quickly to include two sizes of baby plate, a child's dinner plate, Don beakers and mugs, cereal and porridge bowls, a Jaffa fruit saucer, a jam pot, a Casino teapot, cup, saucer, sugar bowl and jugs in various sizes. These shapes were all made in a deep ivory glazed earthenware and decorated with colourful transfer prints. Barbara Vernon's bunnies were usually dressed in sky blue and cherry red and the background was coloured in subtle shades of brown and green.

More shapes had been added by 1940, notably an oval baby plate, a hot water plate with cover and a candle holder. Bunnykins collectors usually like to find an example of each shape featuring a Barbara Vernon design and the jam pot and candle holder, which were withdrawn in 1952, are amongst the hardest to find in the earthenware range.

Some of the early Bunnykins designs were also available in a white bone china body. This finer body was only produced until the Second World War and, as not many bone china pieces survived the rough and tumble of nursery life, they are very rare today. One collector was fortunate enough to find an original boxed bone china breakfast set, complete with silver spoons, whilst another boasts a tea set in pristine condition.

The condition of Bunnykins nursery ware, whether it is bone china or earthenware, is very important for serious collectors who seek out pieces with the minimum of scratches. Sometimes it is very hard to find early baby plates which have not been scraped by enthusiastic eaters scooping up their porridge to enjoy the scene underneath. Collectors also like to find scenes incorporating Barbara Vernon's facsimile signature although sometimes this was cut off the transfer.

Many of Barbara Vernon's scenes had been withdrawn by 1952 and these are amongst the most desirable today. Collectors appreciate her simple designs and the charming subjects which evoke her era, for example one of her bunnies in being dosed with castor oil at *Medicine Time* SF1 and others dance the *Lambeth Walk* HW16. Her quiet sense of humour can also be enjoyed in scenes like *Frightening Spider* SF4 and *Pressing Trousers* HW14 which shows the bunny struggling to remove the creases with a garden roller! Sadly, Barbara Vernon only produced Bunnykins drawings for a few years because of her commitments at the convent and so Walter Hayward, one of Royal Doultons Art Directors, took over the range after the Second World War.

Walter Hayward Designs

Initially Walter Hayward adapted the remaining Barbara Vernon drawings for production but he soon began to create his own scenes although her facsimile signature continued to appear on the ware until the mid 1950s. However, Walter Hayward's work can usually be identified by the presence of some lively little mice that became his trademark. Generally his scenes are much busier than their predecessors and some reflect new topical themes such as the advent of television and space travel. Over the years, he was encouraged to add more and more bunnies, particularly by Doulton's agent in Australia which was one of the strongest markets for Bunnykins. Some of his most ambitious designs, such as *Juggling* LF127 and *Hoopla* LF129, were only available for three years and so these are two of the hardest Hayward designs to find today.

The Bunnykins shapes remained much the same throughout the 1950s and 60s although some larger sizes of Casino teapots and jugs were added in 1952. They were all withdrawn in the late 1960s together with a wide range of scenes when the original earthenware body was replaced with new ivory bone china. By the late 1970s, new shapes had been developed for the china body including the Hug-a-mug which replaced the original Don mug and a range or egg-shaped boxes. Unfortunately, the egg boxes were not made for long and they are now very collectable. Savings books and money balls followed in the early 1980s and these were used occasionally to commemorate special events, such as royal births and weddings.

In the early 1980s, Walter Hayward was commissioned to design a range of scenes celebrating birthdays, christenings and Christmas. He also helped the Bunnykins family celebrate their own birthday with special commemorative pieces to mark their Golden Jubilee in 1984. In addition, all the nursery ware made during 1984 had the inscription Golden Jubilee Celebration added to the backstamp. Bunnykins birthday parties were held all over the world during 1984 and the resulting publicity attracted many new enthusiasts.

An anniversary weekend in Stoke-on-Trent was the catalyst for the largest Bunnykins collection in the U.K. which boasts examples of every scene and shape from 1934 to the present day. The first Bunnykins reference book was published at the end of 1984 and for the first time collectors could see the full extent of the range. Some scenes could only be illustrated from the pattern books and collectors all over the world began hunting for rarities like *Air Mail Delivery* LFa, *Carving the Chicken* LFc and *Dodgems* LF4.

No longer was Bunnykins intended exclusively for youngsters, Walter Hayward designed a set of Bunnykins for Grown Ups featuring bunnies with brief-cases dashing to work. These adult designs only remained in production from 1986 to 1988 so examples are very hard to find today. Walter Hayward's last Bunnykins design following his retirement was the plate to commemorate Australia's Bicentenary in 1988. Meanwhile, another artist was getting to know the Bunnykins family for a series of story books.

Colin Twinn Designs

In 1987, Colin Twinn was commissioned to produce a collection of Bunnykins books for the publishers, Frederick Warne, and many of his drawings were adapted for use on nursery ware. As a successful illustrator of children's books, Twinn had considerable experience with anthropomorphic characters, particularly rabbits, and he created a new look for the Bunnykins family. Pastel colours predominate in his detailed scenes and his bunnies seem softer and fluffier than the originals. Whilst this approach worked well in the little picture books, the new Bunnykins nursery ware designs did not have sufficient impact on the china shop shelves. Established collectors felt that the Bunnykins characters had lost their identity and it would appear that general gift buyers were not enthused either as production of Colin Twinn designs had ceased by the early 1990s.

Many of Colin Twinn's designs appeared on the new shapes which were developed in the late 1980s. An Albion style tea service was introduced in 1987 together with a Stratford tea cup and saucer which replaced the Casino shape. The traditional Don beaker was replaced by a straight sided Malvern beaker and a 10 ½ inch dinner plate was added to the range. Decorative accessories, such as a lamp and two picture plaques, were also available for a few years and these are now sought after by collectors.

Gradually, as Colin Twinn's designs began to disappear from the shops, new stocks of Barbara Vernon and Walter Hayward designs appeared. Around 50 patterns for hollow ware and flat ware had never been withdrawn and these were modified in line with new requirements for colour printing. A tuft of green grass on the left of the backstamp distinguishes the more recent Vernon/Hayward wares from earlier examples. A classic Barbara Vernon scene *Dancing in the Moonlight* was re-drawn for the 60th Anniversary of the Bunnykins range in 1994 and a set of commemorative ware was made for that year only. Royal Doulton's company in Australia commissioned their own exclusive anniversary scene featuring an Aussie picnic complete with kangaroos and koalas and this was one of the last designs by Colin Twinn as a new artist had been found to continue the Bunnykins tradition, Frank Endersby.

Frank Endersby Designs

Frank Endersby is a freelance illustrator who works from his own studio in the idyllic Cotswolds region. During his career, he has worked in a busy graphic design studio and also with a children's book publisher so he has a wide experience of all aspects of design and illustration. He quickly assimilated the essential qualities of the original Bunnykins style and his scenes feature the strong outlines used for the original characters as well as their bright blue and red clothes. To date he has worked on 20 new sets of Bunnykins designs and each set incorporates three scenes, the larger for decorating plates and two smaller ones to use on the front and reverse of cups and other hollow ware. These scenes began to appear in the shops in 1995 but it was a couple of years before dedicated collectors had located all his designs. Early indications are that the new Frank Endersby designs are being very well received by gift buyers and collectors alike, so much so that the original Vernon/Hayward scenes have now been phased out of production.

A few new Bunnykins shapes have been introduced in recent years, such as the divided children's dish and the photograph frame, but the most exciting new concept was the annual Bunnykins Christmas plate made exclusively for members of Royal Doulton International Collectors Club. These lively designs by Frank Endersby have a wealth of colourful detail, including some of Walter Hayward's cheeky mice and the running rabbits wearing Christmas hats! The limited distribution and short production period is guaranteed to make these very special Bunnykins pieces.

COLLECTING BUNNYKINS FIGURINES

Bunnykins figures made their debut in 1939 but the war soon halted production and the original six characters are extremely rare today. It is believed that they were modelled by Charles Noke, the Art Director who developed the HN range of Royal Doulton figures, as they resemble some of his early character animals. These large scale figures, which range in size from 3 to 7 inches,

have little in common with Barbara Vernon's design which might explain why they were never revived after the war.

As well as these characters figures, Noke also introduced a Bunny shaped breakfast set, featuring a teapot, cream jug, sugar bowl, sugar sifter and egg cup, but this suffered a similar fate in the war years. The idea of Bunny shaped ware to accompany the successful nursery ware was not revived until 1967 when a Bunny money bank was added to the range and this remained in production until 1981.

The DB Range

When Royal Doulton took over the Beswick factory in 1969, they acquired the modelling skills of Albert Hallam who worked on the Beatrix Potter range figures. These little character animals were amongst Beswick's most successful product and it was decided to create a similar collection of Bunnykins figures. The first nine figures were launched in 1972 with DB pattern numbers and they averaged 4 inches in height. All were inspired by Walter Hayward's nursery ware patterns, for example *The Artist* DB13 is derived from *The Portrait Painter* SF20. This approach continued until 1974 when there was a total of 15 characters in the range but a new look developed in the 1980s.

Harry Sales Designs

Harry Sales, the Design Manager of the Beswick factory, took over responsibility for the Bunnykins range in 1980. He believed that the rabbit character should reflect the interests of contemporary children and his first figure of a guitar-playing rock star *Mr. Bunnybeat Strumming* DB16 was followed by a space traveller *Astro Bunnykins Rocket Man* DB20. After seeing his colleagues' response to these entertaining designs, it occurred to Harry that Bunnykins figures could also have an adult audience and he began to work on a collection of sporting subjects at the time of the Los Angeles Olympics in 1984. Adults began to purchase these figures as whimsical gifts, sharing Harry's sense of humour in subjects like *Freefall Bunnykins DB41 whose pained expression suggested a not so perfect landing.*

This new direction coincided with the Bunnykins Golden Jubilee when nursery ware first began to be taken seriously by collectors. Before long, the figures were also included in the hunt and early discontinued models, such as *Mr. Bunnykins Autumn Days* DB5 and *Daisy Bunnykins Spring Time* DB7 were sought at collectors fairs and markets. In 1987, the Royal Doulton International Collectors Club commissioned a figure exclusively for its members and *Collector Bunnykins* DB54 is now one of the most expensive figures on the secondary market.

Several special commissions were produced in the late 1980s and these now command premium prices. National subjects such as *Australian Bunnykins* DB58 were made to celebrate that country's bicentenary and new colourways of existing models were produced for sale at special events in the USA, notably *Mr. And Mrs. Bunnykins at the Easter Parade* DB51 and 52.

Graham Tongue Designs

When Harry Sales left Royal Doulton in 1986 to pursue a freelance career, Graham Tongue became the Beswick Studio Manager and he has been responsible for a number of Bunnykins figures, either as designer or modeller. His most popular figure is *Bedtime Bunnykins* DB55 which was made in four different colourways for special occasions. He also produced some figures inspired by Colin Twinn's nursery ware illustrations, for example *Lollipopman Bunnykins* DB65, but these were less successful and were withdrawn after a few years. For a few years following his retirement in 1995, Graham has continued to model Bunnykins figures at his own studio and he created *Ballerina Bunnykins* DB176 and *Cavalier Bunnykins* DB179, a limited edition design.

Limited Edition Designs

The first limited edition Bunnykins figures were commissioned in 1990 for sale at a Doulton collectors fair in London. The *Oompah Band* was renamed the *Royal Doulton Collectors Band* for this occasion and the new blue colourway was so successful that other special editions swiftly followed. Denise Andrews, a freelance illustrator from Suffolk, was invited to produce special designs which were modelled by the team of resident artists at the Beswick studio. Her footballing and cricketing characters augmented the earlier sporting range and her colourful *Clown* and *Jester Bunnykins* have entertained collectors all over the world. Over the years, limited edition sizes have grown from 250 to 3,500 but many new Bunnykins figures are over-subscribed as soon as they are launched. Collectors were bewitched by *Trick or Treat Bunnykins* DB162, which was issued in 1995 and was soon changing hands for many times its issue price. In 1996, Royal Doulton introduced their first Bunnykins Figure of the Year and collectors responded enthusiastically to this new initiative.

Resin Bunnykins Figurines

In 1995, the Bunnykins characters became movie stars when an animated feature film was screened in North America and the UK. *Happy Birthday Bunnykins* was later distributed in video form and inspired a new collection of Bunnykins figures in a resin body. Resin is the name given to a cold cast sculptural material which retains intricate modelling detail more effectively than conventional fired clay bodies. The resin Bunnykins figures are smaller in scale than their ceramic cousins and are decorated primarily in pastel colours. During 1996 and 1997, twenty models were issued in the resin range, including two ambitious musical boxes and two photograph frames, but they did not appeal to collectors or gift buyers and were all withdrawn at the end of 1997. Fortunately the traditional ceramic figures continue to go from strength to strength.

The Success of the DB Range

After just 30 years in production, the DB figures are amongst the most collectable Royal Doulton products and Bunnykins fans are multiplying faster than rabbits. With this in mind, it is a good idea to buy the new Bunnykins figures as soon as they are issued. Royal Doulton have now allocated 313 DB numbers and, although a few intervening numbers have not been issued, committed collectors now have quite a challenge to find them all. Figures are now withdrawn regularly from the range, adding to the excitement of the chase so, in the words of the song, if you want to keep up you'll have to ..run rabbit…run rabbit…run..run..run!

ROYAL DOULTON

INTERNATIONAL COLLECTORS CLUB

Founded in 1980, the Royal Doulton International Collectors Club provides an information service on all aspects of the company's products, past and present. A club magazine, "Gallery," is published four times a year with information on new products and current events that will keep the collector up-to-date on the happenings in the world of Royal Doulton. Upon joining the club, each new member will receive a free gift and invitations to special events and exclusive offers throughout the year.

To join the Royal Doulton Collectors Club, please contact the club directly by writing to the address opposite or calling the appropriate number.

International Collectors Club
Sir Henry Doulton House
Forge Lane, Etruria
Stoke-on-Trent, Staffordshire
ST1 5NN, England

Telephone:
  U.K.: 8702 412696
  Overseas: +44 1782 404045
  U.K. Fax: +44 (0) 1782 404000
  On-line at www.doulton-direct.co.uk
  E-mail: icc@royal-doulton.com

VISITOR CENTRE

Opened in the Summer of 1996, the Royal Doulton Visitor Centre houses the largest collection of Royal Doulton figurines in the world. Demonstration areas offer the collector a first hand insight on how figurines are assembled and decorated. Also at the Visitor Centre is a restaurant and a retail shop offering both best quality ware and slight seconds. Factory tours may be booked, Monday to Friday.

Royal Doulton Visitor Centre
Nile Street, Burslem
Stoke-on-Trent, ST6 2AJ, England
  Visitor Centre: Tel.: +44 (0) 1782 292434
          Fax: +44 (0) 1782 292424

  Factory Store: Tel.: +44 (0) 1782 292451

WEBSITE AND E-MAIL ADDRESS

Web Sites:
  www.royal-doulton.com
  www.doulton-direct.com.au
  www.royal-doulton-brides.com

E-mail:
  Visitor Centre: visitor@royal-doulton.com
  Consumer Enquiries: enquiries@royal-doulton.com
  Museum Curator: heritage@royal-doulton.com
  Doulton-Direct: direct@royal-doulton.cm

ROYAL DOULTON FACTORY SHOPS

Royal Doulton Group Factory Shop
Lawley Street, Longton,
Stoke-on-Trent ST3 2PH, England
  Tel.: +44 (0) 1782 291237

Royal Doulton Factory Shop
Forge Lane, Etruria
Stoke-on-Trent ST1 5NN, England
  Tel.: +44 (0) 1782 284056

Royal Doulton Factory Shop
Victoria Road, Fenton,
Stoke-on-Trent ST4 2PJ, England
  Tel.: +44 (0) 1782 291869

DOULTON CHAPTERS

Detroit Chapter
Ronald Griffin, President
629 Lynne Avenue
Ypsilanti, MI 48198-3829

Edmonton Chapter
Mildred's Collectibles
6813 104 Street, Edmonton, AB

New England Chapter
Lee Piper, President
Meridith Nelson, Vice President
Michael Lynch, Secretary
Scott Reichenberg, Treasurer
E-mail doingantiq@aol.com

Northern California Chapter
Edward L. Khachadourian, President
P.O. Box 214, Moraga, Ca. 94556-0214
Tel.: (925) 376-2221 Fax: (925) 376-3581
E-mail: khack@pacbell.net

Northwest, Bob Haynes, Chapter
Alan Matthew, President
15202 93rd Place N.E., Bothell,
WA., 98011 Tel.: (425) 488-9604

Rochester Chapter
Judith L. Trost, President
103 Garfield Street, Rochester,
NY, 14611 Tel.: (716) 436-3321

Ohio Chapter
Reg Morris, President
5556 Whitehaven Avenue
North Olmstead, OH, 44070
Tel.: (216) 779-5554

Western Pennsylvania Chapter
John Re, President
9589 Parkedge Drive,
Allison Park, PA 15101
Tel.: (412) 366-0201
Fax: (412) 366-2558

THE DOULTON MARKETS

LAND AUCTIONS

AUSTRALIA

Goodman's
  7 Anderson Street,
  Double Bay, Sydney, 2028, N.S.W., Australia
  Tel.: +61 (0) 2 9327 7311; Fax: +61 (0) 2 9327 2917
  Enquiries: Suzanne Brett
  www.goodmans.com.au
  E-mail: info@goodmans.com.au

Sotheby's
  118-122 Queen Street, Woollahra,
  Sydney, 2025, N.S.W., Australia
  Tel.: +61 (0) 2 9362 1000; Fax: +61 (0) 2 9362 1100
  www.sothebys.com E-mail:

CANADA

Empire Auctions
  Montreal
  5500 Paré Street, Montreal, Quebec H4P 2M1
  Tel.: (514) 737-6586; Fax: (514) 342-1352
  Enquiries: Isadore Rubinfeld
  E-mail: montreal@empireauctions.com

Empire Auctions (cont.)
  Ottawa
  1380 Cyrville Road, Gloucester, Ontario
  Tel.: (613) 748-5343; Fax: (613) 748-0354
  Enquiries: Elliot Melamed
  E-mail: ottawa@empireauctions.com

  Toronto
  165 Tycos Drive
  Toronto, Ontario, M6B 1W6
  Tel.: (416) 784-4261; Fax: (416) 784-4262
  Enquiries: Michael Rogozinsky
  www.empireauctions.com
  E-mail: toronto@empireauctions.com

Maynard's Industries Ltd.

Arts / Antiques
  415 West 2nd Avenue, Vancouver, BC, V5Y 1E3
  Tel.: (604) 876-1311; Fax: (604) 876-1323
  www.maynards.com
  E-mail: antiques@maynards.com

Ritchie's

288 King Street East, Toronto, Ontario, M5A 1K4
Tel.: (416) 364-1864; Fax: (416) 364-0704
Enquiries: Caroline Kaiser
www.ritchies.com
E-mail: auction@ritchies.com

Waddington's

111 Bathurst Street, Toronto, Ontario, M5V 2R1
Tel.: (416) 504-9100; Fax: (416) 504-0033
Enquiries: Bill Kime
www.waddingtonsauctions.com
E-mail: info@waddingtonsauctions.com

UNITED KINGDOM

BBR Auctions

Elsecar Heritage Centre, Nr. Barnsley
South Yorkshire S74 8HJ, England
Tel.: +44 (0) 1226 745156; Fax: +44 (0) 1226 351561
Enquiries: Alan Blakeman
www.bbrauctions.co.uk
E-mail: sales@bbrauctions.com

Bonhams

Bond Street:
101 New Bond Street, London, W15 1SR, England
Chelsea:
65-69 Lots Road, Chelsea, London, SW10 0RN, England
Knightsbridge:
Montpelier Street, Knightsbridge, London, SW7 1HH
Tel.: +44 (0) 20 7393 3900; Fax: +44 (0) 20 7393 3905
Enquiries:
  Decorative Arts: Joy McCall
  Tel.: +44 (0) 20 7393 3942
  Comtemporary Ceramics: Gareth Williams
  Tel.: +44 (0) 20 7393 3941
  Doulton Beswick Wares: Mark Oliver
  Tel.: +44 (0) 20 7468 8233
www.bonhams.com
E-mail: info@bonhams.com

Christie's

London
8 King Street, London, SW1 England
Tel.: +44 (0) 20 7839 9060; Fax: +44 (0) 20 7839 1611
South Kensington
85 Old Brompton Road, London, SW7 3LD, England
Tel.: +44 (0) 20 7581 7611; Fax: +44 (0) 20 7321 3321
Enquires: Decorative Arts:
  Tel.: +44 (0) 20 7321 3237
www.christies.com; E-mail: info@christies.com

Potteries Specialist Auctions

271 Waterloo Road, Cobridge, Stoke-on-Trent
Staffordshire, ST6 3HR, England
Tel.: +44 (0) 1782 286622; Fax: +44 (0) 1782 213777
Enquiries: Stella Ashbrooke
www.potteriesauctions.com
E-mail: enquiries@potteriesauctions.com

Sotheby's
London
34-35 New Bond Street, London, W1A 2AA, England
Tel.: +44 (0) 20 7293 5000; Fax: +44 (0) 20 7293 5989
Olympia
Hammersmith Road, London WI4 8UX, England
Tel.: +44 (0) 20 7293 5555; Fax: +44 (0) 20 7293 6939

Sotheby's
Sussex
Summers Place, Billingshurst, Sussex
RH14 9AF, England
Tel.: +44 (0) 1403 833500; Fax: +44 (0) 1403 833699
www.sothebys.com:
E-mail: info@sothebys.com

Louis Taylor

Britannia House
10 Town Road, Hanley
Stoke-on-Trent, Staffordshire, England
Tel.: +44 (0) 1782 214111; Fax: +44 (0) 1782 215283
Enquiries: Clive Hillier

Thomson Roddick & Medcalf

60 Whitesands
Dumfries, DG1 2RS
Scotland
Tel.: +44 (0) 1387 279879; Fax: +44 (0) 1387 266236
Enquiries: C. R. Graham-Campbell

Peter Wilson Auctioneers

Victoria Gallery, Market Street
Nantwich, Cheshire, CW5 5DG, England
Tel.: +44 (0) 1270 610508; Fax: +44 (0) 1270 610508
Enquiries: Peter Wilson

UNITED STATES

Christie's East

219 East 67th Street, New York, NY 10021
Tel.: +1 212 606 0400
www.christies.com

William Doyle Galleries

175 East 87th Street, New York, N.Y. 10128
Tel.: +1 212 427 2730
Fax: +1 212 369 0892

Sotheby's Arcade Auctions

1334 York Avenue, New York, N.Y. 10021
Tel.: +1 212 606 7000
www.sothebys.com

VIRTUAL AUCTIONS

Amazon.com ® Auctions
  Main site: www.amazon.com
  Plus 4 International sites

AOL.com Auctions ®
  Main site: www.aol.com
  Links to – E-bay.com
    – U-bid.com.

E-BAY ® The World's On-line Market Place™
    Main site: www.ebay.com
    Plus 20 International sites.

YAHOO! Auctions ®
    Main site: www.yahoo.com
    Plus 15 International auction sites

FAIRS, MARKETS AND SHOWS

AUSTRALIA
Royal Doulton and Antique Collectable Fair
    Marina Hall, Civic Centre
    Hurstville, Sydney

CANADA
Christie Antique Show
    Christie Conservation Park
    Highway 5, Near Dundas, Ontario
    Always May and September
    Gadsden Promotions Ltd.
    P.O. Box 490, Shelburne, Ontario L0N 1S0
    Tel.: (800) 667-0619
    Fax: (519) 925-6498

UNITED KINGDOM
20th Century Fairs
    266 Glossop Road, Sheffield S10 2HS, England
    Usually in May or June.
    For information on times and dates:
    Tel.: +44 (0) 114 275-0333; Fax: +44 (0) 114 275 4443

Doulton And Beswick Collectors Fair
    National Motorcycle Museum, Meriden, Birmingham,
    Usually March and August.
    For information on times and dates:
    Doulton and Beswick Dealers Association
    Tel.: +44 (0) 181 303-3316

DMG Antiques Fairs Ltd.
    Newark, the largest in the UK with usually six fairs
    annually. For information on times and dates for this
    and many other fairs contact:
    DMG
    Newark, P.O. Box 100, Newark
    Nottinghamshire, NG2 1DJ
    Tel.: +44 (0) 1636 702326; Fax: +44 (0) 1636 707923
    www.dmgantiquefairs.com
    www.antiquesdirectory.co.uk

U.K. Fairs
    Doulton and Beswick Fair for Collectors
    River Park Leisure Centre, Winchester
    Usually held in October
    For information on times and dates contact:
    Enquiries U.K. Fairs; Tel.: +44 (0) 20 8500 3505
    www.portia.co.uk
    E-mail: ukfairs@portia.co.uk

LONDON MARKETS
Alfie's Antique Market
    13-25 Church Street, London; Tuesday - Saturday
Camden Passage Market
    London; Wednesday and Saturday
New Caledonia Market
    Bermondsey Square, London; Friday morning
Portobello Road Market
    Portobello Road, London; Saturday

UNITED STATES
Atlantique City
    Atlantic City Convention Centre
    Atlantic City, NJ
International Gift and Collectible Expo
    Donald E. Stephens Convention Centre
    Rosemont, Illinois
    For information on the above two shows contact:
Krause Publications
    700 East State Street, Iola, WI, 54990-9990
    Tel.: (877) 746-9757; Fax: (715) 445-4389
    www.collectibleshow.com
    E-mail: iceshow@krause.com
Doulton Convention and Sale International
    Fort Lauderdale, Florida, U.S.A.
    Usually February. For information on times and dates:
Pascoe & Company,
    575 S.W. 22nd Ave., Miami, Florida 33135
    Tel.: (305) 643-2550; Fax: (305) 643-2123
    www.pascoeandcompany.com
    E-mail: sales@pascoeandcompany.com=
Royal Doulton Convention & Sale
    Cleveland, Ohio, U.S.A.
    Usually August. For information on times and dates:
    Colonial House Productions
    182 Front Street, Berea, Ohio 44308;
    Tel.: (866) 885-9024; Fax: (866) 854-3117
    www.Colonial-House-Collectibles.com
    E-mail: yworry@aol.com

FURTHER READING

Storybook Figurines

Beatrix Potter Figures and Giftware edited by Louise Irvine
Beswick Price Guide by Harvey May
Bunnykins Collectors Book by Louise Irvine
Cartoon Classics and other Character Figures by Louise Irvine
Royal Doulton Bunnykins Figures by Louise Irvine
Royal Doulton, Royal Albert, Beswick Figurines A Charlton Standard Catalogue by Jean Dale

Animals, Figures and Character Jugs

Beswick Animals: A Charlton Standard Catalogue by Diane & John Callow
and Marilyn & Peter Sweet
Character Jug Collectors Handbook by Kevin Pearson
Collecting Character and Toby Jugs by Jocelyn Lukins
Collecting Doulton Animals by Jocelyn Lukins
Doulton Figure Collectors Handbook by Kevin Pearson
Doulton Flambé Animals by Jocelyn Lukins
Royal Doulton Animals: A Charlton Standard Catalogue by Jean Dale
Royal Doulton Figures by Desmond Eyles, Louise Irvine and Valerie Baynton
Royal Doulton Figurines: A Charlton Standard Catalogue by Jean Dale
Royal Doulton Jugs: A Charlton Standard Catalogue by Jean Dale

General

Beswick Pottery: A Charlton Standard Catalogue by Diane and John Callow
Discovering Royal Doulton by Michael Doulton
Doulton Burslem Advertising Wares by Jocelyn Lukins
Doulton Burslem Wares by Desmond Eyles
Doulton for the Collector by Jocelyn Lukins
Doulton Kingsware Flasks by Jocelyn Lukins
Doulton Lambeth Advertising Wares by Jocelyn Lukins
Doulton Lambeth Wares by Desmond Eyles and Louise Irvine
Doulton Story by Paul Atterbury and Louise Irvine
George Tinwoth by Peter Rose
Hannah Barlow by Peter Rose
John Beswick: A World of Imagination. Catalogue reprint (1950-1996)
Limited Edition Loving Cups by Louise Irvine and Richard Dennis
Phillips Collectors Guide by Catherine Braithwaite
Royal Doulton by Jennifer Queree
Royal Doulton by Julie McKeown
Royal Doulton Series Ware by Louise Irvine (Vols. 1-5)
Sir Henry Doulton Biography by Edmund Gosse

Magazines and Newsletters

Beswick Quarterly (Beswick Newsletter) Contact Laura J. Rock-Smith: 10 Holmes Court,
Sayville N.Y. 11782-2408, U.S.A. Tel./Fax (631) 589-9027

Collecting Doulton Magazine, Contact Barry Hill, Collecting Doulton, P.O. Box 310,
Richmond, Surrey TW10 7FU, England

Cottontails (Bunnykins Newsletter) Contact Claire Green: 6 Beckett Way, Lewes, East
Sussex, BN7 2EB, U.K. E-mail: claireg@2btinternet.com

Rabbitting On (Bunnykins Newsletter) Contact Leah Selig: 2 Harper Street, Merrylands 2160
New South Wales, Australia. Tel./Fax 61 2 9637 2410 (International), 02 637 2410

PART ONE

BUNNYKINS TABLEWARE
Issues of 1934 to 2003

BUNNYKINS BREAKFAST SET
Issues of 1939 - 1945

BUNNYKINS TEAPOTS
Issues of 1994 - 1998

BUNNYKINS TEA SETS
Issues of 1998 - 2003

BUNNYKINS TOBY JUGS
Issues of 1999 - 2003

Candle holder — *Bedtime in Bunks* (SF3)

BUNNYKINS TABLEWARE BACKSTAMPS

BKT-1. 1934 - 1937

1a   1b

1a. The crown and lion, MADE IN ENGLAND upon the ROYAL DOULTON logo, with or without date code.
1b. As 1a, but with "BUNNYKINS" added.

BKT-2. 1937 - c.1940

2a   2b

2a. The "Tug of War" group, (three bunnies from Barbara Vernon;s "Tug of War" scene) supports a crown and lion upon the Royal Doulton logo. "Made in England" is printed in green, the lion is uncoloured. "Bunnykins" below
2b. As 2a, but with date code (1927 + number = date of manufacture).

BKT-3. 1937 - 1953

3a   3c

3a. As 2a, but the lion is now coloured brown and "MADE In ENGLAND" is printed in brown also.

3b. As 3a, but with additional "A" mark for kiln identification. The "A" is printed in green

3c. As 3b, but an extra, crown, lion, Doulton logo is added, with or without date code., the extra logo is green.

3d. As 3c but with BONE CHINA, in green added below England on the lion, crown and Doulton logo stamp (not illustrated).

BKT-4. 1940s

4

4. As 3a, but a completely monochrome logo.

BKT-5. 1954 - 1958

5

5. As 3a, but "MADE IN ENGLAND" is printed in black and under "BUNNYKINS" the registration symbol ® is added; all is encircled with registration and trade mark numbers.

BKT-6a. 1959 - 1975 Earthenware
BKT-6b. 1968 - 1975 Fine Bone China

6a   6b

6a. As 5a, but the cirle of registration and trade mark numbers is removed and replaced by "REGD TRADE MARK" below the registration symbol ®.

6b. As 6a, but now with " ENGLISH FINE BONE CHINA" added between the Tug of War group and "BUNNYKINS".

BKT-7. 1976 - 1984

7a   7b

7a   As 6a, but the " BUNNYKINS" and the registration symbol ® are now on one line with © ROYAL DOULTON / TABLEWARE LTD 1936, on two lines below.

7b   As 7a but now with "ENGLISH FINE BONE CHINA" added between the Tug of War group and "BUNNYKINS" ®

BKT-8. 1976 - 1984

8a   8b

8a.   As 7a, but with 19 − 84 on either side of the "Tug of War logo, below is "GOLDEN JUBLIEE CELEBRATION"

8b   As 8a but with "ENGLISH FINE BONE CHINA" added between the "Tug of War" group and "BUNNYKINS" ®

BKT-9. 1985 - 1987

9a   9b

9a.   As 7a, but with (U.K.) added to the single copyright line © 1936 ROYAL DOULTON.

9b   As 9a but with "ENGLISH FINE BONE CHINA" added between the Tug of War group and "BUNNYKINS"

BKT-10. 1988 - c.1993

10a   10b

10a. As 7a but with © 1936 ROYAL DOULTON (U.K.) replaced by © 1988 ROYAL DOULTON.

10b. As 10a but with "ENGLISH FINE BONE CHINA" added between the "Tug of War" group and "BUNNYKINS" ®

BKT-11. c.1993 - 2002

11a   11b

11a. As 7a, but © 1988 is replaced by the original date © 1936.

11b   As 11a but with "ENGLISH FINE BONE CHINA" added between the "Tug of War" group and "BUNNYKINS" ®

BKT-SPECIAL

Over the years special backstamps were created incorporating the Tug of War logo, and the various text changes with other special design elements such as the logo for the Australian Bicentenary or a wreath of holly leaves for the Christmas plate. We are classifying this group of backstamps under one heading "Special".

SHAPE GUIDE

This guide includes the standard Bunnykins shapes, their sizes and production dates. Originally Bunnykins was produced in either a deep ivory earthenware or a fine white bone china. The white china body was discontinued during the Second World War so examples are very hard to find today. A list of white china shapes from an early catalogue is included on page 10.

In 1968, an ivory bone china body replaced the original earthenware and many early shapes were withdrawn. Those that remained were remodelled for the new body. Today, the majority of Bunnykins nurseryware is made in ivory bone china, the exceptions being the money ball and savings book which are made in a earthenware body.

Some shapes were remodelled specifically for the Bunnykins range, for example the candle holder. Others were adapted from existing tableware ranges. The Casino tea wares, for instance, were originally designed for a striking art deco pattern of that name and the Jaffa fruit saucer takes its name from a fruit set which was produced with various patterns in 1930s.

The early Casino teapots and jugs were sold in several different sizes that are described as 24s, 30s, 36s and 42s and usually this number is incised on the base. This method of sizing was an industry standard and referred to the number of pieces which could be fitted on to a potter's board as he took them from the wheel. Thus the largest size is 24 as only that number of pieces could be accommodated on the potters board compared to 42 smaller pieces. The capacity in pints is also given for reference. Collectors will find some slight differences in capacity and sizes because of potting variations, such as clay thickness and kiln shrinkage. There were also slight modifications to handles and spouts in the early years.

The baby plates have also been altered over the years and the shape records indicate that the oval design was remodelled in 1947 and the round ones were reduced in weight by 5 ounces, also in 1947. Collectors will notice some variations in the profile and depth of baby plates.

From time to time, shapes have been developed for the Bunnykins range and then not produced. The model books record that a framed stand for Bunnykins subjects was modelled in 1940 but not approved. Stands featuring *Going Shopping* SF10 and *Dancing in the Moonlight* LFb have turned up in recent years. Other unusual shapes that have come to light include a vegetable tureen, a sauce boat, an oval plate and a small vase. In the early 1980s, a money box in the form of a post box was modelled but it did not go into production at that time and two examples were recorded, one in the Royal Doulton archives and another in a private collection. In 2001, a limited edition of this post box shape was produced for the Bunnykins Extravaganza Fair.

As with the original earthenware range, the Bunnykins fine white china shapes were also used for other patterns, for instance the Rex mug can be found with several different nurseryware designs. As yet, not all the fine white china shapes have appeared in the market-place so information is limited. It is believed that the majority of them were exported to the USA and Canada during the Second World War as this is where examples tend to be found.

Rare oval platter - "Dancing in the Moonlight"

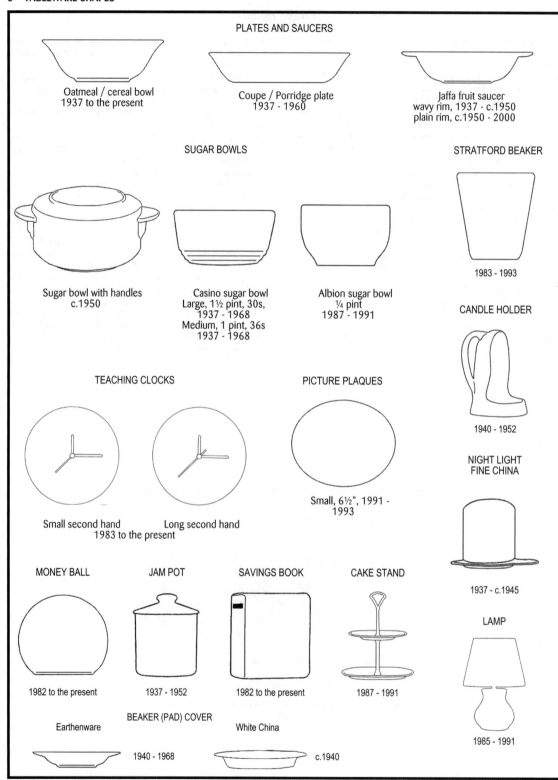

PLATES AND SAUCERS

Oatmeal / cereal bowl
1937 to the present

Coupe / Porridge plate
1937 - 1960

Jaffa fruit saucer
wavy rim, 1937 - c.1950
plain rim, c.1950 - 2000

SUGAR BOWLS

STRATFORD BEAKER

Sugar bowl with handles
c.1950

Casino sugar bowl
Large, 1½ pint, 30s,
1937 - 1968
Medium, 1 pint, 36s
1937 - 1968

Albion sugar bowl
¼ pint
1987 - 1991

1983 - 1993

CANDLE HOLDER

TEACHING CLOCKS

PICTURE PLAQUES

1940 - 1952

Small second hand

Long second hand
1983 to the present

Small, 6½", 1991 -
1993

NIGHT LIGHT
FINE CHINA

1937 - c.1945

MONEY BALL

JAM POT

SAVINGS BOOK

CAKE STAND

LAMP

1982 to the present

1937 - 1952

1982 to the present

1987 - 1991

Earthenware

BEAKER (PAD) COVER

White China

1985 - 1991

1940 - 1968

c.1940

RIM PLATES

Plates in eight sizes
5", 1937 - c.1959
6", 1937 - c.1959
6½", 1937 to the present
7", 1937 - c.1959
7½", 1959 - 1968
8", 1968 to the present
8½", 1937 - 1969
10½", 1987 - 2000

COUPE PLATE

6 7/8", c.1956 - c1971

Bread and butter plate
1940 - 1968

TEA CUPS AND
SAUCERS

Casino 1937 - 1989
modified 1968

Stratford 1987 - 1997

TYPES of JUGS

Casino jug in four sizes
¾ pint, 42s, 1937 - 1968
1 pint, 36s, 1937 - 1968
1½ pint, 30s, 1937 - 1968
2 pint, 24s, 1937 - 1968

Albion jug in three sizes
¼ pint, 1987 - 1991
½ pint, 1988 - 1991
1 pint, 1988 - 1991

DON BEAKERS

Don beaker, 1937 - 1989
Don beaker with handle, 1940 - 1989
Early Don beakers have a running rabbits
border inside the rim, later outside

Standard sizes are listed above, however, other sizes do
exist which are variations on the standards.

EGG SAUCER, CUPS, AND BOXES

Egg saucer
one size, 1991 - 1996

Egg cup, three styles
Footless, 1937 - 1968
Footed, 1940 - 1968
Semi-footed, 1968 to the present

Egg boxes in three sizes
Large, 4¾", 1979 - 1981
Medium, 3¾", 1979 - 1981
Small, 3", 1979 - 1981

BABY PLATES

Round baby plate, small 6"
1937 to the present
modified in 1978 and 1988

Round baby plate, large
7½", 1937 - 1969

Oval baby plate, two sizes
Small 8¼", 1940 - 1952
Large 8½", 1940 - 1968

Slightly different shapes and
depths are found in baby plates

DON MUGS

One handle, 1937 - 1983
modified in 1968

Two handles, 1940 - 1983

HUG-A-MUGS

One handle, 1979 to the present

Two handles, 1979 to the present

MALVERN BEAKER

1989 - 1997

LARGE CUP / MUG

1937 - c.1945

HOT WATER PLATES

Hot Water Plate with Cover
One stopper, 1940 - 1959; Two stopper, 1959 - 1969

TEAPOTS

Albion teapot
1 pint size
1987 - 1991

Casino teapot
1 pint size, 36s, 1937 - 1968
1½ pint size, 30s, 1937 - 1968
2 pint size, 24s, 1952 - 1968

Collectors will find teapots that differ slightly in capacity
from the standard sizes

THE COLLECTORS CHECKLIST OF SHAPES

The following provides the collector with a starting point to developing a checklist of designs vs. shapes. As the Barbara Vernon facsimile signature plays an important role in Bunnykins tableware we have also included that information in the listing. For continuity in the listing, we have noted where a signature was not included in the design.

On checking your collection you may find we have not included a particular design/shape with or without a signature. Why not bring this information to our attention? Please contact:

The Charlton Press at (416) 488-1418 or (800) 442-6042, you can fax us at (416) 488-4656 or (800) 442-1542, or you may e-mail us at chpress@charltonpress.com.

ALBION; 1987 - 1991
Cream jug
¼ pint, 1987 - 1991
without signature
Jug
¼ pint, 1987 - 1991
without signature
½ pint, 1988 - 1991
without signature
1 pint, 1988 - 1991
without signature
Sugar Bowl
¼ pint, 1987 - 1991
without signature
Teapot
1 pint, 1987 - 1991
without signature

BABY PLATES; 1937 to date
Small
oval, 8 ¼", 1940 - 1952
with signature
without signature
round, 6", first issue, 1937 - 1978
with signature
without signature
round, 6", second issue, 1978-1988
without signature
round, 6", third issue, 1988 to date
without signature
Large
oval, 8 ½", 1940 - 1968
with signature
without signature
round, 7 ½", 1937 - 1969
with signature
without signature

BEAKER PAD; 1940 - 1968
with signature
without signature

BREAD AND BUTTER PLATE; 1940 - 1968
with signature
without signature

CAKE STAND; 1987 - 1991
without signature

CANDLE HOLDER; 1940 - 1952
with signature
without signature

CASINO; 1937 - 1968
Jug
42s, ¾ pint, 1937 - 1968
with signature
without signature
36s, 1 pint, 1937 - 1968
with signature
without signature
30s, 1 ½ pint, 1937 - 1968
with signature
without signature
24s, 2 pint, 1937 - 1968
with signature
without signature
Saucer
1937 - 1989
with signature
without signature
Sugar
36s, 1 pint, 1937 - 1968
with signature
without signature
30s, 1 ½ pint, 1937 - 1968
with signature
without signature
Teacup
First issue, 1937 - 1968
with signature
without signature
Second issue, 1968 - 1989
without signature
Teapot
36s, 1 pint, 1937 - 1968
with signature
without signature
30s, 1 ½ pint, 1937 - 1968
with signature
without signature
24s, 2 pint, 1952 - 1968
with signature
without signature

CEREAL / OATMEAL BOWL; 1937 to date
with signature
without signature

CEREAL / PORRIDGE PLATE; 1937 - 1960
with signature
without signature

CLOCK; 1983 to date
without signature

COUPE; 1959 - 1971
without signature

CUP / MUG LARGE; 1937 - c.1945
with signature

DIVIDER DISH; 1993 - 1997
8 ¾", 1993 - 1997
without signature

DON; 1937-1989
Beaker, 1937 - 1989
with signature
without signature
Beaker, one handle, 1940 - 1989
with signature
without signature
Mug, one handle
First issue, 1937 - 1968
with signature
without signature
Second issue, 1968 - 1983
without signature
Mug, two handles, 1940 - 1983
with signature
without signature

EGG BOX; 1979 - 1981
Small, 3", 1979 - 1981
without signature
Medium, 3 ¾", 1979 - 1981
without signature
Large, 4 ¾", 1979 - 1981
without signature

EGG CUPS; 1937 to date
Style One, footless, 1937 - 1968
with signature
without signature
Style Two, footed, 1940 - 1968
with signature
without signature
Style Three, footless modified, 1968 to date
without signature

EGG SAUCER; 1991 - 1996
without signature

HOT WATER PLATE WITH COVER; 1940 - 1969
Plate
First issue, one stopper, 1940 - 1959
with signature
without signature
Second issue, two stoppers, 1959 - 1969
without signature
Cover, 1940 - 1969
with signature
without signature

HUG-A-MUG; 1979 to date
   One handle, 1979 to date
      without signature
   Two handles, 1979 to date
      without signature

JAFFA FRUIT SAUCER; 1937 - 2000
   Wavy rim, 1937 - c.1950
      with signature
      without signature

   Plain rim, c.1950 - 2000
      with signature
      without signature

JAM POT; 1937 - 1952
   with signature
   without signature

LAMP; 1985 - 1991
   without signature

MALVERN BEAKER; 1989 - 1997
   without signature

MONEY BALL; 1982 to date
   without signature

NIGHT LIGHT; 1937 - c.1945
   with signature

PICTURE PLAQUE; 1991 - 1993
   Small, 6 ½", 1991 - 1993
      without signature
   Large, 7 ¼", 1991 - 1993
      without signature

PLATES; 1937 to date
   5", 1937 - c.1959
      with signature
      without signature
   6", 1937 - c.1959
      with signature
      without signature
   6 ½", 1937 to date
      with signature
      without signature
   7", 1937 - c.1959
      with signature
      without signature
   7 ½", 1937 - 1968
      with signature
      without signature

PLATES (cont.)
   8", 1968 to date
      without signature
   8 ½", 1937 - 1969
      with signature
      without signature
   10 ½", 1987 - 2000
      without signature

SAVINGS BOOK; 1982 to date
   without signature

STRATFORD; 1983 - 1997
   Beaker, 1983 - 1993
      without signature
   Saucer, 1987 - 1997
      without signature
   Teacup, 1987 - 1997
      without signature

SUGAR BOWL WITH HANDLES; c.1950
   with signature
   without signature

FINE WHITE CHINA

The following is a list of shapes that were included in a price list of 1937.

- Beaker
  - large
  - small
  - with one handle
- Beaker pad
- Bread and butter plate
- Carlton Jug
  - 24s (1 ¼ pint)
  - 30s (1 pint)
  - 36s (¾ pint)
  - 42s (½ pint)
- Cecil bowl UBC

- Egg cup
- Night light
- Oatmeal saucer
- Phillips bowl
  - 30s
  - 36s
  - 48s
- Plate
  - 4 inches
  - 5 inches
  - 6 inches
  - 7 inches

- Porridge plate
- Prince
  - Cream jug
    - 30s (½ pint)
  - Teapot
    - 30s (1 ½ pint)
    - 42s (1 pint)
- Rex Mug
  - large
  - small
- Teacup and saucer

BUNNYKINS TABLEWARE
Issues of 1934 to the present

ABC THEME — Colin Twinn

ABCDEF SCENE

Design No.: CT94 ABCDEF Scene
Designer: Colin Twinn
Issued: 1994 - 1999

Shape	U.S. $	Can. $	U.K. £	Aust. $
Baby plate, round, small	20.00	27.50	12.50	30.00
Oatmeal / Cereal bowl	15.00	20.00	10.00	25.00
Plate, 8"	15.00	20.00	10.00	25.00

ABCDEF Scene (CT94)

ABC Scene (CT95)

ABC SCENE / A SCENE

Design No.: Front — CT95 ABC Scene
Reverse — CT96 A Scene
Designer: Colin Twinn
Issued: 1994 - 1999

Shape	U.S. $	Can. $	U.K. £	Aust. $
Hug-a-mug, one handle	10.00	15.00	7.50	15.00
Money ball	10.00	15.00	7.50	15.00

A Scene (CT96)

Aerobics

Jogging

AEROBICS / JOGGING

A boxed Bunnykins for Grown Ups set containing a cereal bowl and hug-a-mug with one handle with the *Aerobics/Jogging* design, a 6" plate with the *Aeroplane* design, an 8" plate with the *Breakfast Time* design and a cereal bowl with *Tennis* design was distributed mainly in the U.S.A.

Design:	Front — Aerobics
	Reverse — Jogging
Designer:	Walter Hayward
Issued:	1986 - 1988
Series:	Bunnykins for Grown Ups

Shape	U.S. $	Can. $	U.K. £	Aust. $
Cereal / oatmeal bowl	40.00	60.00	25.00	60.00
Hug-a-mug, one handle	30.00	50.00	15.00	50.00
Complete set (M.I.B)	200.00	300.00	100.00	300.00

Note: See also *Aeroplane* below, *Breakfast Time* page 30 and *Tennis* page 158.

AEROPLANE

A boxed Bunnykins for Grown Ups set containing a cereal bowl and hug-a-mug with one handle with the *Aerobics/Jogging* design, a 6" plate with the *Aeroplane* design, an 8" plate with the *Breakfast Time* design and a cereal bowl with *Tennis* design was distributed mainly in the U.S.A.

Design:	Aeroplane
Designer:	Walter Hayward
Issued:	1986 - 1988
Series:	Bunnykins for Grown Ups

Shape	U.S. $	Can. $	U.K. £	Aust. $
Plate, 6"	40.00	65.00	25.00	65.00
Complete Set (M.I.B)	200.00	300.00	100.00	300.00

Aeroplane

Note: See Also *Aerobics* above, *Breakfast Time* page 30 and *Tennis* page 158.

AFTERNOON TEA / SERVING TEA

Design No.:	Front — HW116 Afternoon Tea
	Reverse — HW116R Serving Tea
Designer:	Walter Hayward
Issued:	1959 - by 1998
Combined with:	*Bugler with Toy Donkey*, HW26R
	Dress Making, HW26
	Hikers, EC124
	Ice Cream on the Beach, HW136R
	Playing with Dolls and Prams, HW115
	Sheltering Under an Umbrella, EC3
	Sledging, Style One, HW141
	Trying on Hats, HW28R

Afternoon Tea (HW116)

Shape	U.S. $	Can. $	U.K. £	Aust. $
Albion cream jug	35.00	55.00	20.00	60.00
Albion jug, ½ pint	85.00	115.00	50.00	125.00
Albion jug, 1 pint	100.00	150.00	60.00	165.00
Albion sugar bowl	30.00	40.00	17.50	45.00
Albion teapot	50.00	70.00	30.00	75.00
Casino jug, 36s	125.00	200.00	85.00	200.00
Casino jug, 42s	100.00	150.00	70.00	150.00
Casino saucer	7.50	12.00	5.00	12.00
Casino sugar bowl, 30s	125.00	200.00	85.00	225.00
Casino sugar bowl, 36s	100.00	150.00	65.00	175.00
Casino teacup	7.50	12.00	5.00	12.00
Casino teapot, 30s	150.00	225.00	100.00	250.00
Divider dish	50.00	75.00	35.00	75.00
Don beaker	25.00	35.00	15.00	40.00
Don beaker, one handle	25.00	35.00	15.00	40.00
Don mug, one handle	10.00	15.00	6.50	18.00
Don mug, two handles	10.00	15.00	6.50	18.00
Egg box				
small	225.00	350.00	150.00	400.00
medium	300.00	450.00	200.00	500.00
large	375.00	550.00	250.00	600.00
Hug-a-mug, one handle	10.00	15.00	7.50	15.00
Hug-a-mug, two handles	10.00	15.00	7.50	15.00
Jaffa fruit saucer (plain)	15.00	20.00	10.00	25.00
Lamp	50.00	75.00	30.00	85.00
Lid of hot water plate	50.00	65.00	30.00	70.00
Malvern beaker	15.00	25.00	10.00	25.00
Money ball	10.00	15.00	7.50	15.00
Picture plaque, small	20.00	30.00	15.00	30.00
Plate, 6 ½"	15.00	20.00	10.00	25.00
Savings book	15.00	22.50	10.00	22.50
Stratford teacup	10.00	15.00	7.50	15.00

Serving Tea (HW116R)

Note: Retirement dates are all approximate. When a design is retired all remaining stocks of the retired litho prints are used until exhausted.

Airmail Delivery (LFa)

AIRMAIL DELIVERY

Design No.	LFa
Designer:	Barbara Vernon
Issued:	By 1937 - by 1952

Shape	U.S. $	Can. $	U.K. £	Aust. $
Baby plate, round, small	300.00	400.00	200.00	425.00
Baby plate, round, large	400.00	525.00	250.00	550.00
Bread and butter plate	500.00	650.00	300.00	675.00
Hot water plate	375.00	500.00	250.00	550.00
Plate, 8 ½"	225.00	300.00	150.00	325.00
Porridge plate	300.00	400.00	200.00	425.00

Note: This design should appear with the Barbara Vernon facsimile signature.

Casino Jugs — Three sizes shown

Family at Breakfast (HW12)   Frightening Spider (SF4)   Going Shopping (SF10)

Four standard sizes of Casino jugs exist; ¾, 1, 1½ and 2 pint capacity. Only these sizes are listed in the shape book. However in between sizes are found in 1¼, 1¾ and 2¼ pint capacity which may have been standard sizes modified for numerous reasons.

¾ Pint	1 Pint	1 ½ Pint	2 Pint
42s - Height 4¼"	36s - Height 4 ¾"	30s - Height 5"	24s - Height 5 ½"

APPLE PICKING

Design No.: SF25
Designer: Walter Hayward
Issued: 1954 - by 1998
Combined with: *Lunch Break*, HW29R
Windy Day, HW27

Shape	U.S. $	Can. $	U.K. £	Aust. $
Baby plate, round, small				
with signature	30.00	40.00	20.00	50.00
without signature	20.00	27.50	12.50	30.00
Cake stand	150.00	250.00	100.00	300.00
Casino jug, 36s				
with signature	150.00	225.00	100.00	250.00
without signature	125.00	200.00	85.00	200.00
Casino saucer				
with signature	15.00	25.00	10.00	25.00
without signature	7.50	12.00	5.00	12.00
Casino sugar, 30s				
with signature	150.00	225.00	100.00	250.00
without signature	125.00	200.00	85.00	225.00
Cereal / oatmeal bowl				
with signature	25.00	35.00	20.00	40.00
without signature	15.00	20.00	10.00	25.00
Hot water plate				
with signature	100.00	135.00	65.00	150.00
without signature	75.00	100.00	45.00	110.00
Picture plaque, large	20.00	30.00	12.50	30.00
Plate, 6 ½"				
with signature	25.00	35.00	15.00	40.00
without signature	15.00	20.00	10.00	25.00
Plate, 7 ½"				
with signature	30.00	40.00	20.00	45.00
without signature	15.00	20.00	10.00	25.00
Plate, 8"	15.00	20.00	10.00	25.00

Note: An 8" plate was issued for the 'U.S. Special Events Tour. 1990,' see page 196.

Apple Picking (SF25)

'Special Events Tour 1990'

Art Class (LF107)

ART CLASS

Design No.: LF107
Designer: Walter Hayward
Issued: 1959 - 1970

Shape	U.S. $	Can. $	U.K. £	Aust. $
Baby plate, oval, large	300.00	400.00	200.00	425.00
Baby plate, oval, small	300.00	400.00	200.00	425.00
Baby plate, round, large	200.00	275.00	125.00	300.00
Plate, 8 ½"	75.00	100.00	45.00	110.00
Porridge plate	100.00	135.00	65.00	145.00

Artist (HW1)

ARTIST

Design No.:   HW1
Designer: Barbara Vernon
Issued: By 1937 - by 1952
Combined with: *Dunce*, HW1R
                 Fishing in the Goldfish Bowl, HW3R
                 Greetings, HW7
                 Netting a Cricket, HW6
                 Pulling on Trousers, HW2

Shape	U.S. $	Can. $	U.K. £	Aust. $
Baby plate, round, small				
with signature	50.00	65.00	30.00	70.00
without signature	30.00	40.00	20.00	45.00
Casino jug, 42s				
with signature	300.00	450.00	200.00	500.00
without signature	250.00	375.00	175.00	400.00
Casino saucer				
with signature	100.00	150.00	65.00	175.00
without signature	75.00	125.00	50.00	125.00
Casino sugar bowl, 30s				
with signature	250.00	375.00	175.00	400.00
without signature	175.00	275.00	125.00	325.00
Casino teacup				
with signature	100.00	150.00	65.00	175.00
without signature	75.00	125.00	50.00	125.00
Don beaker				
with signature	65.00	85.00	40.00	90.00
without signature	35.00	45.00	20.00	50.00
Don beaker, one handle				
with signature	65.00	85.00	40.00	90.00
without signature	35.00	45.00	20.00	50.00
Don mug, one handle				
with signature	50.00	65.00	30.00	75.00
without signature	15.00	20.00	10.00	25.00
Don mug, two handles				
with signature	50.00	65.00	30.00	75.00
without signature	15.00	20.00	10.00	25.00
Jam pot	1,500.00	1,975.00	950.00	2,000.00
Jaffa fruit saucer				
plain rim	50.00	65.00	30.00	70.00
wavy rim	75.00	100.00	50.00	125.00
Plate, 6 ½"				
with signature	30.00	40.00	20.00	45.00
without signature	20.00	25.00	12.00	30.00

FINE WHITE CHINA

		U.K. £	
Beaker, one handle		300.00	
Plate, 5"		650.00	
Plate, 6"		650.00	
Plate, 7"		650.00	
Saucer		300.00	
Teacup		300.00	

Note: White china prices are indications only due to the scarcity of the items. Prices will fluctuate.

ASLEEP IN THE OPEN AIR

Design No.:	HW10
Designer:	Barbara Vernon
Issued:	By 1937 - by 1967
Combined with:	*Bathtime*, Style One, SF18
	Convalescing, SF5
	Gardening, Style One, HW9
	Leapfrog, HW12R
	Washing in the Open Air, HW10R
	Wheelbarrow Race, Style One, HW22

Asleep in the Open Air (HW10)

Shape	U.S. $	Can. $	U.K. £	Aust. $
Casino jug, 30s				
with signature	375.00	525.00	235.00	575.00
without signature	300.00	425.00	190.00	475.00
Casino jug, 36s				
with signature	300.00	425.00	190.00	475.00
without signature	275.00	400.00	175.00	450.00
Casino jug, 42s				
with signature	275.00	400.00	175.00	450.00
without signature	200.00	275.00	125.00	300.00
Casino saucer				
with signature	75.00	100.00	50.00	125.00
without signature	50.00	65.00	30.00	75.00
Casino sugar bowl, 30s				
with signature	200.00	275.00	125.00	300.00
without signature	175.00	175.00	80.00	200.00
Casino sugar bowl 36s				
with signature	150.00	225.00	100.00	250.00
without signature	125.00	175.00	80.00	200.00
Casino teacup				
with signature	75.00	100.00	50.00	125.00
without signature	50.00	65.00	30.00	75.00
Casino teapot, 24s				
with signature	375.00	525.00	235.00	575.00
without signature	300.00	425.00	190.00	475.00

Shape	U.S. $	Can. $	U.K. £	Aust. $
Casino teapot, 30s				
with signature	300.00	425.00	190.00	475.00
without signature	225.00	325.00	150.00	375.00
Casino teapot, 36s				
with signature	275.00	400.00	175.00	450.00
without signature	200.00	275.00	125.00	300.00
Don beaker				
with signature	150.00	225.00	100.00	250.00
without signature	100.00	150.00	65.00	165.00
Don beaker, one handle				
with signature	150.00	225.00	100.00	250.00
without signature	100.00	150.00	65.00	165.00
Don mug, one handle				
with signature	75.00	100.00	50.00	125.00
without signature	35.00	55.00	20.00	60.00
Don mug, two handles				
with signature	75.00	100.00	50.00	125.00
without signature	35.00	55.00	20.00	60.00
Jaffa fruit saucer				
plain rim	35.00	55.00	20.00	60.00
wavy rim	65.00	90.00	40.00	100.00
Plate, 6 ½"				
with signature	60.00	80.00	38.00	85.00
without signature	35.00	55.00	20.00	60.00

Picnic with Kangaroo and Koala,
First Variation (CT84)

AUSTRALIANA BUNNYKINS — Colin Twinn
PICNIC WITH KANGAROO AND KOALA
First Variation, Large Size

The 1994 plates have a leaf border with the inscription Bunnykins 60th Anniversary 1994.

Design No.:   Front — CT84 Picnic with Kangaroo and Koala
                Reverse — CT85 Commemorative Leaf Border
Designer: Colin Twinn
Issued: 1994 - 1994
Backstamp: 'Bunnykins 60th Anniversary Australiana
                Bunnykins. Produced exclusively for Royal
                Doulton Australia.'

Shape	U.S. $	Can. $	U.K. £	Aust. $
Plate, 8"	25.00	35.00	15.00	40.00

PICNIC WITH KANGAROO AND KOALA
Second Variation, Small Size

Design No.:   CT86 Picnic with Kangaroo and Koala
Designer: Colin Twinn
Issued: 1994 - 1994
Backstamp: 'Australiana Bunnykins. Produced exclusively
                for Royal Doulton Australia.'

Shape	U.S. $	Can. $	U.K. £	Aust. $
Baby plate, round, small	25.00	35.00	15.00	40.00
Cereal / oatmeal bowl	15.00	20.00	10.00	20.00

Picnic with Kangaroo and Koala,
Second Variation (CT86)

Backstamp (CT86)

PICNIC SCENE / BUNNY WITH CAKE PLATE

The backstamp on this teacup and saucer does not refer to the 60th Anniversary celebrations.

Design No.:	Front — CT87 Picnic Scene		
	Reverse — CT88 Bunny with Cake Plate		
Designer:	Colin Twinn		
Issued:	1994 - 1994		

Shape	U.S. $	Can. $	U.K. £	Aust. $
Stratford teacup	40.00	60.00	25.00	60.00

Front — Picnic Scene (CT87)

Front — Picinic Scene with Hamper (CT89)

Reverse — Bunny with Cake Plate (CT88)

Reverse — Father Asleep (CT90)

PICNIC SCENE WITH HAMPER / FATHER ASLEEP

Design No.:	Front — CT89 Picnic Scene with Hamper
	Reverse — CT90 Father Asleep
Designer:	Colin Twinn
Issued:	1994 - 1994
Backstamp:	'Australiana Bunnykins. Produced exclusively
	for Royal Doulton Australia.'

Shape	U.S. $	Can. $	U.K. £	Aust. $
Hug-a-mug, one handle	25.00	35.00	15.0 0	40.00
Money ball	15.00	20.00	10.00	20.00

Baking (SF19)

BAKING

Design No.:	SF19
Designer:	Walter Hayward after Barbara Vernon
Issued:	By 1952 - by 1998
Combined with:	*Convalescing*, SF5
	Cricketer, HW22R
	Soldiers Marching to Music, HW16
	Wheelbarrow Race, HW22

Shape	U.S. $	Can. $	U.K. £	Aust. $
Baby plate, round, large				
with signature	75.00	125.00	50.00	150.00
without signature	50.00	75.00	35.00	185.00
Baby plate, round, small				
with signature	30.00	40.00	20.00	50.00
without signature	20.00	27.50	12.50	30.00
Casino jug, 24s				
with signature	325.00	500.00	225.00	550.00
without signature	175.00	275.00	125.00	300.00
Casino jug, 30s				
with signature	250.00	400.00	175.00	425.00
without signature	150.00	250.00	100.00	250.00
Casino saucer				
with signature	15.00	25.00	10.00	25.00
without signature	7.50	12.00	5.00	12.00
Casino teapot, 24s				
with signature	275.00	400.00	175.00	450.00
without signature	175.00	275.00	125.00	325.00
Cereal / oatmeal bowl				
with signature	25.00	35.00	20.00	40.00
without signature	15.00	20.00	10.00	25.00
Hot water plate				
with signature	100.00	135.00	65.00	150.00
without signature	75.00	100.00	45.00	110.00
Jaffa fruit saucer				
plain rim	15.00	20.00	10.00	25.00
wavy rim	35.00	55.00	20.00	60.00
Picture plaque, large	20.00	30.00	12.50	30.00
Plate, 6 ½"				
with signature	25.00	35.00	15.00	40.00
without signature	15.00	20.00	10.00	25.00
Plate, 8"	15.00	20.00	10.00	25.00
Plate, 8 ½"				
with signature	30.00	40.00	20.00	45.00
without signature	15.00	20.00	10.00	25.00

BAKING THEME — Frank Endersby

BAKING CAKES WITH MOTHER

Design No.:	7 Baking Cakes with Mother
Designer:	Frank Endersby
Issued:	1995 to the present

Shape	U.S. $	Can. $	U.K. £	Aust. $
Baby plate, round, small	N/I	46.00	14.00	62.95
Cereal / oatmeal bowl	N/I	33.00	11.00	49.95
Jaffa fruit saucer	15.00	20.00	10.00	25.00
Plate, 6 ½"	N/I	25.00	8.00	34.95
Plate, 8"	N/I	35.00	11.00	49.95

Baking Cakes with Mother (7)

Taking Cake from Oven (8)

TAKING CAKE FROM OVEN / DECORATING THE CAKE

Design No.:	Front — 8 Taking Cake from Oven
	Reverse — 9 Decorating the Cake
Designer:	Frank Endersby
Issued:	1995 to the present
Combined with:	*Carrying Letter, (30)

Shape	U.S. $	Can. $	U.K. £	Aust. $
Hug-a-mug, one handle	30.00	33.00	11.00	49.95
Hug-a-mug, two handles	32.50	39.00	12.00	56.95
Divider dish	50.00	75.00	35.00	75.00
Money ball	33.75	40.00	15.00	62.95
Stratford teacup	20.00	30.00	10.00	30.00

* Indicates scene on divider dish.

Decorating the Cake (9)

Note: 1. Bold type in the listing tables indicate a current design on a current shape.
2. N/I. Not issued individually. The item(s) will be found only in boxed sets in that market.

Bath Night (LF7)

BATH NIGHT

Design No.:   LF7
Designer: Barbara Vernon
Issued: By 1940 - by 1952

Shape	U.S. $	Can. $	U.K. £	Aust. $
Baby plate, oval, small				
with signature	350.00	450.00	225.00	475.00
without signature	300.00	400.00	200.00	425.00
Baby plate, round, large				
with silver rim	300.00	400.00	200.00	425.00
with signature	250.00	325.00	150.00	350.00
without signature	200.00	275.00	125.00	300.00
Bread and butter plate				
with signature	400.00	525.00	250.00	550.00
without signature	350.00	450.00	225.00	475.00
Cereal / oatmeal bowl				
with signature	100.00	135.00	65.00	150.00
without signature	90.00	125.00	55.00	135.00
Plate, 8 ½"				
with signature	100.00	135.00	65.00	145.00
without signature	75.00	100.00	45.00	110.00
Porridge plate				
with signature	125.00	175.00	80.00	185.00
without signature	100.00	135.00	65.00	145.00

Note: Condition is important. Prices listed are based on nurseryware in mint condition. Items in less than mint condition will command lower prices.

BATHTIME, Style One

Design No.:	SF18
Designer:	Walter Hayward after Barbara Vernon
Issued:	By 1952 - 1994
Combined with:	*Asleep in the Open Air*, HW10

Shape	U.S. $	Can. $	U.K. £	Aust. $
Baby plate, round, small				
with signature	30.00	40.00	20.00	50.00
without signature	20.00	27.50	12.50	30.00
Cake stand	150.00	250.00	100.00	300.00
Casino jug, 30s				
with signature	250.00	400.00	175.00	425.00
without signature	150.00	250.00	100.00	250.00
Casino saucer				
with signature	15.00	25.00	10.00	25.00
without signature	7.50	12.00	5.00	12.00
Cereal / oatmeal bowl				
with signature	25.00	35.00	20.00	40.00
without signature	15.00	20.00	10.00	25.00
Hot water plate				
with signature	100.00	135.00	65.00	150.00
without signature	75.00	100.00	45.00	110.00
Jaffa fruit saucer				
plain rim				
with signature	25.00	35.00	20.00	40.00
without signature	15.00	20.00	10.00	25.00
wavy rim	35.00	55.00	20.00	60.00
Picture plaque, large	20.00	30.00	12.50	30.00
Plate, 6 ½"				
with signature	25.00	35.00	15.00	40.00
without signature	15.00	20.00	10.00	25.00
Plate, 7 ½"				
with signature	30.00	40.00	20.00	45.00
without signature	15.00	20.00	10.00	25.00
Plate, 8 ½"				
with signature	30.00	40.00	20.00	45.00
without signature	15.00	20.00	10.00	25.00

Bathtime, Style One (SF18)

BATHTIME THEME — Colin Twinn

Bathtime, Style Two (CT21)

BATHTIME
Style Two, First Variation

Design No.:	CT21 Bathtime
Designer:	Colin Twinn
Issued:	1991 - 1993

Shape	U.S. $	Can. $	U.K. £	Aust. $
Albion jug, 1 pint	100.00	150.00	60.00	165.00
Albion teapot	50.00	70.00	30.00	75.00
Baby plate, round, small	10.00	15.00	7.50	15.00
Cereal / oatmeal bowl	15.00	20.00	10.00	25.00
Picture plaque, large	20.00	30.00	12.50	30.00
Plate, 8"	15.00	20.00	10.00	25.00

Bathtime Scene, Style Two (CT24)

BATHTIME SCENE
Style Two, Second Variation /
BUNNIES IN THE BATH, First Version

Design No.:	Front — CT24 Bathtime Scene
	Reverse — CT25 Bunnies in the Bath, First Version
Designer:	Colin Twinn
Issued:	1991 - 1993
Combined with:	*Bunnies in Bath*, Second Version, CT34
	Bunny on Trike, CT23
	School Gates, Second Variation, CT22

Shape	U.S. $	Can. $	U.K. £	Aust. $
Albion cream jug	35.00	55.00	20.00	60.00
Albion jug, ½ pint	85.00	115.00	50.00	115.00
Albion jug, 1 pint	100.00	150.00	60.00	165.00
Albion teapot	50.00	70.00	30.00	75.00
Hug-a-mug, one handle	10.00	15.00	7.50	15.00
Hug-a-mug, two handles	10.00	15.00	7.50	15.00
Lamp	50.00	75.00	30.00	85.00
Malvern beaker	15.00	25.00	10.00	25.00
Money ball	10.00	15.00	7.50	15.00
Stratford straight beaker	15.00	25.00	10.00	25.00
Stratford teacup	7.50	12.00	5.00	12.00

Note: *Bunnies in the Bath* (CT34) is combined with *Bathtime Scene* (CT24) on a Stratford straight beaker.

Bunnies in the Bath, First Version (CT25)

BUNNIES IN THE BATH
Second Version

Design No.:	CT34
Designer:	Colin Twinn
Issued:	1991 - 1993
Combined with:	*Bathtime Scene*, Style Two,
	Second Variation, (CT24)
	Bunny with Mirror, CT35
	Pushing the Wheelbarrow, CT3

Shape	U.S. $	Can. $	U.K. £	Aust. $
Albion sugar bowl	30.00	40.00	17.50	45.00
Albion teapot	50.00	70.00	30.00	75.00
Egg cup				
Style Three	10.00	15.00	7.50	18.00
Savings book	15.00	22.50	10.00	22.50
Stratford straight beaker	15.00	25.00	10.00	25.00

Bunnies in the Bath, Second Version (CT34)

Rex Mug, *Family at Breakfast* (HW12)

BATHTIME THEME – Frank Endersby

Bathtime, Style Three (22)

BATHTIME
Style Three

Design No.:   22 Bathtime
Designer: Frank Endersby
Issued: 1995 to the present

Shape	U.S. $	Can. $	U.K. £	Aust. $
Baby plate, round, small	N/I	46.00	14.00	62.95
Plate, 6½"	N/I	25.00	8.00	34.95
Plate, 8"	N/I	35.00	11.00	49.95

Blowing and Bursting Bubbles (23)

BLOWING AND BURSTING BUBBLES /
BLOWING BUBBLES AND SAILING BOATS

Design No.:   Front — 23 Blowing and Bursting Bubbles
                Reverse — 24 Blowing Bubbles and Sailing Boats
Designer: Frank Endersby
Issued: 1996 to the present

Shape	U.S. $	Can. $	U.K. £	Aust. $
Hug-a-mug, one handle	30.00	33.00	11.00	49.95
Hug-a-mug, two handles	32.50	39.00	12.00	56.95
Stratford teacup	7.50	12.00	5.00	12.00

Blowing Bubbles and Sailing Boats (24)

BEDTIME IN BUNKS, Style One

Design No.:	SF3
Designer:	Barbara Vernon
Issued:	By 1937 - by 1952
Combined with:	*Family at Breakfast,* HW12
	Feeding the Baby, HW13
	Pulling on Trousers, HW2

Shape	U.S. $	Can. $	U.K. £	Aust. $
Candle holder	2,000.00	2,500.00	1,250.00	2,500.00
Casino jug, 42s	275.00	400.00	175.00	450.00
Hot water plate	200.00	275.00	125.00	300.00
Plate, 7"	90.00	125.00	55.00	135.00
Plate, 7 ½"	100.00	135.00	65.00	145.00
Plate, 8 ½"	100.00	135.00	65.00	145.00

Note: This design should appear with the Barbara Vernon facsimile signature. See next page for *Bedtime In Bunks,* style two.

Bedtime in Bunks, Style One (SF3)

Bedtime Story (SF130)

BEDTIME STORY

Design No.:	SF130
Designer:	Walter Hayward
Issued:	1967 - 1994

Shape	U.S. $	Can. $	U.K. £	Aust. $
Baby plate round, small	20.00	27.50	12.50	30.00
Cake stand	150.00	250.00	100.00	300.00
Casino saucer	7.50	12.00	5.00	12.00
Casino teapot, 24s	175.00	275.00	125.00	325.00
Cereal / oatmeal bowl	15.00	20.00	10.00	25.00
Coupe dish, 6 ¾"			Rare	
Hot water plate	75.00	100.00	45.00	110.00
Jaffa fruit saucer (plain)	15.00	20.00	10.00	25.00
Picture plaque, large	20.00	30.00	12.50	30.00
Plate, 6"	15.00	20.00	10.00	25.00
Plate, 6 ½"	15.00	20.00	10.00	25.00
Plate, 8"	15.00	20.00	10.00	25.00

BEDTIME THEME — Frank Endersby

Bedtime in Bunks, Style Two (13)

BEDTIME IN BUNKS, Style Two

Design No.:	13 Bedtime in Bunks
Designer:	Frank Endersby
Issued:	1995 to the present

Shape	U.S. $	Can. $	U.K. £	Aust. $
Baby plate, round, small	N/I	46.00	14.00	62.95
Cereal / oatmeal bowl	N/I	33.00	11.00	49.95
Plate, 6 ½"	N/I	25.00	8.00	34.95
Plate, 8"	N/I	35.00	11.00	49.95

PILLOW FIGHT, Style Two / PLAYING AND READING

Design No.:	Front — 14 Pillow Fight
	Reverse — 15 Playing and Reading
Designer:	Frank Endersby
Issued:	1995 to the present
Combined with:	*Playing with Ball, (42)

Shape	U.S. $	Can. $	U.K. £	Aust. $
Hug-a-mug, one handle	30.00	33.00	11.00	49.95
Hug-a-mug, two handles	32.50	39.00	12.00	56.95
Divider dish	50.00	75.00	35.00	75.00
Stratford teacup	7.50	12.00	5.00	12.00

* Indicates scene on divider dish.

Pillow Fight, Style Two (14)

Playing and Reading (15)

Note: **1.** Bold type in listing tables indicate a current design on a current shape.
2. N/I. Not issued individually. The item(s) will be found only in boxed sets in that market.

BUNNYKINS

DB1 – Family Photograph
Bunnykins

DB2 – Buntie Bunnykins
Helping Mother

DB3 – Billie Bunnykins
Cooling Off

DB4 – Billie & Buntie Bunnykins
Sleigh Ride, *First Variation*

DB5 – Mr. Bunnykins
Autumn Days

DB6 – Mrs. Bunnykins
Clean Sweep

DB7 – Daisie Bunnykins
Spring Time

DB8 – Dollie Bunnykins Playtime
First Variation

DB9 – Storytime Bunnykins
First Variation

DB10 – Busy Needles
Bunnykins

DB11 – Rise and Shine
Bunnykins

DB12 –Tally Ho! Bunnykins
First Variation

BUNNYKINS

DB13 – The Artist
Bunnykins

DB14 – Grandpa's Story
Bunnykins

DB15 – Sleepytime
Bunnykins

DB16 – Mr. Bunnybeat
Strumming

DB17 – Santa Bunnykins
Happy Christmas

DB18 – Mr. Bunnykins at
the Easter Parade

DB19 – Mrs. Bunnykins at
the Easter Parade

DB20 – Astro Bunnykins
Rocket Man

DB21 – Happy Birthday
Bunnykins

DB22 – Jogging Bunnykins

DB23 – Sousaphone Bunnykins
First Variation

DB24 – Trumpeter Bunnykins
First Variation

BUNNYKINS

DB25 – Cymbals Bunnykins
First Variation

DB26A – Drummer Bunnykins
Style One
First Variation

DB26B – Drummer Bunnykins
Style One
Second Variation

DB27 – Drum-Major
Bunnykins
First Variation

DB28A – Olympic Bunnykins
First Variation

DB28B – Olympic Bunnykins
Second Variation

DB29A – Touchdown Bunnykins
First Variation

DB29B – Touchdown Bunnykins
Second Variation

DB30 – Knockout
Bunnykins

DB31 – Downhill Bunnykins

DB32 – Bogey Bunnykins

DB33 – Tally Ho!
Music Box

BUNNYKINS

DB34 – Santa Bunnykins
Music Box

DB35 – Astro Bunnykins
Rocket Man, Music Box

DB36 – Happy Birthday
Bunnykins, Music Box

DB37 – Jogging Bunnykins
Music Box

DB38 – Mr. Bunnybeat Strumming
Music Box

DB39 – Mrs. Bunnykins at the
Easter parade, Music Box

DB40 – Aerobic Bunnykins

DB41 – Freefall Bunnykins

DB42 – Ace Bunnykins

Note: DB44 Ballet Bunnykins not issued

DB43 – Home Run Bunnykins

DB45 – King John
First Variation

DB46 – Queen Sophie
First Variation

BUNNYKINS

DB47 – Princess Beatrice
First Variation

DB48 – Prince Frederick
First Variation

DB49 – Harry The Herald
First Variation

DB50 – Uncle Sam Bunnykins
First Variation

DB51 – Mr. Bunnykins
at the Easter Parade
Second Variation

DB52 – Mrs. Bunnykins at the Easter
Parade, *Second Variation*

DB53 – Carol Singer Bunnykins
Music Box

DB54 – Collector Bunnykins

DB55 – Bedtime Bunnykins
First Variation

DB56 – Be Prepared Bunnykins

DB57 – Schooldays Bunnykins

DB58 – Australian Bunnykins

BUNNYKINS

DB59 – Storytime Bunnykins
Second Variation

DB60 – Schoolmaster Bunnykins

DB61 – Brownie Bunnykins

DB62 – Santa Bunnykins Happy Christmas
Christmas Tree Ornament

DB63 – Bedtime Bunnykins
Second Variation

DB64 – Policeman
Bunnykins

DB65 – Lollipopman
Bunnykins

DB66 – Schoolboy
Bunnykins

DB67 – Family Photograph
Bunnykins, *Second Variation*

DB68 – Father, Mother &
Victoria Bunnykins

DB69 – William
Bunnykins

DB70 – Susan Bunnykins

BUNNYKINS

DB71 – Polly Bunnykins

DB72 – Tom Bunnykins

DB73 – Harry Bunnykins

DB74A – Nurse Bunnykins
First Variation

DB74B – Nurse Bunnykins
Second Variation

DB75 – Fireman Bunnykins
First Variation

DB76 – Postman Bunnykins

DB77 – Paperboy Bunnykins

DB78 – Tally Ho! Bunnykins
Second Variation

DB79 –Bedtime Bunnykins
Third Variation

DB80 – Dolly Bunnykins Playtime
Second Variation

DB81 – Billie & Buntie Bunnykins
Sleigh Ride, *Second Variation*

BUNNYKINS

DB82 – Ice Cream Bunnykins

DB83 – Susan Bunnykins as
Queen of the May

DB84 – Fisherman Bunnykins
Style One

DB85 – Cook Bunnykins

DB86 – Sousaphone
Bunnykins
Second Variation

DB87 – Trumpeter Bunnykins
Second Variation

DB88 – Cymbals Bunnykins
Second Variation

DB89 – Drummer Bunnykins
Style One, Third Variation

DB90 – Drum-Major Bunnykins
Second Variation

DB91 – King John
Second Variation

DB92 – Queen Sophie
Second Variation

DB93 – Princess Beatrice
Second Variation

BEDTIME WITH DOLLIES

Design No.:	EC125
Designer:	Walter Hayward
Issued:	1959 - 1992
Combined with:	*Cricketer*, HW22R
	Drummer, EC2
	Drummer and Bugler, EC126
	Hikers, EC124
	Holding Hat and Coat, EC4
	Playing with Cup and Spoon, EC6
	Playing with Doll and Pram, EC123
	Raising Hat, Style Two, EC7
	Reading, EC122
	Sheltering Under an Umbrella, EC3
	Trumpeter, EC5
	Trying on Knitting, HW119R
	Unravelling the Knitting, HW119
	Wheelbarrow Race, Style One, HW22

Bedtime with Dollies (EC125)

Shape	U.S. $	Can. $	U.K. £	Aust. $
Albion sugar bowl	30.00	40.00	17.50	45.00
Beaker cover	40.00	55.00	25.00	60.00
Casino sugar bowl, 36s	100.00	150.00	65.00	175.00
Egg cup				
Style One	30.00	40.00	20.00	45.00
Style Two	40.00	55.00	25.00	60.00
Style Three	10.00	15.00	7.50	18.00
Lid of hot water plate	50.00	65.00	30.00	70.00
Money Ball	10.00	15.00	7.50	15.00

Beware of the Bull, (LF108)

BEWARE OF THE BULL

Design No.:	LF108
Designer:	Walter Hayward
Issued:	1959 - 1970

Shape	U.S. $	Can. $	U.K. £	Aust. $
Baby plate, oval, large	150.00	200.00	95.00	225.00
Baby plate, oval, small	150.00	200.00	95.00	225.00
Baby plate, round, large	75.00	100.00	50.00	125.00
Plate, 8"	25.00	35.00	15.00	45.00
Plate, 8 ½"	25.00	35.00	15.00	45.00
Porridge plate	85.00	125.00	55.00	150.00

Bonfire (LF128)

BONFIRE

Design No.:	LF128
Designer:	Walter Hayward
Issued:	1967 - 1970

Shape	U.S. $	Can. $	U.K. £	Aust. $
Baby plate, round, large	350.00	450.00	200.00	475.00
Plate, 8"	175.00	225.00	115.00	250.00
Porridge Bowl	250.00	325.00	150.00	350.00

BREAKFAST TIME

A boxed Bunnykins for Grown Ups set containing a cereal bowl and hug-a-mug with one handle with the *Aerobics/Jogging* design, a 6" plate with the *Aeroplane* design, an 8" plate with the *Breakfast Time* design a cereal bowl in the *Tennis* design was distributed mainly in the U.S.A.

Design No.:	Breakfast Time
Designer:	Walter Hayward
Issued:	1986 - 1988
Series:	Bunnykins for Grown Ups

Shape	U.S. $	Can. $	U.K. £	Aust. $
Plate, 8"	45.00	70.00	30.00	75.00
Complete set (M.I.B.)	200.00	300.00	100.00	300.00

Breakfast Time

Note: See also *Aerobics/Jogging* and *Aeroplane* page 12 and *Tennis* page 158.

BUILDING SAND CASTLES / SAILING BOATS

Design No.:	Front — HW138 Building Sand Castles
	Reverse — HW138R Sailing Boats
Designer:	Walter Hayward
Issued:	1967 - by 1998
Combined with:	*Ice Cream on Beach, HW136R*
	Playing with Doll and Pram, EC123
	Roller Skating Arm in Arm, HW137R
	Roller Skating Race, HW137

Shape	U.S. $	Can. $	U.K. £	Aust. $
Albion cream jug	35.00	55.00	20.00	60.00
Albion jug, ½ pint	85.00	115.00	50.00	115.00
Albion teapot	50.00	70.00	30.00	75.00
Casino teacup	7.50	12.00	5.00	12.00
Don beaker	25.00	35.00	15.00	40.00
Don beaker, one handle	25.00	35.00	15.00	40.00
Don mug, one handles	10.00	15.00	6.50	18.00
Don mug, two handles	10.00	15.00	6.50	18.00
Hug-a-mug, one handle	10.00	15.00	7.50	15.00
Hug-a-mug, two handles	10.00	15.00	7.50	15.00
Lamp	50.00	75.00	30.00	85.00
Lid of hot water plate	50.00	65.00	30.00	70.00
Malvern beaker	15.00	25.00	10.00	25.00
Money ball	10.00	15.00	7.50	15.00
Picture plaque, small	20.00	30.00	12.50	30.00
Stratford straight beaker	15.00	25.00	10.00	25.00
Stratford teacup	7.50	12.00	5.00	12.00
Savings book	15.00	22.50	10.00	22.50

Building Sand Castles (HW138)

Sailing Boats (HW138R)

Bunnykins Build a Snowman (PN198)

BUNNYKINS BUILD A SNOWMAN

Design No.:	PN198
Designer:	Frank Endersby
Issued:	1998 - 1998
Series:	ICC Plate of the Year, Number 2

Shape	U.S. $	Can. $	U.K. £	Aust. $
Plate, 8"	25.00	35.00	15.00	40.00

Divider Dish decorated with Frank Endersby scenes;
Building a Snowman (59), *Sleding*, Style Two (60)
and *Resting in Wheelbarrow (57)*

BUNNYKINS CELEBRATES YOUR CHRISTENING – Walter Hayward

BUNNYKINS CELEBRATE YOUR CHRISTENING
Style One, First Version

Design No.:	SF139 Bunnykins celebrate your Christening
Designer:	Walter Hayward
Issued:	1984 - 1989

Shape	U.S. $	Can. $	U.K. £	Aust. $
Money ball	15.00	20.00	10.00	20.00
Plate, 8"	15.00	20.00	10.00	25.00

Bunnykins Celebrate Your Christening
First Version (SF139)

Bunnykins Celebrate Your Christening
Second Version (HW142)

Style One, Second Version

Design No.:	Front — HW142 Bunnykins celebrate your Christening
	Reverse — HW142R Christening inscription
Designer:	Walter Hayward
Issued:	1984 - 1990

Shape	U.S. $	Can. $	U.K. £	Aust. $
Hug-a-mug, one handle	10.00	15.00	7.50	15.00
Hug-a-mug, two handles	10.00	15.00	7.50	15.00
Money ball	10.00	15.00	7.50	15.00
Savings book	15.00	22.50	10.00	22.50

BUNNYKINS CELEBRATE YOUR CHRISTENING

Christening Inscription (HW142R)

BUNNYKINS CELEBRATES YOUR CHRISTENING – Colin Twinn

Bunnykins Celebrate Your Christening
First Variation (CT38)

BUNNYKINS CELEBRATE YOUR CHRISTENING
Style Two, First Variation, Large Size

Design No.:	Front — CT38 Bunnykins Celebrate your Christening Reverse no. one — without rhyme Reverse no. two — CT65 with rhyme
Designer:	Colin Twinn
Issued:	1990 - 1993
Rhyme:	"Today, as your family welcomes you, To bless who you are and all you will do, The Bunnykins join in your bright celebration. And bring you a message of jubilation For, on this your day, we all wish for you A lifetime of love and much happiness too."

Shape	U.S. $	Can. $	U.K. £	Aust. $
Plate, 8"	15.00	20.00	10.00	25.00

Christening Rhyme (CT65)

Bunnykins Celebrate Your Christening
Second Variation (CT41)

Style Two, Second Variation, Small Size

Design No.:	Front — CT41 Bunnykins celebrate your Christening Reverse — CT42 Christening inscription
Designer:	Colin Twinn
Issued:	1991 - 1993

Shape	U.S. $	Can. $	U.K. £	Aust. $
Hug-a-mug, one handle	10.00	15.00	7.50	15.00
Hug-a-mug, two handles	10.00	15.00	7.50	15.00
Money ball	10.00	15.00	7.50	15.00

Christening Inscription (CT42)

BABY IN CRIB WITH FATHER LOOKING ON
Style Three, First Variation

Design No.:	Front — CT76 Baby in Crib with Father Looking On
	Reverse — CT77 Rhyme
Designer:	Colin Twinn
Issued:	1993 to the present
Rhyme:	"Today, as your family welcomes you,
	To bless who you are and all you will do,
	The Bunnykins join in your bright celebration.
	And bring you a message of jubilation
	For, on this your day, we all wish for you
	A lifetime of love and much happiness too."

Shape	U.S. $	Can. $	U.K. £	Aust. $
Plate, 8"	N/I	35.00	11.00	49.95

Baby in Crib with Father Looking On (CT76)

Baby in Crib (CT78)

BABY IN CRIB
Style Three, Second Variation

Design No.:	Front — CT78 Baby in Crib
	Reverse — CT79 Christening inscription
Designer:	Colin Twinn
Issued:	1993 to the present

Shape	U.S. $	Can. $	U.K. £	Aust. $
Hug-a-mug, one handle	30.00	33.00	11.00	49.95
Hug-a-mug, two handles	32.50	39.00	12.00	56.95
Money ball	33.75	40.00	15.00	62.95

Christening Inscription (CT79)

Note: 1. Bold type in the listing tables indicate a current design on a current shape.
2. N/I, Not issued individually. The item(s) will be found only in boxed sets in that market.

BUNNYKINS COLLECTORS CLUB, AUSTRALIA

Member of Bunnykins Club/Television Time (SF112)

MEMBER OF BUNNYKINS CLUB
BUNNYKINS BUNNIES ARE CHILDREN
LIKE YOU

These plates, with the Member of Bunnykins Club inscription, were made exclusively for the Bunnykins club members in Australia. Other designs with this inscription may exist.

Design No.:
    SF18 — Bathtime, Style One
    SF112 — Television Time
    SF113 — Camp Site
    SF130 — Bedtime Story
    SF131 — Home Decorating
    SF132 — Space Rocket Launch
    SF133 — Flying Kites
    SF134 — Toppling the Fruit Cart
    SF135 — Family in the Garden

Issued: 1979 - 1985

Shape	Design	U.S. $	Can. $	U.K. £	Aust. $
Plate, 6 ½"	Various	200.00	250.00	125.00	275.00

BUNNYKINS HELP SANTA

Design No.:   PN175
Designer: Frank Endersby
Issued: 1997 - 1997
Series: ICC Plate of the Year, Number 1
Backstamp: ICC plus Bunnykins and Frank Endersby facsimile signature

Shape	U.S. $	Can. $	U.K. £	Aust. $
Plate, 8"	25.00	35.00	15.00	40.00

Bunnykins Help Santa (PN175)

BUNNYKINS TEACHING CLOCKS
Walter Hayward, Colin Twinn, Frank Endersby

BUNNYKINS TEACHING CLOCK
Classroom Scene, Style One

Design No.:	Front — SF138 Classroom Scene
	Reverse — Inscription
Designer:	Walter Hayward
Issued:	1983 - to date
Rhyme:	"Learning can be hours of fun
	For Bunnykins and everyone
	To tell the time we learn today
	As we see the clock tick minutes away."

Shape	U.S. $	Can. $	U.K. £	Aust. $
Teaching clock	95.00	100.00	31.00	165.00

Bunnykins Teaching Clock
Classroom Scene, Style One (SF138)

Note: Two second hand varieties exist; long and short.

Bunnykins Teaching Clock
Classroom Scene, Style Two (CT36)

BUNNYKINS TEACHING CLOCK,
Classroom Scene, Style Two, First Version

Design No.:	Front — CT36 Classroom Scene
Designer:	Colin Twinn
Issued:	1991 - 1993
Rhyme:	"Learning can be hours of fun
	For Bunnykins and everyone
	To tell the time we learn today
	As we see the clock tick minutes away."

Shape	U.S. $	Can. $	U.K. £	Aust. $
Teaching clock	30.00	45.00	20.00	50.00

Note: 1. This clock has a short second hand.
2. For information on others shapes with this design see page 44.

Bunnykins Teaching Clock
Four Individual Scenes

BUNNYKINS TEACHING CLOCK
Four Individual Scenes

Design No.: None — Four individual scenes
Designer: Frank Endersby
Issued: 1996 to the present

Shape	U.S. $	Can. $	U.K. £	Aust. $
Teaching clock	95.00	100.00	31.00	165.00

Note: This clock has a short second hand.

CAMP SITE

Design No.: SF113
Designer: Walter Hayward
Issued: 1959 - by 1998

Shape	U.S. $	Can. $	U.K. £	Aust. $
Baby plate, round, small	20.00	27.50	12.50	30.00
Cake stand	150.00	250.00	100.00	300.00
Casino saucer	7.50	12.00	5.00	12.00
Cereal / oatmeal bowl	15.00	20.00	10.00	25.00
Jaffa fruit saucer (plain)	15.00	20.00	10.00	25.00
Hot water plate	75.00	100.00	45.00	110.00
Picture plaque, large	20.00	30.00	12.50	30.00
Plate, 6 ½"	15.00	20.00	10.00	25.00
Plate, 7 ½"	15.00	20.00	10.00	25.00
Plate, 8"	15.00	20.00	10.00	25.00

Camp Site (SF113)

CAMPING THEME — Frank Endersby

CAMPING

Design No.:	34 Camping			
Designer:	Frank Endersby			
Issued:	1996 to the present			

Shape	U.S. $	Can. $	U.K. £	Aust. $
Baby plate, round, small	N/I	46.00	14.00	62.95
Cereal / oatmeal bowl	N/I	33.00	11.00	49.95
Plate, 6 ½"	N/I	25.00	8.00	34.95
Plate, 8"	N/I	35.00	11.00	49.95

Camping (34)

Campfire (35)

CAMPFIRE / ASLEEP IN A SLEEPING BAG

Design No.:	Front — 35 Campfire			
	Reverse — 36 Asleep in a Sleeping Bag			
Designer:	Frank Endersby			
Issued:	1996 to the present			

Shape	U.S. $	Can. $	U.K. £	Aust. $
Hug-a-mug, one handle	30.00	33.00	11.00	49.95
Hug-a-mug, two handles	32.50	39.00	12.00	56.95
Stratford teacup	7.50	12.00	5.00	12.00

Note: 1. Bold type in the listing tables indicate a current design on a current shape.
2. N/I, Not issued individually. The item(s) will be found only in boxed sets in that market.

Asleep in a Sleeping Bag (36)

Carol Singer Bunnykins (CT70)

CAROL SINGER BUNNYKINS
CHRISTMAS TREE ORNAMENT

Design No.:   Front – CT70
                 Reverse – CT71
Designer: Colin Twinn
Issued: 1992 - 1992
Series: Christmas Tree Ornaments

Shape	U.S. $	Can. $	U.K. £	Aust. $
Christmas tree ornament	25.00	35.00	20.00	40.00

Note: For other Christmas ornaments in this series see page 42, 78, 141 and 163.

Christmas 1992 (CT71)

CARVING THE CHICKEN

Design No.:   LFc
Designer: Barbara Vernon
Issued: By 1937 - by 1952

Shape	U.S. $	Can. $	U.K. £	Aust. $
Bread and butter plate	500.00	650.00	300.00	675.00
Casino teapot, 30s	450.00	600.00	275.00	625.00
Plate, 7 ½"	225.00	300.00	150.00	325.00
Plate, 8 ½"	225.00	300.00	150.00	325.00
Porridge plate	300.00	400.00	200.00	425.00

Note: This design should appear with the Barbara Vernon facsimile signature.

Carving the Chicken (LFc)

CHICKEN PULLING A CART

Chicken Pulling A Cart (SF8)

Design No.:	SF8
Designer:	Barbara Vernon
Issued:	By 1940 - by 1952
Combined with:	*Cycling*, HW15R
	Family at Breakfast, HW12
	Family Going out on Washing Day, HW8

Fixing Braces, HW3
Gardener with Wheelbarrow, HW9R
Going Shopping, SF10
Leapfrog, HW12R
Pillow Fight, Style One, SF7

Shape	U.S. $	Can. $	U.K. £	Aust. $
Baby plate, round, small				
with signature	50.00	65.00	30.00	70.00
without signature	30.00	40.00	20.00	45.00
Casino jug, 24s				
with signature	400.00	625.00	275.00	650.00
without signature	350.00	550.00	250.00	550.00
Casino jug, 36s				
with signature	300.00	475.00	200.00	475.00
without signature	250.00	400.00	175.00	400.00
Casino jug, 42s				
with signature	250.00	400.00	175.00	400.00
without signature	200.00	325.00	150.00	325.00
Casino saucer				
with signature	75.00	125.00	50.00	125.00
without signature	50.00	75.00	35.00	75.00
Casino sugar bowl, 30s				
with signature	175.00	275.00	125.00	325.00
without signature	125.00	200.00	85.00	225.00
Casino teapot, 24s				
with signature	375.00	550.00	250.00	600.00
without signature	300.00	450.00	200.00	500.00
Casino teapot, 30s				
with signature	325.00	500.00	225.00	550.00
without signature	250.00	400.00	175.00	450.00

Shape	U.S. $	Can. $	U.K. £	Aust. $
Cereal / oatmeal bowl				
with signature	35.00	45.00	20.00	50.00
without signature	25.00	35.00	15.00	40.00
Don beaker				
with signature	65.00	85.00	40.00	90.00
without signature	35.00	45.00	20.00	50.00
Don Beaker, one handle				
with signature	65.00	85.00	40.00	90.00
without signature	35.00	45.00	20.00	50.00
Jaffa fruit saucer				
plain rim	50.00	65.00	30.00	70.00
wavy rim	75.00	100.00	50.00	125.00
Hot water plate				
with signature	125.00	165.00	80.00	175.00
without signature	100.00	135.00	65.00	150.00
Plate, 6 ½"				
with signature	30.00	40.00	20.00	45.00
without signature	20.00	25.00	12.00	30.00
Plate, 7 ½"				
with signature	65.00	85.00	40.00	95.00
without signature	25.00	35.00	15.00	45.00
Plate, 8 ½"				
with signature	75.00	100.00	45.00	115.00
without signature	25.00	35.00	15.00	45.00

FINE WHITE CHINA

Saucer	Very rare
Teacup	Very rare

Note: This scene was re-issued on an 8" plate in 1984 with the Bunnykins Golden Jubilee backstamp (see page 193).

Christmas Morn

Christmas Morn backstamp

CHRISTMAS MORN
CHRISTMAS TREE ORNAMENT

This Christmas tree ornament has a rabbit-shaped rim. It was commissioned by Royal Doulton U.S.A. and made in the U.S.A.

Design No.:	None
Designer:	Frank Endersby
Issued:	1996 - 1996
Backstamp:	"Christmas Morn" Christmas 1996 Royal Doulton
	"Bunnykins" ® © 1996 Royal Doulton made in U.S.A.
Series:	Christmas Tree Ornaments

Shape	U.S. $	Can. $	U.K. £	Aust. $
Christmas tree ornament	25.00	35.00	20.00	40.00

Note: For other Christmas ornaments in this series see pages 40, 78, 141 and 163.

CHRISTMAS PARTY

Design No.:	LF9
Designer:	Barbara Vernon
Issued:	By 1940 - 1967

Shape	U.S. $	Can. $	U.K. £	Aust. $
Baby plate, oval, large				
with signature	350.00	450.00	225.00	475.00
without signature	300.00	400.00	200.00	425.00
Baby plate, round, large				
with silver rim	450.00	600.00	300.00	625.00
with signature	250.00	325.00	150.00	350.00
without signature	200.00	275.00	125.00	300.00
Bread and butter plate				
with signature	400.00	525.00	250.00	550.00
without signature	350.00	450.00	225.00	475.00
Plate, 8 ½"				
with signature	100.00	135.00	65.00	145.00
without signature	75.00	100.00	45.00	110.00
Porridge plate				
with signature	125.00	175.00	80.00	185.00
without signature	100.00	135.00	65.00	145.00

Christmas Party (LF9)

CHRISTMAS TREE

Design No.: LF16
Designer: Walter Hayward
Issued: 1954 - 1967

Shape	U.S. $	Can. $	U.K. £	Aust. $
Baby plate, oval, large				
with signature	200.00	275.00	125.00	300.00
without signature	150.00	200.00	95.00	225.00
Baby plate, round, large				
with signature	100.00	135.00	65.00	150.00
without signature	75.00	100.00	50.00	125.00
Bread and butter plate				
with signature	250.00	400.00	175.00	400.00
without signature	200.00	325.00	150.00	325.00
Plate, 8 ½"				
with signature	75.00	100.00	45.00	115.00
without signature	25.00	35.00	15.00	45.00
Porridge plate				
with signature	110.00	175.00	70.00	200.00
without signature	85.00	125.00	55.00	150.00

Christmas Tree (LF16)

Christmas Morn Christmas ornament, 1996

CLASSROOM SCENE
Style Two, First Version

Design No.:	CT36 Classroom Scene
Designer:	Colin Twinn
Issued:	1991 - 1993
Combined with:	*Bunny with Mirror, CT35*

For illustration of
this design see
Bunnykins Teaching Clock
page 37.

Shape	U.S. $	Can. $	U.K. £	Aust. $
Albion jug, 1 pint	100.00	150.00	60.00	165.00
Plate, 6"	15.00	20.00	10.00	25.00
Plate, 8"	15.00	20.00	10.00	25.00

Note: For information on the Bunnykins Teaching Clock with this design see page 37.

CLASSROOM SCENE
Style Two, Second Version

Design No.:	CT16 Classroom
Designer:	Colin Twinn
Issued:	1990 - 1993
Combined with:	*Bunny on Trike, CT23*
	Bunny with Mirror, CT35
	Picking Daisies, CT4

Shape	U.S. $	Can. $	U.K. £	Aust. $
Albion cream jug	35.00	55.00	20.00	60.00
Albion jug, ½ pint	85.00	115.00	50.00	115.00
Albion jug, 1 pint	100.00	150.00	60.00	165.00
Albion teapot	50.00	70.00	30.00	75.00
Baby plate, round small	20.00	27.50	12.50	30.00
Cake stand	150.00	250.00	100.00	300.00
Cereal / oatmeal bowl	15.00	20.00	10.00	25.00
Jaffa fruit saucer (plain)	15.00	20.00	10.00	25.00
Stratford straight beaker	15.00	25.00	10.00	25.00

Classroom Scene, Style Two (CT16)

CONDUCTING THE ORCHESTRA

Design No.:	LF5
Designer:	Barbara Vernon
Issued:	By 1940 - by 1952
Combined with:	*Frightening Spider*, SF4

Shape	U.S. $	Can. $	U.K. £	Aust. $
Baby plate, oval, large				
with signature	200.00	275.00	125.00	300.00
without signature	150.00	200.00	95.00	225.00
Baby plate, round, large				
with silver rim			Rare	
with signature	100.00	135.00	65.00	150.00
without signature	75.00	100.00	50.00	125.00
Bread and butter plate				
with signature	250.00	400.00	175.00	400.00
without signature	200.00	325.00	150.00	325.00
Casino jug, 24s				
with signature	400.00	625.00	275.00	650.00
without signature	350.00	550.00	250.00	550.00
Hot water plate				
with signature	125.00	165.00	80.00	175.00
without signature	100.00	135.00	65.00	150.00
Plate, 8 ½"				
with signature	75.00	100.00	45.00	115.00
without signature	25.00	35.00	15.00	45.00
Porridge plate				
with signature	110.00	175.00	70.00	200.00
without signature	85.00	125.00	50.00	150.00

Conducting the Orchestra (LF5)

Convalescing (SF5)

CONVALESCING

Design No.:	SF5
Designer:	Barbara Vernon
Issued:	By 1940 - by 1952
Combined with:	*Asleep in the Open Air*, HW10
	Baking, SF19
	Leapfrog, HW12R
	Soldiers Marching to the Music, HW18
	Washing in the Open Air, HW10R

Shape	U.S. $	Can. $	U.K. £	Aust. $
Baby plate, round, small	50.00	65.00	30.00	70.00
Bread and butter plate	250.00	400.00	175.00	400.00
Casino jug, 42s	250.00	400.00	175.00	400.00
Casino saucer	75.00	125.00	50.00	125.00
Casino teapot, 24s	375.00	550.00	250.00	600.00
Cereal / oatmeal bowl	35.00	45.00	20.00	50.00
Jaffa fruit saucer				
plain rim	50.00	65.00	30.00	70.00
wavy rim	75.00	100.00	50.00	125.00
Hot water plate	125.00	165.00	80.00	175.00
Plate, 6 ½"	30.00	40.00	20.00	45.00
Plate, 7 ½"	65.00	85.00	40.00	95.00

Note: This design should appear with the Barbara Vernon facsimile signature.

Cowboys and Indians (HW140)

Cowboy on Rocking Horse (HW140R)

COWBOYS AND INDIANS / COWBOY ON ROCKING HORSE

Design No.: Front — HW140 Cowboys and Indians
Reverse — HW140R Cowboy on Rocking Horse
Designer: Walter Hayward
Issued: 1967 - by 1998
Combined with: *Hobby Horse*, Style Two, EC121
Ice Cream on the Beach, HW136R
Peashooter, HW118R
Punch and Judy Show, HW136
Roller Skating Arm in Arm, HW137R
Trying on Hats, HW28R

Shape	U.S. $	Can. $	U.K. £	Aust. $
Albion cream jug	35.00	55.00	20.00	60.00
Albion teapot	50.00	70.00	30.00	75.00
Casino teacup	7.50	12.00	5.00	12.00
Divider dish	50.00	75.00	35.00	75.00
Don beaker	25.00	35.00	15.00	40.00
Don beaker, one handle	25.00	35.00	15.00	40.00
Don mug, one handle	10.00	15.00	6.50	18.00
Don mug, two handles	10.00	15.00	6.50	18.00
Egg box				
small	225.00	350.00	150.00	400.00
medium	300.00	450.00	200.00	500.00
large	375.00	550.00	250.00	600.00
Hug-a-mug, one handle	10.00	15.00	7.50	15.00
Hug-a-mug, two handles	10.00	15.00	7.50	15.00
Lamp	50.00	75.00	30.00	85.00
Lid of hot water plate	50.00	65.00	30.00	70.00
Malvern beaker	15.00	25.00	10.00	25.00
Money ball	10.00	15.00	7.50	15.00
Picture plaque, small	20.00	30.00	12.50	30.00
Savings book	15.00	22.50	10.00	22.50
Stratford teacup	7.50	12.00	5.00	12.00

* Indicates scene on divider dish.

CRICKET GAME

Design No.:	LF12			
Designer:	Walter Hayward after Barbara Vernon			
Issued:	1952 - 1967			

Shape	U.S. $	Can. $	U.K. £	Aust. $
Baby plate, oval, large				
with signature	150.00	200.00	95.00	225.00
without signature	100.00	135.00	65.00	150.00
Baby plate, oval, small				
with signature	150.00	200.00	95.00	225.00
without signature	100.00	135.00	65.00	150.00
Baby plate, round large				
with signature	75.00	125.00	50.00	150.00
without signature	50.00	75.00	35.00	85.00
Bread and butter plate				
with signature	250.00	400.00	175.00	400.00
without signature	200.00	325.00	150.00	325.00
Plate, 8 ½"				
with signature	30.00	40.00	20.00	45.00
without signature	15.00	20.00	10.00	25.00
Porridge plate				
with signature	110.00	175.00	70.00	200.00
without signature	85.00	125.00	55.00	150.00

Cricket Game (LF12)

Cuddling under a Mushroom (HW4)

CUDDLING UNDER A MUSHROOM

Design No.:	HW4			
Designer:	Barbara Vernon			
Issued:	By 1937 - by 1952			
Combined with:	*Footballer*, HW13R			
	Golfer, HW4R			
	Netting a Cricket, HW6			

Shape	U.S. $	Can. $	U.K. £	Aust. $
Casino sugar bowl, 30s				
with signature	200.00	275.00	125.00	300.00
without signature	125.00	175.00	80.00	200.00
Casino teacup				
with signature	75.00	100.00	50.00	125.00
without signature	50.00	65.00	30.00	75.00
Don beaker				
with signature	150.00	225.00	100.00	200.00
without signature	100.00	150.00	65.00	165.00
Don beaker, one handle				
with signature	150.00	225.00	100.00	200.00
without signature	100.00	150.00	65.00	165.00
Don mug, one handle				
with signature	75.00	100.00	50.00	125.00
without signature	35.00	55.00	20.00	60.00
Don mug, two handles				
with signature	75.00	100.00	50.00	125.00
without signature	35.00	55.00	20.00	60.00
Lid of hot water plate				
with signature	175.00	250.00	110.00	275.00
without signature	125.00	175.00	80.00	200.00

FINE WHITE CHINA

Saucer			Very Rare	
Teacup			Very Rare	

Cycling (HW15R)

CYCLING

Design No.:	HW15R
Designer:	Barbara Vernon
Issued:	By 1937 - by 1967
Combined with:	*Family at Breakfast*, HW12
	Family Going Out on Washing Day, HW8
	Family with Pram, Style One, HW15
	Feeding the Baby, HW13
	Fixing Braces, HW3
	Golfer, HW4R
	Kissing Under Mistletoe, HW11R
	Pressing Trousers, HW14
	Proposal, HW11
	Reading the Times, HW2R

Shape	U.S. $	Can. $	U.K. £	Aust. $
Beaker cover				
with signature	200.00	275.00	125.00	300.00
without signature	150.00	225.00	100.00	250.00
Casino jug, 42s				
with signature	275.00	400.00	175.00	450.00
without signature	200.00	275.00	125.00	300.00
Casino sugar bowl, 36s				
with signature	150.00	225.00	100.00	250.00
without signature	125.00	175.00	80.00	200.00
Casino teacup				
with signature	75.00	100.00	50.00	125.00
without signature	50.00	65.00	30.00	75.00
Casino teapot, 30s				
with signature	300.00	425.00	190.00	475.00
without signature	225.00	325.00	150.00	375.00
Don beaker, one handle				
with signature	150.00	225.00	100.00	250.00
without signature	100.00	150.00	65.00	165.00
Don mug, one handle				
with signature	75.00	100.00	50.00	125.00
without signature	35.00	55.00	20.00	60.00
Don mug, two handles				
with signature	75.00	100.00	50.00	125.00
without signature	35.00	55.00	20.00	60.00
Jam pot	1,500.00	1,975.00	950.00	2,000.00
Lid of hot water plate				
with signature	175.00	250.00	110.00	275.00
without signature	125.00	175.00	80.00	200.00

FINE WHITE CHINA

Rex mug	1,000.00
Teacup	300.00

Note: Rex mugs are found combining *Cycling* (HW15R) with any of the following: *Family at Breakfast*, (HW12), *Pressing Trousers* (HW14), or *Proposal* (HW11).

CYCLING THEME — Frank Endersby

CYCLE RIDE

Design No.:   46 Cycle Ride
Designer: Frank Endersby
Issued: 1995 - 2003

Shape	U.S. $	Can. $	U.K. £	Aust. $
Baby plate, round, small	20.00	27.50	12.50	30.00
Jaffa fruit saucer	15.00	20.00	10.00	25.00
Plate, 6 ½"	15.00	20.00	10.00	25.00
Plate, 8"	15.00	20.00	10.00	25.00

Cycle Ride (46)

Resting (47)

RESTING / CLEANING BIKE

Design No.:   Front — 47 Resting, Style Three
              Reverse — 48 Cleaning Bike
Designer: Frank Endersby
Issued: 1995 - 2003

Shape	U.S. $	Can. $	U.K. £	Aust. $
Hug-a-mug, one handle	10.00	15.00	7.50	15.00
Hug-a-mug, two handles	10.00	15.00	7.50	15.00

Cleaning Bike (48)

DAISY CHAINS / SMELLING FLOWERS

Daisy Chains (HW25)

Smelling Flowers (HW25R)

Design No.:	Front — HW25 Daisy Chains
	Reverse — HW25R Smelling Flowers
Designer:	Walter Hayward

Issued:	1954 - by 1998
Combined with:	*Hikers*, EC124
	Holding Hat and Coat, EC4
	Ice Cream Vendor, HW23
	Playing with Cup and Spoon, EC6

Shape	U.S. $	Can. $	U.K. £	Aust. $
Albion cream jug	35.00	55.00	20.00	60.00
Albion jug, ½ pint	85.00	115.00	50.00	125.00
Albion jug, 1 pint	100.00	150.00	60.00	165.00
Albion teapot	50.00	70.00	30.00	75.00
Casino jug, 36s				
with signature	175.00	275.00	125.00	275.00
without signature	125.00	200.00	85.00	200.00
Casino jug, 42s				
with signature	150.00	225.00	100.00	225.00
without signature	100.00	150.00	70.00	150.00
Casino saucer				
with signature	15.00	25.00	10.00	25.00
without signature	7.50	12.00	5.00	12.00
Casino teacup				
with signature	15.00	25.00	10.00	25.00
without signature	7.50	12.00	5.00	12.00
Casino teapot, 30s				
with signature	200.00	325.00	125.00	350.00
without signature	150.00	225.00	100.00	250.00
Don beaker				
with signature	50.00	65.00	30.00	75.00
without signature	25.00	35.00	15.00	40.00
Don beaker, one handle				
with signature	50.00	65.00	30.00	75.00
without signature	25.00	35.00	15.00	40.00
Don mug, one handle				
with signature	40.00	55.00	25.00	60.00
without signature	10.00	15.00	6.50	18.00

Shape	U.S. $	Can. $	U.K. £	Aust. $
Don mug, two handles				
with signature	40.00	55.00	25.00	60.00
without signature	10.00	15.00	6.50	18.00
Egg box				
small	225.00	350.00	150.00	400.00
medium	300.00	450.00	200.00	500.00
large	375.00	550.00	250.00	600.00
Hug-a-mug, one handle	10.00	15.00	7.50	15.00
Hug-a-mug, two handles	10.00	15.00	7.50	15.00
Jaffa fruit saucer (plain)	15.00	20.00	10.00	25.00
Lamp	50.00	70.00	30.00	85.00
Lid of hot water plate				
with signature	75.00	100.00	45.00	110.00
without signature	50.00	65.00	30.00	70.00
Malvern beaker	15.00	25.00	10.00	25.00
Money ball	10.00	15.00	7.50	15.00
Picture plaque, small	20.00	30.00	12.50	30.00
Picture plaque, large	20.00	30.00	12.50	30.00
Plate, 6 ½"				
with signature	25.00	35.00	15.00	40.00
without signature	15.00	20.00	10.00	25.00
Savings book	15.00	22.50	10.00	22.50
Stratford straight beaker	15.00	22.50	10.00	22.50
Stratford teacup	7.50	12.00	5.00	12.00

Note: 1. A Hug-a-mug (two handles) was issued for the U.S. Special Event Tour in 1993, see page 198.
   2. A Casino jug combines *Daisy Chains*, (HW25) with *Ice Cream Vendor*, (HW23).

DANCING IN THE MOONLIGHT
First Version

Design No.: LFb
Designer: Barbara Vernon
Issued: 1937 - by 1952

Shape	U.S. $	Can. $	U.K. £	Aust. $
Baby plate, round, large				
with signature	400.00	525.00	250.00	550.00
without signature	350.00	450.00	200.00	475.00
Bread and butter plate				
with signature	500.00	650.00	300.00	675.00
without signature	400.00	525.00	250.00	550.00
Plate, 8 ½"				
with signature	225.00	300.00	150.00	325.00
without signature	175.00	225.00	115.00	250.00
Porridge plate				
with signature	300.00	400.00	200.00	425.00
without signature	250.00	325.00	150.00	350.00

Dancing in the Moonlight, First Version (LFb)

DANCING IN THE MOONLIGHT
Second Version, Second Variation, Small Size

Design No.: CT92
Designer: Justin Clarke based on a design by Barbara Vernon
Issued: Circa 1994
Combined with: *Bunny with Cake Plate*, (CT88)

Shape	U.S. $	Can. $	U.K. £	Aust. $
Cereal / oatmeal bowl	15.00	20.00	10.00	25.00
Don beaker, one handle	10.00	15.00	7.50	20.00
Don mug, one handle	10.00	15.00	7.50	20.00
Malvern beaker	10.00	15.00	7.50	20.00

Note: See also Bunnykins 60th Anniversary page 195.

Dancing Round the Barrel Organ (HW139)

Skipping Game (HW139R)

DANCING ROUND THE BARREL ORGAN / SKIPPING GAME

Design No.: Front — HW139 Dancing Round the Barrel Organ
Reverse — HW139R Skipping Game
Designer: Walter Hayward
Issued: 1967 - by 1998
Combined with: *Hiker Resting with Ice Cream*, HW23R
Ice Cream Vendor, HW23
Peashooter, HW118R
Sailing Boats, HW138R

Shape	U.S. $	Can. $	U.K. £	Aust. $
Albion cream jug	35.00	55.00	20.00	60.00
Albion jug, ½ pint	85.00	115.00	50.00	125.00
Albion jug, 1 pint	100.00	150.00	60.00	165.00
Albion teapot	50.00	70.00	30.00	75.00
Casino jug, 36s	125.00	200.00	85.00	200.00
Casino saucer	7.50	12.00	5.00	12.00
Casino teacup	7.50	12.00	5.00	12.00
Divider dish	50.00	75.00	35.00	75.00
Don beaker	25.00	35.00	15.00	40.00
Don beaker, one handle	25.00	35.00	15.00	40.00
Don mug, one handle	10.00	15.00	6.50	18.00
Don mug, two handles	10.00	15.00	6.50	18.00
Egg box				
small	225.00	350.00	150.00	400.00
medium	300.00	450.00	200.00	500.00
large	375.00	550.00	250.00	600.00
Hug-a-mug, one handle	10.00	15.00	7.50	15.00
Hug-a-mug, two handles	10.00	15.00	7.50	15.00
Jaffa fruit saucer (plain)	15.00	20.00	10.00	25.00
Lamp	50.00	75.00	30.00	85.00
Malvern beaker	15.00	25.00	10.00	25.00
Money ball	10.00	15.00	7.50	15.00
Picture plaque, small	20.00	30.00	12.50	30.00
Plate, 6 ½"	15.00	20.00	10.00	25.00
Savings book	15.00	22.50	10.00	22.50
Stratford straight beaker	15.00	22.50	10.00	22.50
Stratford teacup	7.50	12.00	5.00	12.00

* Indicates scene on divider dish.

Note: A savings book was issued for the U.S. Special Events Tour 1994. The front features *Skipping Game* (HW139R) and the reverse is inscribed 'To' and 'From' for the customer to complete and '*US Special Events Tour 1994*,' see page 199.

DINNER THEME — Frank Endersby

SERVING DINNER / CARRYING PLATES

Design No.:	Front — 44 Serving Dinner
	Reverse — 45 Carrying Plates
Designer:	Frank Endersby
Issued:	1995 - 2003
Combined with:	*Sitting on Suitcase, (51)

Shape	U.S. $	Can. $	U.K. £	Aust. $
Hug-a-mug, one handle	10.00	15.00	7.50	15.00
Hug-a-mug, two handles	10.00	15.00	7.50	15.00
Divider dish	50.00	75.00	35.00	75.00
Stratford teacup	7.50	12.00	5.00	12.00

* Indicates scenes on divider dish.

Preparing Dinner (43)

Serving Dinner (44)

PREPARING DINNER

Design No.:	43 — Preparing Dinner
Designer:	Frank Endersby
Issued:	1995 - 2003

Shape	U.S. $	Can. $	U.K. £	Aust. $
Baby plate, round, small	20.00	27.50	12.50	30.00
Jaffa fruit saucer	15.00	20.00	10.00	25.00
Plate, 6 ½"	15.00	20.00	10.00	25.00
Plate, 8"	15.00	20.00	10.00	25.00

Carrying Plates (45)

Disturbing Sleeping Father (HW118)

Pea Shooter (HW118R)

DISTURBING SLEEPING FATHER / PEA SHOOTER

Design No.:	Front — HW118 Disturbing Sleeping Father
	Reverse — HW118R Pea Shooter
Designer:	Walter Hayward
Issued:	1959 - by 1998
Combined with:	*Dancing with Doll*, HW115R
	Nipped by a Crab, HW21R
	Sledging, Style One, HW141
	Snowball Fight, HW141R
	Wheelbarrow Race, Style One, (HW22)

Shape	U.S. $	Can. $	U.K. £	Aust. $
Albion cream jug	35.00	55.00	20.00	60.00
Albion jug, ½ pint	85.00	115.00	50.00	125.00
Albion jug, 1 pint	100.00	150.00	60.00	165.00
Albion teapot	50.00	70.00	30.00	75.00
Casino jug, 36s	125.00	200.00	85.00	200.00
Casino jug, 42s	100.00	150.00	70.00	150.00
Casino saucer	7.50	12.00	5.00	12.00
Casino teacup	7.50	12.00	5.00	12.00
Divider dish	50.00	75.00	35.00	75.00
Don beaker	25.00	35.00	15.00	40.00
Don beaker, one handle	25.00	35.00	15.00	40.00
Don mug, one handle	10.00	15.00	6.50	18.00
Don mug, two handles	10.00	15.00	6.50	18.00
Egg box				
small	225.00	350.00	150.00	400.00
medium	300.00	450.00	200.00	500.00
large	375.00	550.00	250.00	600.00
Hug-a-mug, one handle	10.00	15.00	7.50	15.00
Hug-a-mug, two handles	10.00	15.00	7.50	15.00
Jaffa fruit saucer (plain)	15.00	20.00	10.00	25.00
Lamp	50.00	75.00	30.00	85.00
Lid of hot water plate	50.00	65.00	30.00	70.00
Malvern beaker	15.00	25.00	10.00	25.00
Money ball	10.00	15.00	7.50	15.00
Picture plaque, small	20.00	30.00	12.50	30.00
Plate, 6 ½"	15.00	20.00	10.00	25.00
Stratford straight beaker	15.00	22.50	10.00	22.50
Stratford teacup	7.50	12.00	5.00	12.00

* Indicates scene on divider dish.

Note: An Albion teapot combines *Pea Shooter* (HW118R) with *Wheelbarrow Race*, Style One (HW22).

DODGEM CARS

Design No.:	LF4
Designer:	Barbara Vernon
Issued:	By 1940 - by 1952

Shape	U.S. $	Can. $	U.K. £	Aust. $
Baby plate, oval, large				
with signature	350.00	450.00	225.00	475.00
without signature	300.00	400.00	200.00	425.00
Baby plate, round large				
with signature	250.00	325.00	150.00	350.00
without signature	200.00	275.00	125.00	300.00
Bread and butter plate				
with signature	400.00	525.00	250.00	550.00
without signature	350.00	450.00	225.00	475.00
Cereal / oatmeal bowl				
with signature	100.00	135.00	65.00	150.00
without signature	90.00	125.00	55.00	135.00
Plate 8 ½"				
with signature	100.00	135.00	65.00	145.00
without signature	75.00	100.00	45.00	110.00
Porridge plate				
with signature	125.00	175.00	80.00	185.00
without signature	100.00	135.00	65.00	145.00

Dodgem Cars (LF4)

DOG CARRIAGE

Design No.:	LFe
Designer:	Barbara Vernon
Issued:	By 1937 - by 1952

Shape	U.S. $	Can. $	U.K. £	Aust. $
Baby plate, oval, large				
with signature	500.00	650.00	300.00	675.00
without signature	450.00	600.00	275.00	625.00
Baby plate, round large				
with signature	400.00	525.00	250.00	550.00
without signature	350.00	450.00	200.00	475.00
Bread / butter plate, handles				
with signature	500.00	650.00	300.00	675.00
without signature	400.00	525.00	250.00	550.00
Cereal / oatmeal bowl				
with signature	300.00	400.00	200.00	425.00
without signature	250.00	325.00	150.00	350.00
Plate, 7 ½"				
with signature	375.00	500.00	250.00	550.00
without signature	325.00	450.00	200.00	500.00
Plate, 8 ½"				
with signature	225.00	300.00	150.00	325.00
without signature	175.00	225.00	115.00	250.00
Porridge plate				
with signature	300.00	400.00	200.00	425.00
without signature	250.00	325.00	150.00	350.00

Dog Carriage (LFe)

The Doll's House (HW120)

Playing with Doll and Teddy (HW120R)

THE DOLL'S HOUSE / PLAYING WITH DOLL AND TEDDY

Design No.:	Front — HW120 The Doll's House
	Reverse — HW120R Playing with Doll and Teddy
Designer:	Walter Hayward
Issued:	1959 - by 1998
Combined with:	*Dancing with Doll, HW115R
	Hikers, EC124
	*Nipped by a Crab, HW21R
	Reading, EC122
	*Serving Tea, HW116R

Shape	U.S. $	Can. $	U.K. £	Aust. $
Albion cream jug	35.00	55.00	20.00	60.00
Albion jug, ½ pint	85.00	115.00	50.00	125.00
Albion teapot	50.00	70.00	30.00	75.00
Cake stand	150.00	250.00	100.00	300.00
Casino jug, 42s	100.00	150.00	70.00	150.00
Casino saucer	7.50	12.00	5.00	12.00
Casino teacup	7.50	12.00	5.00	12.00
Divider dish	50.00	75.00	35.00	75.00
Don beaker	25.00	35.00	15.00	40.00
Don beaker, one handle	25.00	35.00	15.00	40.00
Don mug, one handle	10.00	15.00	6.50	18.00
Don mug, two handles	10.00	15.00	6.50	18.00
Egg box				
small	225.00	350.00	150.00	400.00
medium	300.00	450.00	200.00	500.00
large	375.00	550.00	250.00	600.00
Hug-a-mug, one handle	10.00	15.00	7.50	15.00
Hug-a-mug, two handles	10.00	15.00	7.50	15.00
Jaffa fruit saucer (plain)	15.00	20.00	10.00	25.00
Lamp	50.00	75.00	30.00	85.00
Lid of hot water plate	50.00	65.00	30.00	70.00
Malvern beaker	15.00	25.00	10.00	25.00
Money ball	10.00	15.00	7.50	15.00
Picture plaque, small	20.00	30.00	12.50	30.00
Plate, 6 ½"	15.00	20.00	10.00	25.00
Savings book	15.00	22.50	10.00	22.50
Stratford straight beaker	15.00	22.50	10.00	22.50
Stratford teacup	7.50	12.00	5.00	12.00

* Indicates scene on divider dish.

DRESS MAKING /
BUGLER WITH TOY DONKEY

Dress Making (HW26)

Bugler with Toy Donkey (HW26R)

Design No.: Front — HW26 Dress Making
Reverse — HW26R Bugler with Toy Donkey
Designer: Walter Hayward
Issued: 1954 - by 1998
Combined with: *Mr. Piggly's Store*, SF14
Proposal, HW11

Combined with: *Roller Skating Arm in Arm*, HW137R
Serving Tea, HW116R
Sleeping in a Rocking Chair, EC1
Snowball Fight, HW141R
Toast for Tea Today, SF23
Windy Day, HW27

Shape	U.S. $	Can. $	U.K. £	Aust. $
Albion cream jug	35.00	55.00	20.00	60.00
Albion jug, ½ pint	85.00	115.00	50.00	125.00
Albion jug, 1 pint	100.00	150.00	60.00	165.00
Albion teapot	50.00	70.00	30.00	75.00
Casino jug, 30s				
with signature	200.00	300.00	150.00	300.00
without signature	150.00	250.00	100.00	250.00
Casino jug, 36s				
with signature	150.00	225.00	100.00	225.00
without signature	125.00	200.00	85.00	200.00
Casino jug, 42s				
with signature	125.00	200.00	90.00	200.00
without signature	100.00	150.00	70.00	150.00
Casino saucer				
with signature	15.00	25.00	10.00	25.00
without signature	7.50	12.00	5.00	12.00
Casino teacup				
with signature	15.00	25.00	10.00	25.00
without signature	7.50	12.00	5.00	12.00
Casino teapot, 24s				
with signature	225.00	350.00	150.00	400.00
without signature	175.00	275.00	125.00	325.00
Casino teapot, 30s				
with signature	200.00	325.00	125.00	350.00
without signature	150.00	225.00	100.00	250.00
Divider dish	50.00	75.00	35.00	75.00
Don beaker				
with signature	50.00	65.00	30.00	75.00
without signature	25.00	35.00	15.00	40.00

Shape	U.S. $	Can. $	U.K. £	Aust. $
Don beaker, one handle				
with signature	50.00	65.00	30.00	75.00
without signature	25.00	35.00	15.00	40.00
Don mug, one handle				
with signature	40.00	55.00	25.00	60.00
without signature	10.00	15.00	6.50	18.00
Don mug, two handles				
with signature	40.00	55.00	25.00	60.00
without signature	10.00	15.00	6.50	18.00
Egg box				
small	225.00	350.00	150.00	400.00
medium	300.00	450.00	200.00	500.00
large	375.00	550.00	250.00	600.00
Hug-a-mug, one handle	10.00	15.00	7.50	15.00
Hug-a-mug, two handles	10.00	15.00	7.50	15.00
Jaffa fruit saucer (plain)				
with signature	25.00	35.00	20.00	40.00
without signature	15.00	20.00	10.00	25.00
Lamp	50.00	75.00	30.00	85.00
Lid of hot water plate				
with signature	75.00	100.00	45.00	110.00
without signature	50.00	65.00	30.00	70.00
Malvern beaker	15.00	25.00	10.00	25.00
Money ball	10.00	15.00	7.50	15.00
Picture plaque, small	20.00	30.00	12.50	30.00
Savings book	15.00	22.50	10.00	22.50
Stratford straight beaker	15.00	22.50	10.00	22.50
Stratford teacup	7.50	12.00	5.00	12.00

Dressing Up, First Version (SF22)

DRESSING UP
First Version

Design No.:	SF22
Designer:	Walter Hayward
Issued:	1954 - by 1998
Combined with:	*Toast for Tea Today*, SF23

Shape	U.S. $	Can. $	U.K. £	Aust. $
Albion jug, 1 pint	100.00	150.00	60.00	165.00
Baby plate, round, small				
with signature	30.00	40.00	20.00	50.00
without signature	20.00	27.50	12.50	30.00
Cake stand	150.00	250.00	100.00	300.00
Casino jug, 30s				
with signature	200.00	300.00	150.00	300.00
without signature	150.00	250.00	100.00	250.00
Casino saucer				
with signature	15.00	25.00	10.00	25.00
without signature	7.50	12.00	5.00	12.00
Casino teapot, 30s				
with signature	175.00	275.00	125.00	300.00
without signature	125.00	200.00	85.00	200.00
Cereal / oatmeal bowl				
with signature	25.00	35.00	20.00	40.00
without signature	15.00	20.00	10.00	25.00
Jaffa fruit saucer (plain)	15.00	25.00	10.00	25.00
Hot water plate				
with signature	100.00	135.00	65.00	150.00
without signature	75.00	100.00	45.00	110.00
Picture plaque, large	20.00	30.00	12.50	30.00
Plate, 6 ½"				
with signature	25.00	35.00	15.00	40.00
without signature	15.00	20.00	10.00	25.00
Plate, 8"	15.00	20.00	10.00	25.00

DRESSING UP
Second Version

This design incorporates scenes from SF22 and EC4.

Design No.:	None
Designer:	Monica Ford based on designs by Walter Hayward
Issued:	1987 - 1993

Shape	U.S. $	Can. $	U.K. £	Aust. $
Plate, 10 ½"	35.00	55.00	25.00	60.00

Dressing Up, Second Version

DRUMMER

Design No.:	EC2
Designer:	Barbara Vernon
Issued:	1937 to the present

Combined with:

Bedtime with Dollies, EC125
Cricketer, HW22R
Drummer and Bugler, EC126
Hikers, EC124
Hobby Horse, Style Two, EC121
Holding Hat and Coat, EC4
Playing with Cup and Spoon, EC6
Playing with Doll and Pram, EC123

Raising Hat, Style Two, EC7
Reading, EC122
Sheltering Under an Umbrella, EC3
Sleeping in a Rocking Chair, EC1
Trumpeter, EC5
Wheelbarrow Race, Style One, HW22
Windy Day, HW27

Drummer (EC2)

Shape	U.S. $	Can. $	U.K. £	Aust. $
Albion sugar bowl	30.00	40.00	17.50	45.00
Beaker cover				
with signature	50.00	65.00	30.00	70.00
without signature	40.00	55.00	25.00	60.00
Casino sugar bowl				
with signature	125.00	200.00	85.00	225.00
without signature	100.00	150.00	65.00	175.00
Egg cup				
Style One	30.00	40.00	20.00	45.00
Style Two	40.00	55.00	25.00	60.00
Style Three	N/I	**15.00**	**5.00**	**19.95**
Money Ball	33.75	40.00	15.00	62.95

Drummer and Bugler (EC126)

DRUMMER AND BUGLER

Design No.:	EC126
Designer:	Walter Hayward
Issued:	1959 to the present
Combined with:	Bedtime with Dollies, EC125
	Drummer, EC2
	Hat Shop, HW28
	Hikers, EC124
	Hobby Horse, Style Two, EC121
	Holding Hat and Coat, EC4
	Playing with Cup and Spoon, EC6
	Playing with Doll and Pram, EC123
	Raising Hat, Style Two, EC7
	Reading, EC122
	Sleeping in a Rocking Chair, EC1
	Trumpeter, EC5
	Trying on Hats, HW28R

Shape	U.S. $	Can. $	U.K. £	Aust. $
Albion sugar bowl	30.00	40.00	17.50	45.00
Beaker cover	40.00	55.00	25.00	60.00
Egg cup				
Style One	30.00	40.00	20.00	45.00
Style Two	40.00	55.00	25.00	60.00
Style Three	N/I	**15.00**	**5.00**	**19.95**
Lid of hot water plate	50.00	65.00	30.00	70.00

The Duet (LF13)

DUET, THE

Design No.:	LF13			
Designer:	Walter Hayward after Barbara Vernon			
Issued:	By 1952 - 1970			

Shape	U.S. $	Can. $	U.K. £	Aust. $
Baby plate, oval, large				
with signature	200.00	275.00	125.00	300.00
without signature	150.00	200.00	95.00	225.00
Baby plate, round large				
with signature	100.00	135.00	65.00	150.00
without signature	75.00	100.00	50.00	125.00
Bread and butter plate				
with signature	250.00	400.00	175.00	400.00
without signature	200.00	325.00	150.00	325.00
Cereal / oatmeal bowl				
with signature	35.00	45.00	20.00	50.00
without signature	25.00	35.00	15.00	40.00
Hot water plate				
with signature	125.00	165.00	80.00	175.00
without signature	100.00	135.00	65.00	150.00
Plate, 8"	25.00	35.00	15.00	45.00
Plate, 8 ½"				
with signature	75.00	100.00	75.00	115.00
without signature	25.00	35.00	15.00	45.00
Porridge plate				
with signature	110.00	175.00	70.00	200.00
without signature	85.00	125.00	55.00	150.00

Key fobs commemorating the 2000 Australian Tour
Trumpeter (EC5), Drummer (EC2), Drummer and Bugler (EC126)

DUNCE

Design No.:	HW1R
Designer:	Barbara Vernon
Issued:	By 1937 - by 1952
Combined with:	*Artist*, HW1
	Embracing at a Window, HW5
	Greetings, HW7
	Netting a Cricket, HW6
	Pressing Trousers, HW14
	Proposal, HW11

Dunce (HW1R)

Shape	U.S. $	Can. $	U.K. £	Aust. $
Casino jug, 42s				
with signature	275.00	400.00	175.00	450.00
without signature	200.00	275.00	125.00	300.00
Casino sugar bowl, 30s				
with signature	200.00	275.00	125.00	300.00
without signature	125.00	175.00	80.00	200.00
Casino sugar bowl, 36s				
with signature	150.00	225.00	100.00	250.00
without signature	125.00	175.00	80.00	200.00
Casino teacup				
with signature	75.00	100.00	50.00	125.00
without signature	30.00	65.00	30.00	75.00
Casino teapot, 36s				
with signature	275.00	400.00	175.00	450.00
without signature	200.00	275.00	125.00	300.00
Don beaker				
with signature	150.00	225.00	100.00	250.00
without signature	100.00	150.00	65.00	165.00
Don beaker, one handle				
with signature	150.00	225.00	100.00	250.00
without signature	100.00	150.00	65.00	250.00
Don mug, one handle				
with signature	75.00	100.00	50.00	125.00
without signature	35.00	55.00	20.00	60.00
Don mug, two handles				
with signature	75.00	100.00	50.00	125.00
without signature	35.00	55.00	20.00	60.00
Jam pot	1,500.00	1,975.00	950.00	2,000.00
Lid of hot water plate				
with signature	175.00	250.00	110.00	275.00
without signature	125.00	175.00	80.00	200.00
FINE WHITE CHINA				
Beaker, one handle	300.00	400.00	200.00	425.00
Rex mug	1,000.00	1,350.00	625.00	1,450.00

Note: *Dunce* (HW1R) is combined with *Proposal* (HW11) on the Rex mug.

Embracing at a Window (HW5)

EMBRACING AT A WINDOW

Design No.:   HW5
Designer: Barbara Vernon
Issued: By 1937 - by 1952
Combined with: *Dunce*, HW1R
    Fixing Braces, HW3
    Leapfrog, HW12R
    Top Hat, HW14R

Shape	U.S. $	Can. $	U.K. £	Aust. $
Casino saucer	150.00	200.00	95.00	225.00
Casino teacup	150.00	200.00	95.00	225.00
Casino teapot, 30s	600.00	800.00	375.00	850.00
Don beaker	300.00	500.00	200.00	550.00
Don beaker, one handle	300.00	500.00	200.00	550.00
Don mug, one handle	150.00	200.00	95.00	225.00
Don mug, two handles	150.00	200.00	95.00	225.00
Jaffa fruit saucer	250.00	325.00	150.00	350.00
Jam pot	1,500.00	1,975.00	950.00	2,000.00
Plate, 6 ½"	125.00	165.00	80.00	175.00

Note: This design should appear with the Barbara Vernon facsimile signature.

Jam Pot combining *Proposal* (HW11), and *Netting a Cricket* (HW6)

ENGINE PULLING A CARRIAGE / TO THE STATION

Engine Pulling a Carriage (HW17)

To the Station (HW17R)

Design No.: Front — HW17 Engine Pulling a Carriage
Reverse — HW17R To the Station
Designer: Walter Hayward after Barbara Vernon
Issued: By 1952 - by 1998

Combined with: *Family with Pram,* Style One, HW15
Ice Cream on the Beach, HW136R
Ice Cream Vendor, HW23
Raising Hat, Style Two, EC7
See-saw, Style One, SF14
Snowball Fight, HW141R

Shape	U.S. $	Can. $	U.K. £	Aust. $
Albion cream jug	35.00	55.00	20.00	60.00
Albion jug, ½ pint	85.00	115.00	50.00	125.00
Albion teapot	50.00	70.00	30.00	75.00
Casino jug, 36s				
with signature	175.00	275.00	125.00	275.00
without signature	125.00	200.00	85.00	200.00
Casino jug, 42s				
with signature	150.00	225.00	100.00	225.00
without signature	100.00	150.00	70.00	150.00
Casino saucer				
with signature	22.50	36.00	15.00	36.00
without signature	7.50	12.00	5.00	12.00
Casino sugar bowl, 36s				
with signature	125.00	200.00	85.00	225.00
without signature	100.00	150.00	65.00	175.00
Casino teacup				
with signature	22.50	36.00	15.00	36.00
without signature	7.50	12.00	5.00	12.00
Casino teapot, 24s				
with signature	275.00	400.00	175.00	450.00
without signature	175.00	275.00	125.00	325.00
Casino teapot, 30s				
with signature	250.00	375.00	165.00	400.00
without signature	150.00	225.00	100.00	250.00
Don beaker				
with signature	50.00	65.00	30.00	75.00
without signature	25.00	35.00	15.00	40.00
Don beaker, one handle				
with signature	50.00	65.00	30.00	75.00

Shape	U.S. $	Can. $	U.K. £	Aust. $
Don beaker, one handle				
without signature	25.00	35.00	15.00	40.00
Don mug, one handle				
with signature	40.00	55.00	25.00	60.00
without signature	10.00	15.00	6.50	18.00
Don mug, two handles				
with signature	40.00	55.00	25.00	60.00
without signature	10.00	15.00	6.50	18.00
Egg box				
small	225.00	350.00	150.00	400.00
medium	300.00	450.00	200.00	500.00
large	375.00	550.00	250.00	600.00
Jaffa fruit saucer (plain)	15.00	20.00	10.00	25.00
Lamp	50.00	75.00	30.00	85.00
Lid of hot water plate				
with signature	75.00	100.00	45.00	110.00
without signature	50.00	65.00	30.00	70.00
Malvern beaker	15.00	25.00	10.00	25.00
Money ball	10.00	15.00	7.50	15.00
Picture plaque, small	20.00	30.00	12.50	30.00
Plate, 6 ½"				
with signature	25.00	35.00	15.00	40.00
without signature	15.00	20.00	10.00	25.00
Plate, 7 ½"				
with signature	30.00	40.00	20.00	45.00
without signature	10.00	20.00	10.00	25.00
Savings book	15.00	22.50	10.00	22.50
Stratford straight beaker	15.00	22.50	10.00	22.50
Stratford teacup	7.50	12.00	5.00	12.00

FAIRGROUND THEME — Frank Endersby

Swinging Boats (31)

SWINGING BOATS

Design No.:	31 Swinging Boats
Designer:	Frank Endersby
Issued:	1995 to the present

Shape	U.S. $	Can. $	U.K. £	Aust. $
Baby plate, round, small	N/I	46.00	14.00	62.95
Cereal / oatmeal bowl	N/I	33.00	11.00	49.95
Plate, 6 ½"	N/I	25.00	8.00	34.95
Plate, 8"	N/I	35.00	11.00	49.95

Coconut Shy (32)

COCONUT SHY / PLAYING WITH BALLOONS

Design No.:	Front — 32 Coconut Shy
	Reverse — 33 Playing with Balloons
Designer:	Frank Endersby
Issued:	1995 to the present
Combined with:	*Butterfly Net*, (6)

Shape	U.S. $	Can. $	U.K. £	Aust. $
Hug-a-mug, one handle	**30.00**	**33.00**	**11.00**	**49.95**
Hug-a-mug, two handles	**32.50**	**39.00**	**12.00**	**56.95**
Divider dish	50.00	75.00	35.00	75.00
Malvern beaker	15.00	25.00	10.00	25.00
Money ball	**33.75**	**40.00**	**15.00**	**62.95**
Stratford teacup	7.50	12.00	5.00	12.00

* Indicates scene on divider dish.

Note: 1. Bold type in the listing tables indicate a current design on a current shape.
 2. N/I, Not issued individually. The item(s) will be found only in boxed sets in that market.

Playing with Balloons (33)

FAMILY AT BREAKFAST

Design No.:	HW12
Designer:	Barbara Vernon
Issued:	By 1937 - by 1952
Combined with:	*Bedtime in Bunks*, SF3
	Chicken Pulling a Cart, SF8
	Cycling, HW15R
	Feeding the Baby, HW13
	Fixing Braces, HW3
	Footballer, HW13R
	Golfer, HW4R
	Kissing Under the Mistletoe, HW11R
	Lambeth Walk, HW16
	Leapfrog, HW12R
	Proposal, HW11
	Pulling On Trousers, HW2
	Raising Hat, Style One, HW16R
	Smoking in the Doorway, SF2
	Washing Day, HW8R
	Wedding, LFd

Family at Breakfast (HW12)

Shape	U.S. $	Can. $	U.K. £	Aust. $
Baby plate, round, small				
with signature	50.00	65.00	30.00	70.00
without signature	30.00	40.00	20.00	45.00
Candle holder	2,000.00	2,500.00	1,250.00	2,500.00
Casino jug, 36s				
with signature	300.00	475.00	200.00	475.00
without signature	250.00	400.00	175.00	400.00
Casino jug, 42s				
with signature	250.00	400.00	175.00	400.00
without signature	200.00	325.00	150.00	325.00
Casino saucer				
with signature	75.00	125.00	50.00	125.00
without signature	50.00	75.00	35.00	75.00
Casino sugar bowl, 30s				
with signature	200.00	325.00	125.00	350.00
without signature	150.00	225.00	100.00	250.00
Casino sugar bowl, 36s				
with signature	175.00	275.00	125.00	325.00
without signature	125.00	200.00	85.00	225.00
Casino teacup				
with signature	75.00	125.00	50.00	125.00
without signature	50.00	75.00	35.00	75.00
Casino teapot, 30s				
with signature	325.00	500.00	225.00	550.00
without signature	250.00	400.00	175.00	450.00
Casino teapot, 36s				
with signature	250.00	375.00	165.00	400.00
without signature	225.00	350.00	150.00	375.00
Cereal / oatmeal bowl				
with signature	35.00	45.00	20.00	50.00
without signature	25.00	35.00	15.00	40.00
Cup / mug, large	800.00	1,000.00	500.00	1,100.00
Don beaker				
with signature	65.00	85.00	40.00	90.00
without signature	35.00	45.00	20.00	50.00

Shape	U.S. $	Can. $	U.K. £	Aust. $
Don beaker, one handle				
with signature	65.00	85.00	40.00	90.00
without signature	35.00	45.00	20.00	50.00
Don mug, one handle				
with signature	50.00	65.00	30.00	75.00
without signature	15.00	20.00	10.00	25.00
Don mug, two handles				
with signature	50.00	65.00	30.00	75.00
without signature	15.00	20.00	10.00	25.00
Hot water plate				
with signature	125.00	165.00	80.00	175.00
without signature	100.00	135.00	65.00	150.00
Jaffa fruit saucer (wavy)				
with signature	75.00	100.00	50.00	125.00
without signature	50.00	65.00	30.00	70.00
Jam pot	1,500.00	1,975.00	950.00	2,000.00
Lid of hot water plate				
with signature	100.00	135.00	65.00	150.00
without signature	75.00	100.00	50.00	115.00
Plate, 6 ½"				
with signature	30.00	40.00	20.00	45.00
without signature	20.00	25.00	12.00	30.00
Plate, 7 ½"				
with signature	65.00	85.00	40.00	95.00
without signature	25.00	35.00	15.00	45.00
FINE WHITE CHINA				
Beaker, one handle	300.00	400.00	200.00	425.00
Rex mug	1,000.00	1,350.00	625.00	1,400.00
Saucer	300.00	400.00	200.00	425.00
Teacup	300.00	400.00	200.00	425.00

Note: *Family at Breakfast* (HW12) is combined with *Gardener with Wheelbarrow* (HW9R) on the fine white china beaker, and with *Cycling* (HW15R) on the Rex mug.

Family Cycling (LF11)

FAMILY CYCLING

Design No.:   LF11
Designer: Walter Hayward
Issued: By 1952 - 1970

Shape	U.S. $	Can. $	U.K. £	Aust. $
Baby plate, oval, large				
with signature	200.00	275.00	125.00	300.00
without signature	150.00	200.00	95.00	225.00
Baby plate, round large				
with signature	100.00	135.00	65.00	150.00
without signature	75.00	100.00	50.00	125.00
Bread and butter plate				
with signature	250.00	400.00	175.00	400.00
without signature	200.00	325.00	150.00	325.00
Cereal / oatmeal bowl				
with signature	35.00	45.00	20.00	50.00
without signature	25.00	35.00	15.00	40.00
Hot water plate				
with signature	125.00	165.00	80.00	175.00
without signature	100.00	135.00	65.00	150.00
Plate, 8 ½"				
with signature	75.00	100.00	45.00	115.00
without signature	25.00	35.00	15.00	45.00
Porridge plate				
with signature	110.00	175.00	70.00	200.00
without signature	85.00	125.00	55.00	150.00

Note: Retirement dates are all approximate. When a design is retired all
remaining stocks of the retired litho prints are used until exhausted.

FAMILY GOING OUT ON WASHING DAY

Design No.:	HW8
Designer:	Barbara Vernon
Issued:	By 1937 - by 1967
Combined with:	*Chicken Pulling a Cart*, SF8
	Cycling, HW15R
	Leapfrog, HW12R
	Netting a Cricket, HW6
	Sheltering Under Umbrella, EC3
	Trumpeter, EC5
	Washing Day, HW8R

Family Going out on Washing Day (HW8)

Shape	U.S. $	Can. $	U.K. £	Aust. $
Casino jug, 24s				
with signature	475.00	675.00	300.00	725.00
without signature	400.00	550.00	250.00	600.00
Casino saucer				
with signature	75.00	100.00	50.00	125.00
without signature	50.00	65.00	30.00	75.00
Casino sugar bowl, 36s				
with signature	150.00	225.00	100.00	250.00
without signature	125.00	175.00	80.00	200.00
Casino teacup				
with signature	75.00	100.00	50.00	125.00
without signature	50.00	65.00	30.00	75.00
Casino teapot, 30s				
with signature	300.00	425.00	190.00	475.00
without signature	225.00	325.00	150.00	375.00
Don beaker				
with signature	150.00	225.00	100.00	250.00
without signature	100.00	150.00	65.00	165.00
Don beaker, one handle				
with signature	150.00	225.00	100.00	250.00
without signature	100.00	150.00	65.00	165.00
Don mug, one handle				
with signature	75.00	100.00	50.00	125.00
without signature	35.00	55.00	20.00	60.00
Don mug, two handles				
with signature	75.00	100.00	50.00	125.00
without signature	35.00	55.00	20.00	60.00
Jaffa fruit saucer				
plain rim				
with signature	95.00	125.00	60.00	135.00
without signature	65.00	85.00	40.00	95.00
wavy rim				
with signature	125.00	165.00	80.00	85.00
without signature	85.00	110.00	55.00	60.00
Plate, 6 ½"				
with signature	90.00	125.00	55.00	135.00
without signature	60.00	85.00	40.00	95.00

Family in the Garden (SF135)

FAMILY IN THE GARDEN

Design No.: SF135
Designer: Walter Hayward
Issued: 1967 - by 1998

Shape	U.S. $	Can. $	U.K. £	Aust. $
Albion jug, 1 pint	100.00	150.00	60.00	165.00
Baby plate, round, large	50.00	75.00	35.00	85.00
Baby plate, round, small	20.00	27.50	12.50	30.00
Cake stand	150.00	250.00	100.00	300.00
Cereal / oatmeal bowl	15.00	20.00	10.00	25.00
Hot water plate	75.00	100.00	45.00	110.00
Jaffa fruit saucer (plain)	15.00	20.00	10.00	25.00
Picture plaque, large	20.00	30.00	12.50	30.00
Plate, 6 ½"	15.00	20.00	10.00	25.00
Plate, 8"	15.00	20.00	10.00	25.00

FAMILY PHOTOGRAPH

Design No.: LF15
Designer: Walter Hayward
Issued: By 1954 - 1970

Shape	U.S. $	Can. $	U.K. £	Aust. $
Baby plate, oval, large				
with signature	200.00	275.00	125.00	300.00
without signature	150.00	200.00	95.00	225.00
Baby plate, round large				
with signature	100.00	135.00	65.00	150.00
without signature	75.00	100.00	50.00	125.00
Bread and butter plate				
with signature	300.00	450.00	200.00	500.00
without signature	150.00	225.00	100.00	250.00
Cereal / oatmeal bowl				
with signature	35.00	45.00	20.00	50.00
without signature	25.00	35.00	15.00	40.00
Plate, 8"	25.00	35.00	15.00	40.00
Plate, 8 ½"	25.00	35.00	15.00	40.00
Porridge plate				
with signature	110.00	175.00	70.00	200.00
without signature	85.00	125.00	55.00	150.00

Family Photograph (LF15)

FAMILY WITH PRAM
Style One

Design No.:   HW15
Designer: Barbara Vernon
Issued: By 1937 - by 1952
Combined with: *Cycling,* HW15R
        Engine Pulling a Carriage, HW17
        Footballer, HW13R
        Leapfrog, HW12R
        Proposal, HW11
        Pulling on Trousers, HW2
        Raising Hat, Style One, HW16R
        Raising Hat, Style Two, EC7
        Rowboat, HW21
        Washing in the Open Air, HW10R

Family with Pram, Style One (HW15)

Shape	U.S. $	Can. $	U.K. £	Aust. $
Baby plate, oval, large	200.00	275.00	125.00	300.00
Baby plate, round, large	100.00	135.00	65.00	150.00
Casino jug, 30s	300.00	475.00	200.00	475.00
Casino saucer	75.00	125.00	50.00	125.00
Casino sugar bowl, 30s	200.00	325.00	125.00	350.00
Casino teacup	75.00	125.00	50.00	125.00
Casino teapot, 24s	375.00	550.00	250.00	600.00
Casino teapot, 30s	325.00	500.00	225.00	550.00

Shape	U.S. $	Can. $	U.K. £	Aust. $
Don beaker	65.00	85.00	40.00	90.00
Don beaker, one handle	65.00	85.00	40.00	90.00
Don mug, one handle	50.00	65.00	30.00	75.00
Don mug, two handles	50.00	65.00	30.00	75.00
Jaffa fruit saucer	50.00	65.00	30.00	70.00
Jam pot	1,500.00	1,975.00	950.00	2,000.00
Lid of hot water plate	100.00	135.00	65.00	150.00
Plate, 6 ½"	30.00	40.00	20.00	45.00
Plate, 7 ½"	20.00	25.00	15.00	30.00

Note: **1.** This design should appear with the Barbara Vernon facsimile signature.
      2. This design is found on in-between sizes of Casino jugs.

Family with Pram (HW15) / Raising Hat (HW16R)

FAMILY WITH PRAM / RAISING HAT

The unusual combination of *Family with Pram,* Style One (HW15) and *Raising Hat,* Style One (HW16R), has been found on large round and oval baby plates, a casino sugar bowl, a casino teapot and a 7½" plate.

Design No.:   HW15 / HW16R
Designer: Barbara Vernon
Issued: By 1937 - by 1952

Shape	U.S. $	Can. $	U.K. £	Aust. $
Baby plate, oval, large			Rare	
Baby plate, round, large			Rare	
Casino sugar bowl			Rare	
Casino teapot, 30s			Rare	
Plate, 7 ½"	250.00	350.00	150.00	375.00

Family with Pram, Style Two (CT14)

Standing by Pram (CT6)

FAMILY WITH PRAM
Style Two

Design No.:	Front — CT14 Family with Pram
	Reverse — CT6 Standing by Pram
Designer:	Colin Twinn
Issued:	1989 - 1993
Combined with:	*Bunny on Rocking Horse*, CT29
	Father Bunnykins with Fishing Rod, CT27
	Home from Fishing, CT26
	Nursery, First Version, CT19
	Picking Daisies, CT4

Shape	U.S. $	Can. $	U.K. £	Aust. $
Albion cream jug	35.00	55.00	20.00	60.00
Albion jug, ½ pint	85.00	115.00	50.00	125.00
Albion jug, 1 pint	100.00	150.00	60.00	165.00
Cake stand	150.00	250.00	100.00	300.00
Divider dish	75.00	125.00	50.00	125.00
Hug-a-mug, one handle	10.00	15.00	7.50	15.00
Hug-a-mug, two handles	10.00	15.00	7.50	15.00
Lamp	50.00	75.00	30.00	85.00
Malvern beaker	15.00	25.00	10.00	25.00
Money ball	10.00	15.00	7.50	15.00
Stratford teacup	7.50	12.00	5.00	12.00

Note: *Standing by Pram*, CT6 is combined with *Picking Daisies*, CT4 on Albion 1 pint and ½ pint jugs.

FEEDING THE BABY

Feeding the Baby (HW13)

Design No.:	HW13
Designer:	Barbara Vernon
Issued:	By 1937 - by 1967
Combined with:	*Bedtime in Bunks*, SF3
	Cycling, HW15R
	Family at Breakfast, HW12
	Footballer, HW13R
	Golfer, HW4R
	Kissing under the Mistletoe, HW11R

Leapfrog, HW12R
Pressing Trousers, HW14
Pulling on Trousers, HW2
Raising Hat, Style One, HW16R
Santa Claus, SF9
Sleeping in a Rocking Chair, EC1
Top Hat, HW14R
Trumpeter, EC5
Washing in the Open Air, HW10R

Shape	U.S. $	Can. $	U.K. £	Aust. $
Baby plate, round, small				
with signature	50.00	65.00	30.00	70.00
without signature	30.00	40.00	20.00	45.00
Candle holder	2,000.00	2,500.00	1,250.00	2,500.00
Casino jug, 36s				
with signature	300.00	475.00	200.00	475.00
without signature	250.00	400.00	175.00	400.00
Casino jug, 42s				
with signature	250.00	400.00	175.00	400.00
without signature	200.00	325.00	150.00	325.00
Casino saucer				
with signature	75.00	125.00	50.00	125.00
without signature	50.00	75.00	35.00	75.00
Casino sugar bowl, 30s				
with signature	200.00	325.00	125.00	350.00
without signature	150.00	225.00	100.00	250.00
Casino teacup				
with signature	75.00	125.00	50.00	125.00
without signature	50.00	75.00	35.00	75.00
Casino teapot, 36s				
with signature	250.00	375.00	165.00	400.00
without signature	225.00	350.00	150.00	400.00
Cup / mug, large	800.00	1,000.00	500.00	1,100.00
Don beaker				
with signature	65.00	85.00	40.00	90.00
without signature	35.00	45.00	20.00	50.00

Shape	U.S. $	Can. $	U.K. £	Aust. $
Don beaker, one handle				
with signature	65.00	85.00	40.00	90.00
without signature	35.00	45.00	20.00	50.00
Don mug, one handle				
with silver rim	350.00	475.00	225.00	500.00
with signature	50.00	65.00	30.00	75.00
without signature	15.00	20.00	10.00	25.00
Don mug, two handles				
with signature	50.00	65.00	30.00	75.00
without signature	15.00	20.00	10.00	25.00
Jaffa fruit saucer				
plain rim	50.00	65.00	30.00	70.00
wavy rim	75.00	100.00	50.00	125.00
Jam pot	1,500.00	1,975.00	950.00	2,000.00
Lid of hot water plate				
with signature	100.00	135.00	65.00	150.00
without signature	75.00	100.00	50.00	115.00
Plate, 6 ½"				
with signature	30.00	40.00	20.00	45.00
without signature	20.00	25.00	12.00	30.00
Sugar bowl with handles	3,500.00	6,000.00	2,500.00	7,000.00
FINE WHITE CHINA				
Saucer	300.00	400.00	200.00	425.00
Teacup	300.00	400.00	200.00	425.00

FIRE STATION THEME — Frank Endersby

Washing the Fire Engine (10)

WASHING THE FIRE ENGINE

Design No.:	10 Washing the Fire Engine
Designer:	Frank Endersby
Issued:	1995 to the present

Shape	U.S. $	Can. $	U.K. £	Aust. $
Cereal / oatmeal bowl	N/I	33.00	11.00	49.95
Jaffa fruit saucer	15.00	20.00	10.00	25.00
Plate, 6 ½"	N/I	25.00	8.00	34.95
Plate, 8"	N/I	35.00	11.00	49.95

Pumping Water (11)

PUMPING WATER / TRYING ON HAT

Design No.:	Front — 11 Pumping Water
	Reverse — 12 Trying on Hat
Designer:	Frank Endersby
Issued:	1995 to the present
Combined with:	*Carrying Net, (6)

Shape	U.S. $	Can. $	U.K. £	Aust. $
Hug-a-mug, one handle	30.00	33.00	11.00	49.95
Hug-a-mug, two handles	32.50	39.00	12.00	56.95
Divider dish	50.00	75.00	35.00	75.00
Malvern beaker	15.00	25.00	10.00	25.00
Money ball	33.75	40.00	15.00	62.95
Stratford teacup	7.50	12.00	5.00	12.00

* Indicates scenes on divider dish.

Trying on Hat (12)

Note: 1. Bold type in the listing tables indicate a current design on a current shape.
2. N/I, Not issued individually. The item(s) will be found only in boxed sets in that market.

FISHING THEME — Frank Endersby

FISHING AT THE POND

Design No.:	4 Fishing at the Pond
Designer:	Frank Endersby
Issued:	1995 to the present

Shape	U.S. $	Can. $	U.K. £	Aust. $
Baby plate, round, small	N/I	33.00	11.00	49.95
Jaffa fruit saucer	15.00	20.00	10.00	25.00
Plate, 6 ½"	N/I	25.00	8.00	34.95
Plate, 8"	N/I	35.00	11.00	49.95

Fishing at the Pond (4)

Resting by Pond (5)

RESTING BY POND / CARRYING NET

Design No.:	Front — 5 Resting by Pond
	Reverse — 6 Carrying Net
Designer:	Frank Endersby
Issued:	1995 to the present
Combined with:	*Playing with Balloons*, (33)

Shape	U.S. $	Can. $	U.K. £	Aust. $
Hug-a-mug, one handle	30.00	33.00	11.00	49.95
Hug-a-mug, two handles	32.50	39.00	12.00	56.95
Divider dish	50.00	75.00	35.00	75.00
Money ball	33.75	40.00	15.00	62.95
Stratford teacup	7.50	12.00	5.00	12.00

* Indicates scene on divider dish.
.

Carrying Net (6)

Fishing in the Goldfish Bowl (HW3R)

FISHING IN THE GOLDFISH BOWL

Design No.:	HW3R
Designer:	Barbara Vernon
Issued:	By 1937 - by 1952
Combined with:	*Artist*, HW1
	Fixing Braces, HW3
	Mr. Piggly's Stores, SF14
	Netting a Cricket, HW6
	Playing with Cup and Spoon, EC6
	Pressing Trousers, HW14
	Pulling on Trousers, HW2
	Sheltering Under an Umbrella, EC3

Shape	U.S. $	Can. $	U.K. £	Aust. $
Casino jug, 24s	475.00	675.00	300.00	725.00
Casino jug, 36s	300.00	425.00	190.00	475.00
Casino teacup	75.00	100.00	50.00	125.00
Don beaker	150.00	225.00	100.00	250.00
Don mug, one handle	75.00	100.00	50.00	125.00

FINE WHITE CHINA

Teacup		Very Rare

Note: This design should appear with the Barbara Vernon facsimile signature.

FISHING ON THE PIER

Design No.:	LF3
Designer:	Barbara Vernon
Issued:	By 1940 - by 1952

Shape	U.S. $	Can. $	U.K. £	Aust. $
Baby plate, round, large				
with silver rim		Rare		
with signature	400.00	525.00	250.00	550.00
without signature	350.00	450.00	225.00	475.00
Bread and butter plate				
with signature	500.00	650.00	300.00	675.00
without signature	400.00	525.00	250.00	550.00
Cereal / oatmeal bowl				
with signature	200.00	275.00	125.00	300.00
without signature	175.00	225.00	115.00	250.00
Plate, 8 ½"				
with signature	225.00	300.00	150.00	325.00
without signature	175.00	225.00	115.00	250.00
Porridge plate				
with signature	300.00	400.00	200.00	425.00
without signature	250.00	325.00	150.00	350.00

Fishing on the Pier (LF3)

FIXING BRACES

Design No.:	HW3
Designer:	Barbara Vernon
Issued:	By 1937 - by 1952
Combined with:	*Chicken Pulling a Cart*, SF8
	Cycling, HW15R
	Embracing at a Window, HW5
	Family at Breakfast, HW12
	Fishing in the Goldfish Bowl, HW3R
	Going Shopping, SF10
	Leapfrog, HW12R
	Smoking in the Doorway, SF2

Fixing Braces (HW3)

Shape	U.S. $	Can. $	U.K. £	Aust. $
Candle holder	2,000.00	2,500.00	1,250.00	2,500.00
Casino jug, 24s	400.00	625.00	275.00	650.00
Casino jug, 36s	300.00	475.00	200.00	475.00
Casino saucer	75.00	125.00	50.00	125.00
Casino teacup	75.00	125.00	50.00	125.00
Cup / mug, large			Rare	
Don beaker	65.00	85.00	40.00	90.00
Don beaker, one handle	65.00	85.00	40.00	90.00
Don mug, one handle	50.00	65.00	30.00	75.00
Don mug, two handles	50.00	65.00	30.00	75.00
Jaffa fruit saucer				
plain rim	50.00	65.00	30.00	70.00
wavy rim	75.00	100.00	50.00	125.00
Plate, 6 ½"	30.00	40.00	20.00	45.00

FINE WHITE CHINA

Night light	Very Rare
Rex mug	Very Rare

Note: This design should appear with the Barbara Vernon facsimile signature.

Flying Kites (SF133)

FLYING KITES

Design No.:	SF133
Designer:	Walter Hayward
Issued:	1967 - by 1998

Shape	U.S. $	Can. $	U.K. £	Aust. $
Albion jug, 1 pint	100.00	150.00	60.00	165.00
Baby plate, round, small	20.00	27.50	12.50	30.00
Cake stand	150.00	250.00	100.00	300.00
Casino saucer	7.50	12.00	5.00	12.00
Cereal / oatmeal bowl	15.00	20.00	10.00	25.00
Jaffa fruit saucer (plain)	15.00	20.00	10.00	25.00
Hot water plate	75.00	100.00	45.00	110.00
Picture plaque, large	20.00	30.00	12.50	30.00
Plate, 6 ½"	15.00	20.00	10.00	25.00
Plate, 8"	15.00	20.00	10.00	25.00

Footballer (HW13R)

FOOTBALLER

Design No.:	HW13R
Designer:	Barbara Vernon
Issued:	By 1937 - by 1967
Combined with:	*Cuddling under a Mushroom*, HW4
	Family at Breakfast, HW12
	Family with Pram, Style One, HW15
	Feeding the Baby, HW13
	Gardening, Style One (HW9)
	Lambeth Walk, HW16
	Pressing Trousers, HW14
	Proposal, HW11
	Reading the Times, HW2R
	Sleeping in a Rocking Chair, EC1

Shape	U.S. $	Can. $	U.K. £	Aust. $
Beaker Cover	75.00	100.00	45.00	110.00
Casino jug, 42s				
with signature	250.00	400.00	175.00	400.00
without signature	200.00	325.00	150.00	325.00
Casino sugar bowl, 36s				
with signature	175.00	275.00	125.00	325.00
without signature	125.00	200.00	85.00	225.00
Casino teacup				
with signature	75.00	125.00	50.00	125.00
without signature	50.00	75.00	35.00	75.00
Don beaker				
with signature	65.00	85.00	40.00	90.00
without signature	35.00	45.00	20.00	50.00
Don beaker, one handle				
with signature	65.00	85.00	40.00	90.00
without signature	35.00	45.00	20.00	50.00
Don mug, one handle				
with silver rim		Rare		
with signature	50.00	65.00	30.00	75.00
without signature	15.00	20.00	10.00	25.00
Don mug, two handles				
with signature	50.00	65.00	30.00	75.00
without signature	15.00	20.00	10.00	25.00
Lid of hot water plate				
with signature	100.00	135.00	65.00	150.00
without signature	75.00	100.00	50.00	115.00
Sugar bowl with handles		Very rare		

FINE WHITE CHINA

Shape	U.S. $	Can. $	U.K. £	Aust. $
Rex mug, small, 2 ½"	1,000.00	1,350.00	625.00	1,400.00
Teacup	300.00	400.00	200.00	425.00

Note: 1. The Rex mug can be found combined with one of the following: *Pressing Trousers* (HW14), *Proposal* (HW11) or *Lambeth Walk*, First Version (HW16).

2. Fine white china prices are indications only due to the scarcity of the shapes, prices will vary.

FRIGHTENING SPIDER

Design No.: SF4
Designer: Barbara Vernon
Issued: By 1937 - by 1952
Combined with: *Conducting the Orchestra*, LF5
Greetings, HW7
Medicine Time, SF1
Pressing Trousers, HW14

Shape	U.S. $	Can. $	U.K. £	Aust. $
Baby plate, round, large	100.00	135.00	65.00	150.00
Baby plate, round, small	50.00	65.00	30.00	70.00
Casino jug, 24s	400.00	625.00	275.00	650.00
Casino jug, 36s	300.00	475.00	200.00	475.00
Casino saucer	75.00	125.00	50.00	125.00
Casino teapot, 24s	375.00	550.00	250.00	600.00
Cereal / oatmeal bowl	35.00	45.00	20.00	50.00
Jaffa fruit saucer				
plain rim	50.00	65.00	30.00	70.00
wavy rim	75.00	100.00	50.00	125.00
Hot water plate	125.00	165.00	80.00	175.00
Plate, 6 ½"	30.00	40.00	20.00	45.00
Plate, 7"	65.00	85.00	40.00	95.00
Plate, 7 ½"	65.00	85.00	40.00	95.00
Plate, 8"	75.00	100.00	45.00	115.00
FINE WHITE CHINA				
Saucer	300.00	400.00	200.00	425.00
Teacup	300.00	400.00	200.00	425.00

Frightening Spider (SF4)

Note: This design should appear with the Barbara Vernon facsimile signature. A round baby plate has been recorded featuring the facsimile name of Dorothy Vernon instead of Barbara Vernon.

Frightening Spider with "Dorothy Vernon" facsimile name

Fun in the Snow

FUN IN THE SNOW
CHRISTMAS TREE ORNAMENT

This Christmas tree ornament, which has a rabbit-shaped rim, was commissioned by Royal Doulton U.S.A. and produced in the U.S.A. The words Fun in the Snow appear on the reverse.

Design No.:	None
Designer:	Frank Endersby
Issued:	1995 - 1995
Series:	Christmas Tree Ornaments

Shape	U.S. $	Can. $	U.K. £	Aust. $
Christmas tree ornament	25.00	35.00	20.00	50.00

Note: For other Christmas ornaments in this series see page 40, 42, 141 and 163.

GAME OF GOLF

Design No.:	SF11
Designer:	Barbara Vernon
Issued:	By 1940 - by 1952
Combined with:	*Gardening*, Style One, HW9
	Picnic, Second Version, LF10
	Pulling on Trousers, HW2

Game of Golf (SF11)

Shape	U.S. $	Can. $	U.K. £	Aust. $
Baby plate, round, large				
with signature	100.00	135.00	65.00	150.00
without signature	75.00	100.00	50.00	125.00
Baby plate, round, small				
with signature	50.00	65.00	30.00	70.00
without signature	30.00	40.00	20.00	45.00
Casino jug, 36s				
with signature	300.00	475.00	200.00	475.00
without signature	250.00	400.00	175.00	400.00
Casino saucer				
with signature	75.00	125.00	50.00	125.00
without signature	50.00	75.00	35.00	75.00
Casino teapot, 24s				
with signature	375.00	550.00	250.00	600.00
without signature	300.00	450.00	200.00	500.00
Casino teapot, 30s				
with signature	400.00	600.00	275.00	700.00
without signature	300.00	450.00	200.00	500.00
Cereal / oatmeal bowl				
with signature	35.00	45.00	20.00	50.00
without signature	25.00	35.00	15.00	40.00
Jaffa fruit saucer				
plain rim	50.00	65.00	30.00	75.00
wavy rim	75.00	100.00	50.00	125.00
Lid for hot water plate				
with signature	100.00	135.00	65.00	150.00
without signature	75.00	100.00	50.00	115.00
Plate, 6 ½"				
with signature	30.00	40.00	20.00	45.00
without signature	20.00	25.00	12.00	30.00
Plate, 7 ½"				
with signature	65.00	85.00	40.00	95.00
without signature	25.00	35.00	15.00	45.00

Note: See also *Golfer* (HW4R) page 85.

GARAGE THEME – Frank Endersby

PETROL IN THE SPORTS CAR

Design No.:   37 Petrol in the Sports Car
Designer: Frank Endersby
Issued: 1995 to the present

Shape	U.S. $	Can. $	U.K. £	Aust. $
Baby plate, round, small	N/I	33.00	11.00	49.95
Plate, 6 ½"	N/I	25.00	8.00	34.95
Plate, 8"	N/I	35.00	11.00	49.95

Petrol in the Sports Car (37)

Pumping Tyre (38)

PUMPING TYRE / SITTING ON OIL DRUM

Design No.:   Front — 38 Pumping Tyre
                  Reverse — 39 Sitting on Oil Drum
Designer: Frank Endersby
Issued: 1995 to the present
Combined with: *Pillar Money Box*

Shape	U.S. $	Can. $	U.K. £	Aust. $
Hug-a-mug, one handle	30.00	33.00	11.00	49.95
Hug-a-mug, two handles	32.50	39.00	12.00	56.95
Malvern beaker	15.00	25.00	10.00	25.00

Sitting on Oil Drum (39)

Gardener with Wheelbarrow (HW9R)

GARDENER WITH WHEELBARROW

Design No.:	HW9R
Designer:	Barbara Vernon
Issued:	By 1937 - by 1967
Combined with:	*Chicken Pulling a Cart, SF8*
	Gardening, Style One, HW9
	Leapfrog, HW12R
	Netting a Cricket, HW6

Shape	U.S. $	Can. $	U.K. £	Aust. $
Casino jug, 42s				
with signature	250.00	400.00	175.00	400.00
without signature	200.00	325.00	150.00	325.00
Casino sugar bowl, 30s				
with signature	200.00	325.00	125.00	350.00
without signature	150.00	225.00	100.00	250.00
Casino sugar bowl, 36s				
with signature	175.00	275.00	125.00	325.00
without signature	125.00	200.00	85.00	225.00
Casino teacup				
with signature	75.00	125.00	50.00	125.00
without signature	50.00	75.00	35.00	75.00
Cup / mug, large		Rare		
Don beaker				
with signature	65.00	85.00	40.00	90.00
without signature	35.00	45.00	20.00	50.00
Don mug, one handle				
with silver rim		Rare		
with signature	50.00	65.00	30.00	75.00
without signature	15.00	20.00	10.00	25.00
Don mug, two handles				
with signature	50.00	65.00	30.00	75.00
without signature	15.00	20.00	10.00	25.00
Lid of hot water plate				
with signature	100.00	135.00	65.00	150.00
without signature	75.00	100.00	50.00	115.00

Note: 1. Retirement dates are all approximate. When a design is retired all remaining stocks of the retired litho prints are used until exhausted.
2. Condition is important. Prices listed are based on nurseryware in mint condition. Items in less than mint condition will command lower prices.

GARDENING
Style One

Gardening, Style One (HW9)

Design No.: HW9
Designer: Barbara Vernon
Issued: By 1937 - by 1967

Combined with: *Asleep in the Open Air*, HW10
Footballer, HW13R
Game of Golf, SF11
Gardener with Wheelbarrow, HW9R
Greetings, HW7
Leapfrog, HW12R
Washing in the Open Air, HW10R

Shape	U.S. $	Can. $	U.K. £	Aust. $
Baby plate, round, small				
with signature	200.00	275.00	125.00	300.00
without signature	150.00	200.00	100.00	225.00
Casino jug, 36s				
with signature	300.00	425.00	190.00	475.00
without signature	275.00	400.00	175.00	450.00
Casino jug, 42s				
with signature	275.00	400.00	175.00	450.00
without signature	200.00	275.00	125.00	300.00
Casino saucer				
with signature	75.00	100.00	50.00	125.00
without signature	50.00	65.00	30.00	75.00
Casino sugar bowl, 36s				
with signature	150.00	225.00	100.00	250.00
without signature	125.00	175.00	80.00	200.00
Casino teacup				
with signature	75.00	100.00	50.00	125.00
without signature	50.00	65.00	30.00	75.00
Casino teapot, 24s				
with signature	375.00	525.00	235.00	575.00
without signature	300.00	425.00	190.00	475.00
Cereal / oatmeal bowl				
with signature	100.00	135.00	65.00	150.00
without signature	90.00	125.00	55.00	135.00

Shape	U.S. $	Can. $	U.K. £	Aust. $
Don beaker				
with signature	150.00	225.00	100.00	250.00
without signature	100.00	150.00	65.00	165.00
Don beaker, one handle				
with signature	150.00	225.00	100.00	250.00
without signature	100.00	150.00	65.00	165.00
Don mug, one handle				
with silver rim	350.00	475.00	225.00	500.00
with signature	75.00	100.00	50.00	125.00
without signature	35.00	55.00	20.00	60.00
Don mug, two handles				
with signature	75.00	100.00	50.00	125.00
without signature	35.00	55.00	20.00	60.00
Jaffa fruit saucer				
plain rim	95.00	135.00	65.00	150.00
wavy rim	125.00	175.00	80.00	200.00
Jam pot	1,500.00	1,975.00	950.00	2,000.00
Lid of hot water plate				
with signature	175.00	250.00	110.00	275.00
without signature	125.00	175.00	80.00	200.00
Plate, 6 ½"				
with signature	60.00	80.00	38.00	85.00
without signature	35.00	55.00	20.00	60.00

GARDENING THEME — Frank Endersby

Gardening, Style Two (55)

GARDENING
Style Two

Design No.:	55 Gardening
Designer:	Frank Endersby
Issued:	1995 - 2003

Shape	U.S. $	Can. $	U.K. £	Aust. $
Baby plate, round, small	N/I	33.00	11.00	49.95
Cake stand	150.00	250.00	100.00	300.00
Plate, 6 ½"	N/I	25.00	8.00	34.95
Plate, 8"	N/I	35.00	11.00	49.95
Plate, 10 ½"	35.00	55.00	25.00	60.00

Playing in Tree House (56)

PLAYING IN TREE HOUSE / RESTING IN WHEELBARROW

Design No.:	Front — 56 Playing in Tree House
	Reverse — 57 Resting in Wheelbarrow
Designer:	Frank Endersby
Issued:	1995 - 2003
Combined with:	*Butterfly Net, (6)

Shape	U.S. $	Can. $	U.K. £	Aust. $
Hug-a-mug, one handle	30.00	33.00	11.00	49.95
Hug-a-mug, two handles	32.50	39.00	12.00	56.95
Divider Dish	50.00	75.00	35.00	75.00
Money Ball	33.75	40.00	15.00	62.95

* Indicates scene on divider dish.

Resting in Wheelbarrow (57)

GEOGRAPHY LESSON

Design No.:	LF17			
Designer:	Walter Hayward			
Issued:	1954 - 1970			

Shape	U.S. $	Can. $	U.K. £	Aust. $
Baby plate, oval, large				
with signature	200.00	275.00	125.00	300.00
without signature	150.00	200.00	95.00	225.00
Baby plate, round, large				
with signature	100.00	135.00	65.00	150.00
without signature	75.00	100.00	50.00	125.00
Bread and butter plate				
with signature	250.00	400.00	175.00	400.00
without signature	200.00	325.00	150.00	325.00
Cereal / oatmeal bowl				
with signature	35.00	45.00	20.00	50.00
without signature	25.00	35.00	15.00	40.00
Plate, 8"	75.00	100.00	45.00	115.00
Plate, 8 ½"				
with signature	75.00	100.00	45.00	115.00
without signature	25.00	35.00	15.00	45.00
Porridge plate				
with signature	110.00	175.00	70.00	200.00
without signature	85.00	125.00	55.00	150.00

Geography Lesson (LF17)

Getting Dressed (LF2)

GETTING DRESSED

Design No.:	LF2			
Designer:	Barbara Vernon			
Issued:	By 1940 - by 1952			

Shape	U.S. $	Can. $	U.K. £	Aust. $
Baby plate, round, large				
with signature	400.00	525.00	250.00	550.00
without signature	350.00	450.00	225.00	475.00
Bread / butter plate, handles				
with signature	500.00	650.00	300.00	675.00
without signature	400.00	525.00	250.00	550.00
Hot water plate				
with signature	375.00	500.00	250.00	550.00
without signature	325.00	450.00	200.00	500.00
Plate, 8 ½"				
with signature	225.00	300.00	150.00	325.00
without signature	175.00	225.00	115.00	250.00
Porridge plate				
with signature	300.00	400.00	200.00	425.00
without signature	250.00	325.00	150.00	350.00

Going Shopping (SF10)

GOING SHOPPING

Design No.:	SF10
Designer:	Barbara Vernon
Issued:	By 1940 - by 1952
Combined with:	*Chicken Pulling a Cart*, SF8
	Fixing Braces, HW3
	Lambeth Walk, second version, HW16

Shape	U.S. $	Can. $	U.K. £	Aust. $
Baby plate, round, small				
with signature	50.00	65.00	30.00	70.00
without signature	30.00	40.00	20.00	45.00
Casino jug, 30s				
with signature	300.00	475.00	200.00	475.00
without signature	225.00	325.00	150.00	325.00
Casino saucer				
with signature	75.00	125.00	50.00	125.00
without signature	50.00	75.00	35.00	75.00
Casino teapot, 24s				
with signature	375.00	550.00	250.00	600.00
without signature	300.00	450.00	200.00	500.00
Cereal / oatmeal bowl				
with signature	35.00	45.00	20.00	50.00
without signature	25.00	35.00	15.00	40.00
Don beaker				
with signature	65.00	85.00	40.00	90.00
without signature	35.00	45.00	20.00	50.00
Don beaker, one handle				
with signature	65.00	85.00	40.00	90.00
without signature	35.00	45.00	20.00	50.00
Jaffa fruit saucer (wavy)				
with signature	75.00	100.00	50.00	125.00
without signature	50.00	65.00	30.00	70.00
Hot water plate				
with signature	125.00	165.00	80.00	175.00
without signature	100.00	135.00	65.00	150.00
Plate, 6 ½"				
with signature	30.00	40.00	20.00	45.00
without signature	20.00	25.00	12.00	30.00
Plate, 7 ½"				
with signature	65.00	85.00	40.00	95.00
without signature	25.00	35.00	15.00	45.00

FINE WHITE CHINA

Cereal / oatmeal bowl   Very Rare

Note: **1.** Early Don beakers may come with a border of running rabbits inside the beaker, a little down from the rim.
  2. Condition is important. Prices listed are based on nurseryware in mint condition. Items in less than mint condition will command lower prices.

GOLFER

Design No.:	HW4R
Designer:	Barbara Vernon
Issued:	By 1937 - by 1952
Combined with:	
Cuddling under a Mushroom, HW4	*Pressing Trousers*, HW14
Cycling, HW15R	*Proposal*, HW11
Family at Breakfast, HW12	*Pulling on Trousers*, HW2
Feeding the Baby, HW13	*Reading the Times*, HW2R

Shape	U.S. $	Can. $	U.K. £	Aust. $
Casino jug, 36s	300.00	475.00	200.00	475.00
Casino jug, 42s	250.00	400.00	175.00	400.00
Casino teacup	75.00	125.00	50.00	125.00
Don beaker	65.00	85.00	40.00	90.00
Don beaker, one handle	65.00	85.00	40.00	90.00
Don mug, one handle	50.00	65.00	30.00	75.00
Don mug, two handles	50.00	65.00	30.00	75.00
FINE WHITE CHINA				
Rex mug	1,000.00	1,350.00	625.00	1,400.00

Golfer (HW4R)

Note: 1. This design should appear with the Barbara Vernon facsimile signature. See also *Game of Golf* (SF11) page 78.
2. *Golfer* (HW4R) is combined with *Proposal* (HW11) on the Rex mug.

GREETINGS

Design No.:	HW7
Designer:	Barbara Vernon
Issued:	By 1937 - by 1952
Combined with:	*Artist*, HW1
	Dunce, HW1R
	Fixing Braces, HW3
	Frightening Spider, SF4
	Gardening, Style One, HW9

Greetings (HW7)

Shape	U.S. $	Can. $	U.K. £	Aust. $
Baby plate, round, small	50.00	65.00	30.00	70.00
Casino jug, 36s	300.00	475.00	200.00	475.00
Casino jug, 42s	250.00	400.00	175.00	400.00
Casino saucer	75.00	125.00	50.00	125.00
Casino teacup	75.00	125.00	50.00	125.00
Casino teapot, 24s	375.00	550.00	250.00	600.00
Casino teapot, 30s	325.00	500.00	225.00	550.00
Cereal / oatmeal bowl	35.00	45.00	20.00	50.00
Don beaker	65.00	85.00	40.00	90.00
Don beaker, one handle	65.00	85.00	40.00	90.00

Shape	U.S. $	Can. $	U.K. £	Aust. $
Don mug, one handle	50.00	65.00	30.00	75.00
Don mug, two handles	50.00	65.00	30.00	75.00
Jaffa fruit saucer				
plain rim	50.00	65.00	30.00	70.00
wavy rim	75.00	100.00	50.00	125.00
Lid of hot water plate	100.00	135.00	65.00	150.00
Plate, 6 ½"	30.00	40.00	20.00	45.00
Plate, 7 ½"	65.00	85.00	40.00	95.00
FINE CHINA				
Plate, 5"	650.00	850.00	400.00	875.00
Plate, 7"	650.00	850.00	400.00	875.00
Rex mug	1,000.00	1,350.00	625.00	1,400.00

Note: This design should appear with the Barbara Vernon facsimile signature.

HAPPY BIRTHDAY FROM BUNNYKINS — Walter Hayward

Happy Birthday From Bunnykins,
Style One, (SF136)

Style One

Design No.:	Front — SF136 Happy Birthday from Bunnykins
	Reverse — Birthday Inscription
Designer:	Walter Hayward
Issued:	1982 - 1989
Inscription:	"Birthdays are lots and lots of fun,
	With cards and gifts for everyone
	There are cakes and jellies and lots to eat,
	Parties and games and your favourite treat.
	So on this your very special day
	The Bunnykins wish you a Happy Birthday"

Shape	U.S. $	Can. $	U.K. £	Aust. $
Plate, 8"	15.00	25.00	10.00	30.00

Reverse Birthday Inscription

HAPPY BIRTHDAY FROM BUNNYKINS — Colin Twinn

Style Two, First Version

The rhyme used on the reverse of this plate is the same as that used on style one, however a new border and copyright date are shown.

Design No.:   Front — CT37 Happy Birthday from Bunnykins
                  Reverse — CT64 Birthday Inscription
Designer: Colin Twinn
Issued: 1990 - 1992
Inscription: Birthdays are lots and lots of fun,
                  With cards and gifts for everyone
                  There are cakes and jellies and lots to eat
                  Parties and games and your favourite treat.
                  So on this your very special day
                  The Bunnykins wish you a Happy Birthday

Shape	U.S. $	Can. $	U.K. £	Aust. $
Plate, 8"	15.00	25.00	10.00	30.00

Happy Birthday from Bunnykins
Style Two, First Version (CT37)

Happy Birthday from Bunnykins
Style Two, Second Version (CT60)

Birthday Inscription (CT64)

Style Two, Second Version

Design No.:   Front — CT60 Happy Birthday from Bunnykins
                  Reverse — CT61 Inscription
Designer: Colin Twinn
Issued: 1992 - 1992

Shape	U.S. $	Can. $	U.K. £	Aust. $
Hug-a-mug, one handle	10.00	15.00	7.50	15.00

Happy Birthday Bunnykins
Inscription (CT61)

Note: See page no. 197 for two money balls issued for the 1992 U.S. Special Events Tour.

HAPPY EASTER FROM BUNNYKINS — Colin Twinn

Happy Easter from Bunnykins
First Version (CT40)

First Version, Large Design

Design No.:	Front — CT40 Happy Easter from Bunnykins
	Reverse no. one - without inscription
	Reverse no. two — CT67 with inscription
Designer:	Colin Twinn
Issued:	1990 - 1992
Rhyme:	The Easter Bunnykins romp and play,
	Loving the joy of this Easter Day.
	Gone is the frost, the long winter lost,
	The sunshine brings light and new blossoms bright,
	So Bunnykins send you this warm invitation
	To Easter party, a grand celebration.

Shape	U.S. $	Can. $	U.K. £	Aust. $
Plate, 8"	15.00	25.00	10.00	30.00

Happy Easter from Bunnykins
Second Version (CT62)

Second Version, Small Design

Design No.:	Front — CT62 Happy Easter from Bunnykins
	Reverse — CT63 Happy Easter Inscription
Designer:	Colin Twinn
Issued:	1992 - 1992

Shape	U.S. $	Can. $	U.K. £	Aust. $
Hug-a-mug, one handle	10.00	15.00	7.50	15.00

Happy Easter Inscription (CT63)

HAT SHOP / TRYING ON HATS

Hat Shop (HW28)

Trying on Hats (HW28R)

Design No.: Front — HW28 Hat Shop
Reverse — HW28R Trying on Hats
Designer: Walter Hayward
Issued: Hat Shop - 1954 - by 1998
Trying on Hats - 1954 - 2003

Combined with: *Afternoon Tea*, HW116
Dancing with Doll, HW115R
Drummer and Bugler, EC126
Serving Tea, HW116R
Trumpeter, EC5

Shape	U.S. $	Can. $	U.K. £	Aust. $
Albion cream jug	35.00	55.00	20.00	60.00
Albion jug, ½ pint	85.00	115.00	50.00	125.00
Albion jug, 1 pint	100.00	150.00	60.00	165.00
Albion teapot	50.00	70.00	30.00	75.00
Casino jug, 36s				
with signature	175.00	275.00	125.00	275.00
without signature	125.00	200.00	85.00	300.00
Casino jug, 42s				
with signature	150.00	225.00	100.00	225.00
without signature	100.00	150.00	70.00	150.00
Casino saucer				
with signature	15.00	25.00	10.00	25.00
without signature	7.50	12.00	5.00	12.00
Casino teacup				
with signature	15.00	25.00	10.00	25.00
without signature	7.50	12.00	5.00	12.00
Divider dish	50.00	75.00	35.00	75.00
Don beaker				
with signature	50.00	65.00	30.00	75.00
without signature	25.00	35.00	15.00	40.00
Don beaker, one handle				
with signature	50.00	65.00	30.00	75.00
without signature	25.00	35.00	15.00	40.00
Don mug, one handle				
with signature	40.00	55.00	25.00	60.00
without signature	10.00	15.00	6.50	18.00

Shape	U.S. $	Can. $	U.K. £	Aust. $
Don mug, two handles				
with signature	40.00	55.00	25.00	60.00
without signature	10.00	15.00	6.50	18.00
Egg box				
small	225.00	350.00	150.00	400.00
medium	300.00	450.00	200.00	500.00
large	375.00	550.00	250.00	600.00
Hug-a-mug, one handle	10.00	15.00	7.50	15.00
Hug-a-mug, two handles	10.00	15.00	7.50	15.00
Jaffa fruit saucer (plain)	15.00	20.00	10.00	25.00
Lamp	50.00	75.00	30.00	85.00
Lid of hot water plate				
with signature	75.00	100.00	45.00	110.00
without signature	50.00	65.00	30.00	70.00
Malvern beaker	15.00	25.00	10.00	25.00
Money ball	10.00	15.00	7.50	15.00
Picture plaque, small	20.00	30.00	12.50	30.00
Plate, 6 ½"				
with signature	25.00	35.00	15.00	40.00
without signature	15.00	20.00	10.00	25.00
Savings book	15.00	22.50	10.00	22.50
Stratford straight beaker	15.00	25.00	10.00	25.00
Stratford teacup	7.50	12.00	5.00	12.00

Note: *Trying on Hats* (HW28R) was paired with *Dancing with Doll* (HW115R) on the Savings book. The divider dish combines *Afternoon Tea* (HW116), *Serving Tea* (HW116R) and *Trying on Hats* (HW28R) and the lid of the hot water plate combines *Hat Shop* (HW28), *Trying on Hats* (HW28R) and *Drummer and Bugler* (EC126).

HAYMAKING / LUNCH BREAK

Haymaking (HW29)

Lunch Break (HW29R)

Design No.:	Front — HW29 Haymaking
	Reverse — HW29R Lunch Break
Designer:	Walter Hayward
Issued:	1954 - by 1998

Combined with: *Apple Picking*, SF25
Dancing with Doll, HW115R
Holding Hat and Coat, EC4
Sleeping in a Rocking Chair, EC1
Toast for Tea Today, SF3

Shape	U.S. $	Can. $	U.K. £	Aust. $
Albion cream jug	35.00	55.00	20.00	60.00
Albion jug, ½ pint	85.00	115.00	50.00	125.00
Albion jug, 1 pint	100.00	150.00	60.00	165.00
Albion teapot	50.00	70.00	30.00	75.00
Casino jug, 36s				
with signature	175.00	275.00	125.00	275.00
without signature	125.00	200.00	85.00	200.00
Casino jug, 42s				
with signature	150.00	225.00	100.00	225.00
without signature	100.00	150.00	70.00	150.00
Casino saucer				
with signature	15.00	25.00	10.00	25.00
without signature	7.50	12.00	5.00	12.00
Casino sugar, 30s				
with signature	175.00	275.00	125.00	300.00
without signature	125.00	200.00	85.00	225.00
Casino teacup				
with signature	15.00	25.00	10.00	25.00
without signature	7.50	12.00	5.00	12.00
Casino teapot, 30s				
with signature	250.00	375.00	165.00	400.00
without signature	150.00	225.00	100.00	250.00
Don beaker				
with signature	50.00	65.00	30.00	75.00
without signature	25.00	35.00	15.00	40.00
Don beaker, one handle				
with signature	50.00	65.00	30.00	75.00
without signature	25.00	35.00	15.00	40.00

Shape	U.S. $	Can. $	U.K. £	Aust. $
Don mug, one handle				
with signature	40.00	55.00	25.00	60.00
without signature	10.00	15.00	6.50	18.00
Don mug, two handles				
with signature	40.00	55.00	25.00	60.00
without signature	10.00	15.00	6.50	18.00
Egg box				
small	225.00	350.00	150.00	400.00
medium	300.00	450.00	200.00	500.00
large	375.00	550.00	250.00	600.00
Hug-a-mug, one handle	10.00	15.00	7.50	15.00
Hug-a-mug, two handles	10.00	15.00	7.50	15.00
Jaffa fruit saucer (plain)	15.00	20.00	10.00	25.00
Lamp	50.00	75.00	30.00	85.00
Lid of hot water plate				
with signature	75.00	100.00	45.00	110.00
without signature	50.00	65.00	30.00	70.00
Malvern beaker	15.00	25.00	10.00	25.00
Money ball	10.00	15.00	7.50	15.00
Picture plaque, small	20.00	30.00	12.50	30.00
Plate, 6 ½"				
with signature	25.00	35.00	15.00	40.00
without signature	15.00	20.00	10.00	25.00
Savings book	15.00	22.50	10.00	22.50
Stratford straight beaker	15.00	25.00	10.00	25.00
Stratford teacup	7.50	12.00	5.00	12.00

HIKERS

Design No.:	EC124
Designer:	Walter Hayward
Issued:	1959 to the present
Combined with:	*Afternoon Tea*, HW116
	Bedtime with Dollies, EC125
	Daisy Chains, HW25
	The Doll's House, HW120
	Drummer, EC2
	Drummer and Bugler, EC126
	Hobby Horse, Style Two, EC121
	Holding Hat and Coat, EC4
	Nipped by a Crab, HW21R
	Playing with Cup and Spoon, EC6
	Playing with Doll and Pram, EC123
	Playing with Doll and Teddy, HW120R
	Playing with Dolls and Prams, HW115
	Raising Hat, Style Two, EC7
	Reading, EC122
	Row Boat, HW21
	Sheltering Under an Umbrella, EC3
	Sleeping in a Rocking Chair, EC1
	Trumpeter, EC5

Hikers (EC124)

Shape	U.S. $	Can. $	U.K. £	Aust. $
Albion sugar bowl	30.00	40.00	17.50	45.00
Beaker cover	40.00	55.00	25.00	60.00
Egg cup				
Style One	30.00	40.00	20.00	45.00
Style Two	40.00	55.00	25.00	60.00
Style Three	N/I	**15.00**	**5.00**	**19.95**
Lid of hot water plate	50.00	65.00	30.00	70.00
Money Ball	**33.75**	**40.00**	**15.00**	**62.95**

Note: This scene was combined with *Daisy Chains*, (HW25) on a Hug-a-mug for the U.S. Special Events Tour in 1993, see page 198.

Hobby Horse, Style Two (EC121)

HOBBY HORSE
Style Two

Design No.:	EC121
Designer:	Walter Hayward
Issued:	1959 to the present
Combined with:	*Cowboy on Rocking Horse*, HW140R
	Cowboys and Indians, HW140
	Drummer, EC2
	Drummer and Bugler, EC126
	Hikers, EC124
	Holding Hat and Coat, EC4
	Lasso Games, HW117
	Lassoing, HW117R
	Playing with Cup and Spoon, EC6
	Playing with Doll and Pram, EC123
	Raising Hat, Style Two, EC7
	Reading, EC122
	Sheltering Under an Umbrella, EC3
	Sleeping in a Rocking Chair, EC1
	Trumpeter, EC5

Shape	U.S. $	Can. $	U.K. £	Aust. $
Albion sugar bowl	30.00	40.00	17.50	45.00
Beaker cover	40.00	55.00	25.00	60.00
Egg cup				
Style One	30.00	40.00	20.00	45.00
Style Two	40.00	55.00	25.00	60.00
Style Three	N/I	15.00	5.00	19.95
Lid of hot water plate	50.00	65.00	30.00	70.00

China teacup combining. *Pulling on Trousers* (HW2) and *Proposal* (HW11)

HOLDING HAT AND COAT

Design No.:	EC4
Designer:	Barbara Vernon
Issued:	1937 - 2003
Combined with:	*Bedtime with Dollies*, EC125
	Drummer, EC2
	Drummer and Bugler, EC126
	Haymaking, HW29
	Hikers, EC124
	Hobby Horse, Style Two, EC121
	Lunch Break, HW29R
	Playing with Cup and Spoon, EC6
	Playing with Doll and Pram, EC123
	Proposal, HW11
	Pulling on Trousers, HW2
	Raising Hat, Style Two, EC7
	Sheltering Under an Umbrella, EC3
	Skipping, HW20R
	Swinging, HW20
	Trumpeter, EC5
	Wheelbarrow Race, Style One, HW22

Holding Hat and Coat (EC4)

Shape	U.S. $	Can. $	U.K. £	Aust. $
Albion sugar bowl	30.00	40.00	17.50	45.00
Beaker cover				
with signature	50.00	65.00	30.00	70.00
without signature	40.00	55.00	25.00	60.00
Casino sugar bowl, 36s				
with signature	125.00	200.00	85.00	225.00
without signature	100.00	150.00	65.00	175.00
Egg cup				
Style One	30.00	40.00	20.00	45.00
Style Two				
with signature	50.00	65.00	30.00	70.00
without signature	40.00	55.00	25.00	60.00
Style Three	10.00	15.00	7.50	18.00
Lid of hot water plate				
with signature	75.00	100.00	45.00	110.00
without signature	50.00	65.00	30.00	70.00
Money ball	10.00	15.00	7.50	15.00

FINE CHINA
Beaker cover
    with signature   Very Rare

Home Decorating (SF131)

HOME DECORATING

Design No.:	SF131
Designer:	Walter Hayward
Issued:	1967 - by 1998

Shape	U.S. $	Can. $	U.K. £	Aust. $
Baby plate, round, small	20.00	27.50	12.50	30.00
Cake stand	150.00	250.00	100.00	300.00
Casino saucer	7.50	12.00	5.00	12.00
Cereal / oatmeal bowl	15.00	20.00	10.00	25.00
Coupe plate, 6 ¾"			Very Rare	
Hot water plate	75.00	100.00	45.00	110.00
Jaffa fruit saucer (plain)	15.00	20.00	10.00	25.00
Picture plaque, large	20.00	30.00	12.50	30.00
Plate, 6 ½"	15.00	20.00	10.00	25.00
Plate, 8"	15.00	20.00	10.00	25.00
Plate, 10 ½"	20.00	25.00	12.00	30.00

HOME FROM FISHING
First Variation, Large Size

Design No.:	CT18 Home from Fishing
Designer:	Colin Twinn
Issued:	1990 - 1993

Shape	U.S. $	Can. $	U.K. £	Aust. $
Albion cream jug	35.00	55.00	20.00	60.00
Albion jug, 1 pint	100.00	150.00	60.00	165.00
Baby plate, round, small	20.00	27.50	12.50	30.00
Divider dish	75.00	125.00	50.00	125.00
Jaffa fruit saucer	15.00	20.00	10.00	25.00
Picture plaque, large	20.00	30.00	12.50	30.00
Picture plaque, small	20.00	30.00	12.50	30.00
Plate, 8"	15.00	20.00	10.00	25.00

Home from Fishing, First Variation (CT18)

HOME FROM FISHING
Second Variation, Small Size /
FATHER BUNNYKINS WITH FISHING ROD

Design No.:	Front — CT26 Home from Fishing
	Reverse — CT27 Father Bunnykins with
	Fishing Rod
Designer:	Colin Twinn
Issued:	1990 - 1993
Combined with:	*Bunny on Rocking Horse*, CT29
	Family with Pram, Style Two, CT14
	Standing by Pram, CT6

Shape	U.S. $	Can. $	U.K. £	Aust. $
Albion cream jug	35.00	55.00	20.00	60.00
Albion jug, ½ pint	85.00	115.00	50.00	125.00
Albion jug, 1 pint	100.00	150.00	60.00	165.00
Albion teapot	50.00	70.00	30.00	75.00
Hug-a-mug, one handle	10.00	15.00	7.50	15.00
Hug-a-mug, two handles	10.00	15.00	7.50	15.00
Lamp	50.00	75.00	30.00	85.00
Malvern beaker	15.00	25.00	10.00	25.00
Money ball	10.00	15.00	7.50	15.00
Picture plaque, small	20.00	30.00	12.50	30.00
Savings book	15.00	22.50	10.00	22.50
Stratford straight beaker	15.00	25.00	10.00	25.00
Stratford teacup	7.50	12.00	5.00	12.00

Note: *Bunny on Rocking Horse* (CT29) is combined with *Home from Fishing* (CT26) on a savings book.

Home from Fishing, Second Variation (CT26)

Father Bunnykins with Fishing Rod (CT27)

Hoopla (LF129)

HOOPLA

Design No.:	LF129
Designer:	Walter Hayward
Issued:	1967 - 1970

Shape	U.S. $	Can. $	U.K. £	Aust. $
Baby plate, oval, large	450.00	600.00	275.00	625.00
Baby plate, round, large	350.00	450.00	225.00	475.00
Plate, 8 ½"	175.00	225.00	115.00	250.00

ICE CREAM THEME — Colin Twinn

Ice Cream Seller, First Variation (CT5)

ICE CREAM SELLER
First Variation, Large Size

Design No.:   CT5 Ice Cream Seller
Designer: Colin Twinn
Issued: 1989 - 1993
Combined with: *Pushing the Wheelbarrow*, CT3
                    Splashing at Sink, CT33
                    Washing Up, CT32

Shape	U.S. $	Can. $	U.K. £	Aust. $
Albion teapot	50.00	70.00	30.00	75.00
Hug-a-mug, one handle	10.00	15.00	7.50	10.00
Hug-a-mug, two handles	10.00	15.00	7.50	10.00
Lamp	50.00	75.00	30.00	85.00
Malvern beaker	15.00	25.00	10.00	25.00
Money ball	10.00	15.00	7.50	15.00
Picture plaque, small	20.00	30.00	12.50	30.00
Stratford straight beaker	15.00	25.00	10.00	25.00
Stratford teacup	7.50	12.00	5.00	12.00

ICE CREAM SELLER
Second Variation, Small Size

Design No.:   CT11 Ice Cream Seller
Designer: Colin Twinn
Issued: 1989 - 1993
Combined with: *Bunny on Trike*, CT23
                    Picking Daisies, CT4

Shape	U.S. $	Can. $	U.K. £	Aust. $
Albion cream jug	35.00	55.00	20.00	60.00
Albion jug, ½ pint	85.00	115.00	50.00	125.00
Albion jug, 1 pint	100.00	150.00	60.00	165.00
Albion teapot	50.00	70.00	30.00	75.00
Baby plate, round, small	20.00	27.50	12.50	30.00
Cake stand	150.00	250.00	100.00	300.00
Cereal / oatmeal bowl	15.00	20.00	10.00	25.00
Plate, 6"	15.00	20.00	10.00	25.00

Ice Cream Seller, Second Variation (CT11)

ICE CREAM VENDOR / HIKER RESTING WITH ICE CREAM

Ice Cream Vendor (HW23)

Hiker Resting with Ice Cream (HW23R)

Design No.: Front — HW23 Ice Cream Vendor
Reverse — HW23R Hiker Resting with Ice Cream

Designer: Walter Hayward

Issued: By 1952 - by 1998

Combined with: *Daisy Chains*, HW25
Peashooter, HW118R
Skipping Game, HW139R
Snowball Fight, HW141R

Shape	U.S. $	Can. $	U.K. £	Aust. $
Albion cream jug	35.00	55.00	20.00	60.00
Albion jug, ½ pint	85.00	115.00	50.00	125.00
Albion jug, 1 pint	100.00	150.00	60.00	165.00
Albion teapot	50.00	70.00	30.00	75.00
Baby plate, round, small				
with signature	30.00	40.00	20.00	50.00
without signature	20.00	27.50	12.50	30.00
Casino jug, 30s				
with signature	250.00	400.00	175.00	425.00
without signature	150.00	250.00	100.00	250.00
Casino jug, 36s				
with signature	175.00	275.00	125.00	275.00
without signature	125.00	200.00	85.00	200.00
Casino jug, 42s				
with signature	150.00	225.00	100.00	225.00
without signature	100.00	150.00	70.00	150.00
Casino saucer				
with signature	15.00	25.00	10.00	25.00
without signature	7.50	12.00	5.00	12.00
Casino sugar bowl, 30s				
with signature	175.00	275.00	125.00	300.00
without signature	125.00	200.00	85.00	225.00
Casino sugar bowl, 36s				
with signature	150.00	225.00	100.00	250.00
without signature	100.00	150.00	65.00	175.00
Casino teacup				
with signature	15.00	25.00	10.00	25.00
without signature	7.50	12.00	5.00	12.00
Casino teapot, 30s				
with signature	250.00	375.00	165.00	400.00
without signature	150.00	225.00	100.00	250.00
Divider dish	50.00	75.00	35.00	75.00
Don beaker				
with signature	50.00	65.00	30.00	75.00

Shape	U.S. $	Can. $	U.K. £	Aust. $
Don beaker				
without signature	25.00	35.00	15.00	40.00
Don beaker, one handle				
with signature	50.00	65.00	30.00	75.00
without signature	25.00	35.00	15.00	45.00
Don mug, one handle				
with signature	40.00	55.00	25.00	60.00
without signature	10.00	15.00	6.50	18.00
Don mug, two handles				
with signature	40.00	55.00	25.00	60.00
without signature	10.00	15.00	6.50	18.00
Egg box				
small	225.00	350.00	150.00	400.00
medium	300.00	450.00	200.00	500.00
large	375.00	550.00	250.00	600.00
Hug-a-mug, one handle	10.00	15.00	7.50	15.00
Hug-a-mug, two handles	10.00	15.00	7.50	15.00
Jaffa fruit saucer				
plain rim	15.00	20.00	10.00	25.00
wavy rim	35.00	55.00	20.00	60.00
Lamp	50.00	75.00	30.00	85.00
Lid of hot water plate				
with signature	75.00	100.00	45.00	110.00
without signature	50.00	65.00	30.00	70.00
Malvern Beaker	25.00	35.00	15.00	40.00
Money ball	15.00	20.00	10.00	25.00
Picture plaque, small	20.00	30.00	12.50	20.00
Plate, 6 ½"				
with signature	25.00	35.00	15.00	40.00
without signature	15.00	20.00	10.00	25.00
Savings book	15.00	22.50	10.00	22.50
Stratford straight beaker	15.00	25.00	10.00	25.00
Stratford teacup	7.50	12.00	5.00	12.00

* Indicates scene on divider dish

Ice Skating (SF24)

ICE SKATING

Design No.:	SF24	
Designer:	Walter Hayward	
Issued:	1954 - 1967	

Shape	U.S. $	Can. $	U.K. £	Aust. $
Baby plate, round, small				
with signature	50.00	65.00	30.00	70.00
without signature	30.00	40.00	20.00	45.00
Baby plate, round, large				
with signature	100.00	135.00	65.00	150.00
without signature	75.00	100.00	50.00	125.00
Casino jug, 24s				
with signature	400.00	625.00	275.00	650.00
without signature	350.00	550.00	250.00	550.00
Casino saucer				
with signature	75.00	125.00	50.00	125.00
without signature	50.00	75.00	35.00	75.00
Casino sugar bowl, 36s				
with signature	150.00	225.00	90.00	225.00
without signature	135.00	200.00	80.00	200.00
Cereal / oatmeal bowl				
with signature	35.00	45.00	20.00	50.00
without signature	25.00	35.00	15.00	40.00
Hot water plate				
with signature	125.00	165.00	80.00	175.00
without signature	100.00	135.00	65.00	150.00
Jaffa fruit saucer (plain)	30.00	40.00	20.00	45.00
Plate, 6 ½"				
with signature	30.00	40.00	20.00	45.00
without signature	20.00	25.00	12.00	30.00
Plate, 7 ½"				
with signature	60.00	85.00	40.00	95.00
without signature	25.00	35.00	15.00	45.00
Plate, 8 ½"				
with signature	75.00	100.00	45.00	115.00
without signature	25.00	35.00	15.00	45.00

Note: Retirement dates are all approximate. When a design is retired all remaining stocks of the retired litho prints are used until exhausted.

JACK AND JILL

Design No.:	Front — CT9 Jack and Jill
	Reverse — CT10 Jack and Jill Nursery Rhyme
Designer:	Colin Twinn
Issued:	1989 - 1993

Shape	U.S. $	Can. $	U.K. £	Aust. $
Hug-a-mug, one handle	10.00	15.00	7.50	15.00

Jack and Jill (CT9)

Jack and Jill Nursery Rhyme (CT10)

Juggling (LF127)

JUGGLING

Design No.:	LF127
Designer:	Walter Hayward
Issued:	1967 - 1970

Shape	U.S. $	Can. $	U.K. £	Aust. $
Baby plate, oval, large	450.00	600.00	275.00	625.00
Baby plate, round, large	350.00	450.00	225.00	475.00
Plate, 8 ½"	175.00	225.00	115.00	250.00
Porridge plate	250.00	325.00	150.00	350.00

Kissing Under the Mistletoe
(with mistletoe)

KISSING UNDER THE MISTLETOE
First Version, With Mistletoe

Design No.:	HW11R
Designer:	Barbara Vernon
Issued:	By 1937 - by 1947
Combined with:	*Cycling*, HW15R
	Family at Breakfast, HW12
	Feeding the Baby, HW13
	Medicine Time, SF1
	Proposal, HW11
	Reading the Times, HW2R

Shape	U.S. $	Can. $	U.K. £	Aust. $
Casino jug, 36s	300.00	425.00	190.00	475.00
Casino jug, 42s	275.00	400.00	175.00	450.00
Casino teacup	75.00	100.00	50.00	125.00
Don beaker	150.00	225.00	100.00	250.00
Don beaker, one handle	150.00	225.00	100.00	250.00
Don mug, one handle	75.00	100.00	50.00	125.00
Don mug, two handles	75.00	100.00	50.00	125.00
FINE WHITE CHINA				
Teacup	300.00	400.00	200.00	425.00

Kissing Under the Mistletoe
(without mistletoe)

KISSING UNDER THE MISTLETOE
Second Version, Without Mistletoe

Design No.:	HW11R
Designer:	Barbara Vernon
Issued:	By 1947 - by 1967
Combined with:	*Cycling*, HW15R
	Family at Breakfast, HW12
	Feeding the Baby, HW13
	Medicine Time, SF1
	Proposal, HW11
	Reading the Times, HW2R

Shape	U.S. $	Can. $	U.K. £	Aust. $
Beaker cover	75.00	100.00	45.00	110.00
Casino jug, 42s				
with signature	150.00	225.00	100.00	225.00
without signature	100.00	150.00	70.00	150.00
Casino teacup				
with signature	75.00	125.00	50.00	125.00
without signature	50.00	75.00	35.00	75.00
Don beaker				
with signature	65.00	85.00	40.00	90.00
without signature	35.00	45.00	20.00	50.00
Don beaker, one handle				
with signature	65.00	85.00	40.00	90.00

Shape	U.S. $	Can. $	U.K. £	Aust. $
Don beaker, one handle				
without signature	35.00	45.00	20.00	50.00
Don mug, one handle				
with signature	50.00	65.00	30.00	75.00
without signature	15.00	20.00	10.00	25.00
Don mug, two handles				
with signature	50.00	65.00	30.00	75.00
without signature	15.00	20.00	10.00	25.00
FINE WHITE CHINA				
Rex mug	1,000.00	1,350.00	625.00	1,400.00

LAMBETH WALK
First Version, Lambeth Walk on Music Sheet

Design No.:	HW16
Designer:	Barbara Vernon
Issued:	By 1937 - by 1949
Combined with:	*Family at Breakfast,* HW12
	Footballer, HW13R
	Leapfrog, HW12R
	Raising Hat, Style One, HW16R
	Top Hat, HW14R

Lambeth Walk, First Version (HW16)

Shape	U.S. $	Can. $	U.K. £	Aust. $
Baby plate, round, small	50.00	65.00	30.00	70.00
Candle holder	2,000.00	2,500.00	1,250.00	2,500.00
Casino jug, 30s	300.00	475.00	200.00	475.00
Casino jug, 36s	250.00	400.00	175.00	425.00
Casino saucer	75.00	125.00	50.00	125.00
Casino teacup	75.00	125.00	50.00	125.00
Don beaker	65.00	85.00	40.00	90.00
Don mug, one handle	50.00	65.00	30.00	75.00
Don mug, two handles	50.00	65.00	30.00	75.00
Jam pot	1,500.00	1,975.00	625.00	2,000.00
Lid of hot water plate	100.00	135.00	65.00	150.00
FINE WHITE CHINA				
Rex mug	1,000.00	1,350.00	625.00	1,400.00
Saucer	300.00	400.00	200.00	425.00

Note: **1.** This design should appear with the Barbara Vernon facsimile signature.
2. A Rex mug combines *Footballer* (HW13R) and *Lambeth Walk,* first version (HW16).

A rare Bunnykins vegetable tureen
Family at Breakfast, (HW12); *Lambeth Walk* (HW16)

Lambeth Walk, Second Version (HW16)

LAMBETH WALK,
Second Version, Musical Score on Music Sheet, Bird Sits Atop Sheet

After 1949 the words Lambeth Walk were replaced by a musical score, and a small bird sat atop the music sheet.

Design No.:	HW16
Designer:	Barbara Vernon
Issued:	By 1949 - 1967
Combined with:	*Bedtime with Dollies*, EC125
	Footballer, HW13R
	Going Shopping, SF10
	Leapfrog, HW12R
	Playing with Dolls, EC123
	Raising Hat, Style One, HW16R
	Santa Claus, SF9
	Sleeping in a Rocking Chair, EC1
	Soldiers Marching, HW18R
	Top Hat, HW14R

Shape	U.S. $	Can. $	U.K. £	Aust. $
Baby plate, round, small				
with signature	50.00	65.00	30.00	70.00
without signature	30.00	40.00	20.00	45.00
Candle holder	2,000.00	2,500.00	1,250.00	2,500.00
Casino jug, 30s				
with signature	200.00	300.00	150.00	300.00
without signature	150.00	250.00	100.00	250.00
Casino jug, 36s				
with signature	150.00	225.00	100.00	225.00
without signature	125.00	200.00	85.00	200.00
Casino jug, 42s				
with signature	125.00	200.00	90.00	200.00
without signature	100.00	150.00	70.00	150.00
Casino saucer				
with signature	15.00	25.00	10.00	25.00
without signature	7.50	12.00	5.00	12.00
Casino sugar bowl, 30s				
with signature	150.00	225.00	100.00	250.00
without signature	125.00	200.00	85.00	225.00
Casino teacup				
with signature	15.00	25.00	10.00	25.00
without signature	7.50	12.00	5.00	12.00
Casino teapot, 24s				
with signature	275.00	400.00	175.00	450.00
without signature	175.00	275.00	125.00	325.00
Cup / mug, large	350.00	475.00	225.00	500.00

Shape	U.S. $	Can. $	U.K. £	Aust. $
Don beaker				
with signature	65.00	85.00	40.00	90.00
without signature	35.00	45.00	20.00	50.00
Don beaker, one handle				
with signature	65.00	85.00	40.00	90.00
without signature	35.00	45.00	20.00	50.00
Don mug, one handle				
with signature	50.00	65.00	30.00	75.00
without signature	15.00	20.00	10.00	25.00
Don mug, two handles				
with signature	50.00	65.00	30.00	75.00
without signature	15.00	20.00	10.00	25.00
Egg cup				
Style One	40.00	55.00	30.00	65.00
Style Two	75.00	115.00	55.00	125.00
Style Three	20.00	25.00	12.00	25.00
Jam pot	1,500.00	2,000.00	950.00	2,000.00
Lid of hot water plate				
with signature	100.00	135.00	65.00	150.00
without signature	75.00	100.00	50.00	115.00
Plate, 6 ½"				
with signature	30.00	40.00	20.00	45.00
without signature	20.00	25.00	12.00	30.00
Sugar bowl with handles		Extremely rare		

Note: Condition is important. Prices listed are based on nurseryware in mint condition. Items in less than mint condition will command lower prices.

LASSO GAMES / LASSOING

Design No.:	Front — HW117 Lasso Games
	Reverse — HW117R Lassoing
Designer:	Walter Hayward
Issued:	1959 - 1967
Combined with:	*Hobby Horse*, Style Two, EC121
	Watering the Flowers, SF15

Shape	U.S. $	Can. $	U.K. £	Aust. $
Casino teacup	50.00	5.00	35.00	75.00
Casino teapot, 30s	325.00	500.00	225.00	550.00
Don beaker	35.00	45.00	20.00	50.00
Don beaker, one handle	35.00	45.00	20.00	50.00
Don mug, one handle	15.00	20.00	10.00	25.00
Don mug, two handles	15.00	20.00	10.00	25.00
Jaffa fruit saucer (plain)	30.00	40.00	20.00	45.00
Lid of hot water plate	75.00	100.00	50.00	115.00
Plate, 6 ½"	20.00	25.00	12.00	30.00

Lasso Games (HW117)

LEAPFROG

Design No.:	HW12R
Designer:	Barbara Vernon
Issued:	By 1937 - by 1952

Combined with:

Asleep in the Open Air, HW10	*Family Going out on Washing Day*, HW8
Chicken Pulling a Cart, SF8	*Family with Pram*, Style One, HW15
Convalescing, SF5	*Gardening*, Style One, HW9
Embracing at a Window, HW5	*Lambeth Walk*, HW16
Family at Breakfast, HW12	*Pressing Trousers*, HW14
Feeding the Baby, HW13	*Proposal*, HW11
Fixing Braces, HW3	*Washing in the Open Air*, HW10R
Gardener with Wheelbarrow, HW9R	

Lassoing (HW117R)

Shape	U.S. $	Can. $	U.K. £	Aust. $
Beaker cover				
Casino jug, 36s				
with signature	300.00	475.00	200.00	475.00
without signature	250.00	400.00	175.00	400.00
Casino jug, 42s				
with signature	250.00	400.00	175.00	400.00
without signature	200.00	325.00	150.00	325.00
Casino sugar bowl, 30s				
with signature	200.00	325.00	125.00	350.00
without signature	150.00	225.00	100.00	225.00
Casino teacup				
with signature	75.00	125.00	50.00	125.00
without signature	50.00	75.00	35.00	75.00
Don beaker				
with signature	65.00	85.00	40.00	90.00
without signature	35.00	45.00	20.00	50.00
Don beaker, one handle				
with signature	65.00	85.00	40.00	90.00
without signature	35.00	45.00	20.00	50.00
Don mug, one handle				
with signature	50.00	65.00	30.00	75.00
without signature	15.00	20.00	10.00	25.00
Jam pot	1,500.00	2,000.00	950.00	2,000.00
FINE WHITE CHINA				
Rex mug	1,000.00	1,350.00	625.00	1,400.00
Saucer	300.00	400.00	200.00	425.00
Teacup	300.00	400.00	200.00	425.00

Leapfrog (HW12R)

Note: *Leapfrog* is combined with *Footballer* (HW13R) on the Rex mug.

Letterbox (SF13)

LETTERBOX

Design No.:	SF13
Designer:	Walter Hayward after Barbara Vernon
Issued:	By 1952 - by 1998

Shape	U.S. $	Can. $	U.K. £	Aust. $
Baby plate, round, small				
with signature	30.00	40.00	20.00	50.00
without signature	20.00	27.50	12.50	30.00
Cake stand	150.00	250.00	100.00	300.00
Casino saucer				
with signature	15.00	25.00	10.00	25.00
without signature	7.50	12.00	5.00	12.00
Casino teapot, 24s				
with signature	275.00	400.00	175.00	450.00
without signature	175.00	275.00	125.00	325.00
Cereal / oatmeal bowl				
with signature	25.00	35.00	20.00	40.00
without signature	15.00	20.00	10.00	25.00
Hot water plate				
with signature	100.00	135.00	65.00	150.00
without signature	75.00	100.00	45.00	115.00
Jaffa fruit saucer (plain)				
with signature	25.00	35.00	20.00	40.00
without signature	15.00	20.00	10.00	25.00
Plate, 6 ½"				
with signature	25.00	35.00	15.00	40.00
without signature	10.00	20.00	10.00	25.00
Plate, 7 ½"				
with signature	30.00	40.00	20.00	45.00
without signature	15.00	20.00	10.00	25.00
Plate, 8"	15.00	20.00	10.00	25.00

Note: A money box in the same shape of a post box was modelled but not put into production. Two examples have been recorded, one in the Royal Doulton Archives and another in a private collection. A Money Box was produced for the Millennium Bunnykins Extravaganza. For illustration of post box see page 190.

MEDICINE TIME

Design No.:	SF1
Designer:	Barbara Vernon
Issued:	By 1937 - by 1952
Combined with:	*Dunce*, HW1R
	Frightening Spider, SF4
	Kissing Under the Mistletoe, HW11R
	Proposal, HW11

Medicine Time (SF1)

Shape	U.S. $	Can. $	U.K. £	Aust. $
Baby plate, round, small				
with signature	200.00	275.00	125.00	300.00
without signature	150.00	200.00	100.00	225.00
Baby plate, round, large				
with signature	250.00	325.00	150.00	350.00
without signature	200.00	275.00	125.00	300.00
Candle holder	2,000.00	2,500.00	1,250.00	2,500.00
Casino jug, 30s				
with signature	375.00	525.00	235.00	575.00
without signature	300.00	425.00	190.00	475.00
Casino saucer				
with signature	75.00	100.00	50.00	125.00
without signature	50.00	65.00	30.00	75.00
Casino teapot, 30s				
with signature	300.00	425.00	190.00	475.00
without signature	225.00	325.00	150.00	375.00
Cereal / oatmeal bowl				
with signature	100.00	135.00	65.00	150.00
without signature	90.00	125.00	55.00	135.00
Hot water plate				
with signature	200.00	275.00	125.00	300.00
without signature	150.00	200.00	100.00	225.00
Plate, 6 ½"				
with signature	90.00	125.00	55.00	135.00
without signature	65.00	85.00	40.00	95.00
Plate, 7"				
with signature	90.00	125.00	55.00	135.00
without signature	65.00	85.00	40.00	95.00
Plate, 8"	75.00	100.00	45.00	110.00
FINE WHITE CHINA				
Coupe	650.00	850.00	400.00	875.00
Night light		Very Rare		
Plate, 6"	650.00	850.00	400.00	875.00
Plate, 7"	650.00	850.00	400.00	875.00

MERRY CHRISTMAS FROM BUNNYKINS — Walter Hayward

Merry Christmas from Bunnykins,
Style One (SF137)

Reverse Inscription (SF137)

Style One

The reverse decoration on this plate has a single holly leaf wreath border and a 1936 copyright date.

Design No.:	Front — SF137 Merry Christmas from Bunnykins
	Reverse — Inscription
Designer:	Walter Hayward
Issued:	1981 - 1989
Rhyme:	'Bunnykins are just like you
	For they love Christmas too,
	They sing and dance as you can see
	And play around the Christmas tree,
	And each year they always say
	We wish it were Christmas every day'

Shape	U.S. $	Can. $	U.K. £	Aust. $
Plate, 8"	15.00	20.00	10.00	20.00

MERRY CHRISTMAS FROM BUNNYKINS — Colin Twinn

Style Two
First Variation, Large Size

The reverse decoration on this plate has a multiple holly leaf wreath border.

Design No.:	Front — CT39 Merry Christmas from Bunnykins			
	Reverse — CT66 Inscription			
Designer:	Colin Twinn			
Issued:	1990 - 1993			
Rhyme:	'Bunnykins are just like you			
	For they love Christmas too.			
	They sing and dance as you can see			
	And play around the Christmas tree			
	And each year they always say			
	"We wish it were Christmas every day."			

Shape	U.S. $	Can. $	U.K. £	Aust. $
Plate, 8"	15.00	20.00	10.00	25.00

Merry Christmas from Bunnykins
First Variation (CT39)

Merry Christmas from Bunnykins
Second Variation (CT43)

Style Two
Second Variation, Small Size

Design No.:	Front — CT43 Merry Christmas from Bunnykins
	Reverse — CT44 Inscription
Designer:	Colin Twinn
Issued:	1992 - 1994

Shape	U.S. $	Can. $	U.K. £	Aust. $
Hug-a-mug, one handle	10.00	15.00	7.50	15.00

Family Christmas Scene, First Version (CT72)

Style Three
FAMILY CHRISTMAS SCENE
First Version, Large Size

Design No.:	CT72 Family Christmas Scene
	CT73 Christmas Inscription
Designer:	Colin Twinn
Issued:	1993 - 1994
Inscription:	´Bunnykins are just like you
	For they love Christmas too.
	They sing and dance as you can see
	And play around the Christmas tree
	And each year they always say
	"We wish it were Christmas every day."

Shape	U.S. $	Can. $	U.K. £	Aust. $
Plate, 8"	15.00	20.00	10.00	25.00

Christmas Inscription, First Version (CT73)

Style Three
FAMILY CHRISTMAS SCENE
Second Version, Small Size

Design No.:	Front — CT74 Family Christmas Scene
	Reverse — CT75 Merry Christmas from Bunnykins
	Inscription
Designer:	Colin Twinn
Issued:	1993 - 1994

Shape	U.S. $	Can. $	U.K. £	Aust. $
Hug-a-mug, one handle	10.00	15.00	7.50	15.00
Malvern beaker	15.00	25.00	10.00	25.00
Money ball	10.00	15.00	7.50	15.00

Merry Christmas from Bunnykins,
Second Version (CT74)

Merry Christmas Inscription,
Second Version (CT75)

BUNNYKINS

DB94 – Prince Frederick
Second Variation

DB95 – Harry The Herald
Second Variation

DB96 – Touchdown Bunnykins
Third Variation

DB97 – Touchdown Bunnykins
Fourth Variation

DB98 – Touchdown Bunnykins
Fifth Variation

DB99 – Touchdown Bunnykins
Sixth Variation

DB100 – Touchdown Bunnykins
Seventh Variation

DB101 – Bride Bunnykins

DB102 – Groom Bunnykins

DB103 – Bedtime Bunnykins
Fourth Variation

DB104 – Carol Singer Bunnykins

DB105 – Sousaphone Bunnykins
Third Variation

BUNNYKINS

DB106 – Trumpeter Bunnykins
Third Variation

DB107 – Cymbals Bunnykins
Third Variation

DB108 – Drummer Bunnykins
Style One, Fourth Variation

DB109 – Drum-Major Bunnykins
Third Variation

DB115 – Harry The Herald
Third Variation

DB116 – Goalkeeper Bunnykins
First Variation

DB117 – Footballer Bunnykins
First Variation

DB118 – Goalkeeper Bunnykins
Second Variation

DB119 – Footballer Bunnykins
Second Variation

DB120 – Goalkeeper Bunnykins
Third Variation

DB121 – Footballer Bunnykins
Third Variation

DB122 – Goalkeeper Bunnykins
Fourth Variation

Note: DB110 to 114 not allocated

BUNNYKINS

DB123 – Soccer Player
Bunnykins

DB124 – Rock and Roll
Bunnykins

DB125 – Milkman Bunnykins

DB126 – Magician Bunnykins
First Variation

DB127 – Guardsman Bunnykins

DB128 – Clown Bunnykins
First Variation

DB129 – Clown Bunnykins
Second Variation

DB130 – Sweetheart Bunnykins
First Variation

DB131 – Master Potter
Bunnykins

DB132 – Halloween Bunnykins

DB133 – Aussie Surfer
Bunnykins

DB134 – John Bull
Bunnykins

BUNNYKINS

DB135 – Mountie Bunnykins

DB136 – Sergeant Mountie
Bunnykins

DB137 – 60th Anniversary
Bunnykins

DB142 – Cheerleader Bunnykins
First Variation

DB143 – Cheerleader Bunnykins
Second Variation

DB144 – Batsman Bunnykins

DB145 – Bowler Bunnykins

DB146 – Christmas Surprise
Bunnykins

DB147 – Rainy Day Bunnykins

Note: DB138 to 141 not allocated

DB148 – Bathtime Bunnykins

DB149 – Easter Greetings
Bunnykins

DB150 – Wicketkeeper Bunnykins

BUNNYKINS

DB151 – Partners in Collecting

DB152 – Boy Skater Bunnykins
First Variation

DB153 – Girl Skater Bunnykins

DB154 – Father Bunnykins
Style One

DB155 – Mother's Day
Bunnykins

DB156 – Gardener Bunnykins

DB157 – Goodnight Bunnykins

DB158 – New Baby Bunnykins

DB159 – Magician Bunnykins
Second Variation

DB160 – Out for a Duck
Bunnykins

DB161 – Jester Bunnykins

DB162 – Trick of Treat Bunnykins

BUNNYKINS

DB163 – Beefeater Bunnykins

DB164 – Juggler Bunnykins

DB165 – Ringmaster Bunnykins

DB166 – Sailor Bunnykins

DB167 – Mother and Baby
Bunnykins, *Style One*

DB168 – Wizard Bunnykins

DB169 – Jockey Bunnykins

DB170 – Fisherman Bunnykins
Style Two

DB171 – Joker Bunnykins

DB172 – Welshlady Bunnykins

DB173 – Bridesmaid Bunnykins

DB174 –Sweetheart Bunnykins
Second Variation

BUNNYKINS

DB175 – Uncle Sam Bunnykins
Second Variation

DB176 – Ballerina Bunnykins

DB177 – Seaside Bunnykins

DB178 – Irishman Bunnykins

DB179 – Cavalier Bunnykins

DB180 – Scotsman Bunnykins

DB181 – Doctor Bunnykins

DB182 – Banjo Player
Bunnykins

DB183 – Fireman Bunnykins
Second Variation

DB184 – Clarinet Player
Bunnykins

DB185 – Double Bass Player
Bunnykins

DB186 – Saxophone Player
Bunnykins

BUNNYKINS

DB187 – Boy Skater Bunnykins
Second Variation

DB188 – Judge Bunnykins

DB189 – Mother Bunnykins

DB190 – Tourist Bunnykins

DB191 – Piper Bunnykins

DB192 – Santa's Helper Bunnykins

DB193 – Detective Bunnykins

DB195 – Sydney Bunnykins

DB194 – Merry Christmas Bunnykins Tableau

DB196 – Angel Bunnykins

DB197 – Mystic Bunnykins

MR. PIGGLY'S STORES

Design No.:	SF14
Designer:	Walter Hayward after Barbara Vernon
Issued:	By 1952 - by 1998
Combined with:	*Dress Making*, HW 26
	Fishing in the Goldfish Bowl, HW3R
	Playing on the River, SF16
	See-saw, Style One, SFS17
	Swinging, HW 20
	Toast for Tea Today, SF23

Mr. Piggly's Stores (SF14)

Shape	U.S. $	Can. $	U.K. £	Aust. $
Baby plate, small, round				
with signature	30.00	40.00	20.00	50.00
without signature	20.00	27.50	12.50	30.00
Bread and butter plate				
with signature	200.00	325.00	125.00	350.00
without signature	125.00	200.00	85.00	225.00
Casino jug, 24s				
with signature	300.00	475.00	200.00	475.00
without signature	175.00	275.00	125.00	300.00
Casino saucer				
with signature	15.00	25.00	10.00	25.00
without signature	7.50	12.00	5.00	12.00
Casino sugar, 30s				
with signature	150.00	225.00	100.00	250.00
without signature	100.00	150.00	65.00	175.00
Casino teapot, 30s				
with signature	250.00	375.00	165.00	400.00
without signature	150.00	225.00	100.00	250.00
Cereal / oatmeal bowl				
with signature	25.00	35.00	20.00	40.00
without signature	15.00	20.00	10.00	25.00
Hot water plate				
with signature	100.00	135.00	65.00	150.00
without signature	75.00	100.00	45.00	110.00
Jaffa fruit saucer (plain)				
with signature	25.00	35.00	20.00	40.00
without signature	15.00	20.00	10.00	25.00
Picture plaque, large	20.00	30.00	12.50	30.00
Plate, 6 ½"				
with signature	25.00	35.00	15.00	40.00
without signature	15.00	20.00	10.00	25.00
Plate, 7 ½"				
with signature	30.00	40.00	20.00	45.00
without signature	15.00	20.00	10.00	25.00
Plate, 8 ½"				
with signature	30.00	40.00	20.00	45.00
without signature	15.00	20.00	10.00	25.00
Porridge plate				
with signature	90.00	150.00	60.00	175.00
without signature	70.00	110.00	45.00	125.00

Mrs. Moppet's Tea Room (LF6)

MRS. MOPPET'S TEA ROOM

Design No.:	LF6
Designer:	Barbara Vernon
Issued:	By 1940 - by 1952

Shape	U.S. $	Can. $	U.K. £	Aust. $
Baby plate, oval, large				
with signature	350.00	450.00	225.00	475.00
without signature	300.00	400.00	200.00	425.00
Baby plate, round, large				
with silver rim		Rare		
with signature	250.00	325.00	150.00	350.00
without signature	200.00	275.00	125.00	300.00
Bread / butter plate, handles				
with signature	400.00	525.00	250.00	550.00
without signature	350.00	450.00	225.00	475.00
Cereal / oatmeal bowl				
with signature	100.00	135.00	65.00	150.00
without signature	90.00	125.00	55.00	135.00
Plate, 8 ½"				
with signature	100.00	135.00	65.00	145.00
without signature	75.00	100.00	45.00	110.00
Porridge plate				
with signature	125.00	175.00	80.00	185.00
without signature	100.00	135.00	65.00	145.00

Style One Egg Cup, *Trumpeter* (EC5),
with Barbara Vernon facsimile signature on side and backstamp/base.

NETTING A CRICKET

Design No.:	HW6
Designer:	Barbara Vernon
Issued:	By 1937 - by 1952
Combined with:	*Artist*, HW1
	Cuddling under a Mushroom, HW4
	Dunce, HW1R
	Family Going out on Washing Day, HW8
	Fishing in the Goldfish Bowl, HW3R
	Gardener with Wheelbarrow, HW9R
	Pressing Trousers, HW14
	Proposal, HW11
	Pulling Trousers, HW2
	Reading the Times, HW2R

Netting a Cricket (HW6)

Shape	U.S. $	Can. $	U.K. £	Aust. $
Casino jug, 24s				
with signature	475.00	675.00	300.00	725.00
without signature	400.00	550.00	250.00	600.00
Casino sugar bowl, 30s				
with signature	200.00	275.00	125.00	300.00
without signature	125.00	175.00	80.00	200.00
Casino sugar bowl, 36s				
with signature	150.00	225.00	100.00	250.00
without signature	125.00	175.00	80.00	200.00
Casino teacup				
with signature	75.00	100.00	50.00	125.00
without signature	50.00	65.00	30.00	75.00
Don beaker				
with signature	150.00	225.00	100.00	250.00
without signature	100.00	150.00	65.00	165.00
Don beaker, one handle				
with signature	150.00	225.00	100.00	250.00
without signature	100.00	150.00	65.00	165.00
Don mug, one handle				
with signature	75.00	100.00	50.00	125.00
without signature	35.00	55.00	20.00	60.00
Don mug, two handles				
with signature	75.00	100.00	50.00	125.00
without signature	35.00	55.00	20.00	60.00
Jaffa fruit saucer				
plain rim	35.00	55.00	20.00	60.00
wavy rim	65.00	90.00	40.00	10000
Jam pot	1,500.00	1,975.00	950.00	2,000.00
Plate, 6 ½"				
with signature	90.00	125.00	55.00	135.00
without signature	65.00	85.00	40.00	95.00
FINE WHITE CHINA				
Don mug, one handle	300.00	400.00	200.00	425.00

Note: Retirement dates are all approximate. When a design is retired all remaining stocks of the retired litho prints are used until exhausted.

NEW ARRIVAL THEME — Colin Twinn

Family Group with Father Standing (CT97)

FAMILY GROUP WITH FATHER STANDING

Design No.:   CT97 Family Group with Father Standing
Designer: Colin Twinn
Issued: 1995 - 1997

Shape	U.S. $	Can. $	U.K. £	Aust. $
Baby plate, round, small	25.00	35.00	15.00	40.00
Cereal / oatmeal bowl	15.00	20.00	10.00	25.00
Plate, 8"	15.00	20.00	10.00	25.00

Family Group with Father Kneeling (CT98)

FAMILY GROUP WITH FATHER KNEELING

Design No.:   Front — CT98 Family Group with Father Kneeling
           Reverse — CT99 New Arrival Inscription
Designer: Colin Twinn
Issued: 1995 - 1997

Shape	U.S. $	Can. $	U.K. £	Aust. $
Hug-a-mug, one handle	10.00	15.00	7.50	15.00
Money ball	10.00	15.00	7.50	15.00

New Arrival Inscription (CT99)

NEW BABY THEME — Frank Endersby

SHOWING BABY AT WINDOW

Design No.:	40 Showing Baby at Window
Designer:	Frank Endersby
Issued:	1996 to the present

Shape	U.S. $	Can. $	U.K. £	Aust. $
Plate, 6 ½"	N/I	25.00	8.00	34.95
Plate, 8"	N/I	35.00	11.00	49.95

Showing Baby at Window (40)

Pushing Pram (41)

PUSHING PRAM / PLAYING WITH BALL

Design No.:	Front — 41 Pushing Pram
	Reverse — 42 Playing with Ball
Designer:	Frank Endersby
Issued:	1996 to the present
Combined with:	*Carrying Letter (30)
	*Decorating the Cake, (9)
	*Playing and reading, (15)

Shape	U.S. $	Can. $	U.K. £	Aust. $
Hug-a-mug, one handle	30.00	33.00	11.00	49.95
Hug-a-mug, two handles	32.50	39.00	12.00	56.95
Divider dish	50.00	75.00	35.00	75.00
Malvern beaker	15.00	25.00	10.00	25.00
Money ball	33.75	40.00	15.00	62.95
Stratford teacup	7.50	12.00	5.00	12.00

* Indicates scene on divider dish.

Playing with Ball (42)

NURSERY THEME — Colin Twinn

Nursery, First Version (CT19)

NURSERY
First Version, Small Size

Design No.: CT19 Nursery
Designer: Colin Twinn
Issued: 1990 - 1993
Combined with: *Family with Pram*, Style Two, CT14
Standing by Pram, CT6

Shape	U.S. $	Can. $	U.K. £	Aust. $
Albion jug, 1 pint	100.00	150.00	60.00	165.00
Baby plate, round, small	20.00	27.50	12.50	30.00
Cake stand	150.00	250.00	100.00	300.00
Cereal / oatmeal bowl	15.00	20.00	10.00	25.00
Lamp	50.00	75.00	30.00	85.00
Money ball	10.00	15.00	7.50	15.00
Picture plaque, large	20.00	30.00	12.50	30.00
Picture plaque, small	20.00	30.00	12.50	30.00
Plate, 6 ½"	15.00	20.00	10.00	25.00
Plate, 8"	15.00	20.00	10.00	25.00

Nursery, Second Version (CT28)

NURSERY
Second Version, Large Size /
BUNNY ON ROCKING HORSE

Design No.: Front — CT28 Nursery
Reverse — CT29 Bunny on Rocking Horse
Designer: Colin Twinn
Issued: 1990 - 1993
Combined with: *Family with Pram*, Style Two, CT14
Father Bunnykins with Fishing Rod, (CT27)

Shape	U.S. $	Can. $	U.K. £	Aust. $
Albion cream jug	35.00	55.00	20.00	60.00
Albion jug, ½ pint	85.00	115.00	50.00	125.00
Albion jug, 1 pint	100.00	150.00	60.00	165.00
Albion teapot	50.00	70.00	30.00	75.00
Egg cup				
Style Three	10.00	15.00	7.50	18.00
Hug-a-mug, one handle	10.00	15.00	7.50	15.00
Hug-a-mug, two handles	10.00	15.00	7.50	15.00
Money ball	10.00	15.00	7.50	15.00
Picture plaque, small	20.00	30.00	12.50	30.00
Savings book	15.00	22.50	10.00	22.50
Stratford straight beaker	15.00	25.00	10.00	25.00
Stratford teacup	7.50	12.00	5.00	12.00

Bunny on Rocking Horse (CT29)

BUNNY WITH MIRROR

Design No.:	Front — CT35 Bunny with Mirror
Designer:	Colin Twinn
Issued:	1990 - 1993
Combined with:	*Bunnies in the Bath*, Second Version, CT34
	Classroom Scene, Style Two, First version, CT36
	Classroom Scene, Style Two, Second version, CT16
	Picking Daisies, CT4

Shape	U.S. $	Can. $	U.K. £	Aust. $
Albion cream jug	35.00	55.00	20.00	60.00
Albion sugar bowl	30.00	40.00	17.50	45.00
Divider dish	75.00	125.00	50.00	125.00
Egg cup				
Style Three	10.00	15.00	7.50	18.00

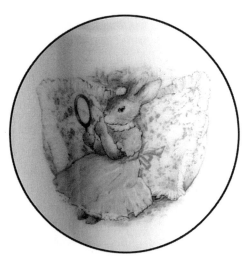

Bunny with Mirror (CT35)

China eggcups, *Pushing the Wheelbarrow* (CT3)
and *Bunnies in the Bath,* second version (CT34).

Orange Vendor (SF12)

ORANGE VENDOR

Design No.:	SF12
Designer:	Walter Hayward after Barbara Vernon
Issued:	By 1952 - 1967
Combined with:	*Writing Letters*, HW19R

Shape	U.S. $	Can. $	U.K. £	Aust. $
Baby plate, round, small				
with signature	30.00	40.00	20.00	50.00
without signature	20.00	27.50	12.50	30.00
Baby plate, round, large				
with signature	75.00	125.00	50.00	150.00
without signature	50.00	75.00	35.00	85.00
Casino jug, 30s				
with signature	200.00	300.00	150.00	300.00
without signature	150.00	250.00	100.00	250.00
Casino saucer				
with signature	15.00	25.00	10.00	25.00
without signature	7.50	12.00	5.00	12.00
Casino teapot, 30s				
with signature	250.00	375.00	165.00	400.00
without signature	150.00	225.00	100.00	250.00
Cereal / oatmeal bowl				
with signature	25.00	35.00	20.00	40.00
without signature	15.00	20.00	10.00	25.00
Hot water plate				
with signature	100.00	135.00	65.00	150.00
without signature	75.00	100.00	45.00	110.00
Jaffa fruit saucer (plain)				
with signature	25.00	35.00	20.00	40.00
without signature	15.00	20.00	10.00	25.00
Plate, 6 ½"				
with signature	25.00	35.00	15.00	40.00
without signature	15.00	20.00	10.00	25.00
Plate, 7 ½"				
with signature	30.00	40.00	20.00	45.00
without signature	15.00	20.00	10.00	25.00
Plate, 8 ½"				
with signature	30.00	40.00	20.00	45.00
without signature	15.00	20.00	10.00	25.00

Note: Retirement dates are all approximate. When a design is retired all remaining stocks of retired litho prints are used until exhausted.

PICNIC
Style One, First Version (without trees)

Design No.:	Unknown			
Designer:	Walter Hayward after Barbara Vernon			
Issued:	1940			

Shape	U.S. $	Can. $	U.K. £	Aust. $
Baby plate, oval, small	500.00	650.00	300.00	675.00
Baby plate, round, large	400.00	525.00	250.00	550.00
Bread and butter plate	500.00	650.00	300.00	675.00
Plate, 8 ½"	225.00	300.00	150.00	325.00

Note: This design should appear with the Barbara Vernon facsimile signature.

Picnic, Style One, First Version

PICNIC
Style One, Second Version (with trees)

This scene was redrawn to better fit, or conform to round shapes.

Design No.:	LF10			
Designer:	Walter Hayward after Barbara Vernon			
Issued:	By 1940 - 1970			
Combined with:	*Game of Golf,* SF11			

Shape	U.S. $	Can. $	U.K. £	Aust. $
Baby plate, oval, large				
with signature	200.00	275.00	125.00	300.00
without signature	150.00	200.00	95.00	225.00
Baby plate, round, large				
with signature	100.00	135.00	65.00	150.00
without signature	75.00	100.00	50.00	125.00
Bread and butter plate				
with signature	250.00	400.00	175.00	400.00
without signature	200.00	325.00	150.00	325.00
Casino teapot, 30s				
with signature	200.00	325.00	125.00	350.00
without signature	150.00	225.00	100.00	250.00
Cereal / oatmeal bowl				
with signature	35.00	45.00	20.00	50.00
without signature	25.00	35.00	15.00	40.00
Hot water plate				
with signature	125.00	165.00	80.00	175.00
without signature	100.00	135.00	65.00	150.00
Plate, 8 ½"				
with signature	75.00	100.00	45.00	115.00
without signature	25.00	35.00	15.00	45.00
Porridge plate				
with signature	110.00	175.00	70.00	200.00
without signature	85.00	125.00	55.00	150.00

Picnic, Style One, Second Version (LF10)

PICNIC CAKE STALL THEME — Colin Twinn

Picnic and Cake Stall (CT2)

PICNIC AND CAKE STALL

Design No.:	CT2 Picnic and Cake Stall
Designer:	Colin Twinn
Issued:	1989 - 1993

Shape	U.S. $	Can. $	U.K. £	Aust. $
Plate, 8"	30.00	40.00	20.00	45.00
Plate 10 ½"	35.00	55.00	25.00	60.00

Cake Stall (CT12)

CAKE STALL / PICKING DAISIES

Design No.:	Front — CT12 Cake Stall
	Reverse — CT4 Picking Daisies
Designer:	Colin Twinn
Issued:	1989 - 1993
Combined with:	*Bunny with Mirror*, CT35
	Classroom Scene, Style Two, Second Version, CT16
	Ice Cream Seller, Second Variation, CT11
	Pushing the Wheelbarrow, CT3
	Queen of the May, First Variation, CT7
	Queen of the May, Second Variation, CT13
	Standing by Pram, CT6

Shape	U.S. $	Can. $	U.K. £	Aust. $
Albion cream jug	35.00	55.00	20.00	60.00
Albion jug, ½ pint	85.00	115.00	50.00	125.00
Albion jug, 1 pint	100.00	150.00	60.00	165.00
Albion teapot	50.00	70.00	30.00	75.00
Hug-a-mug, one handle	10.00	15.00	7.50	15.00
Hug-a-mug, two handles	10.00	15.00	7.50	15.00
Malvern beaker	15.00	25.00	10.00	25.00
Stratford straight beaker	15.00	25.00	10.00	25.00
Stratford teacup	7.50	12.00	5.00	12.00

Picking Daisies (CT4)

Note: *Cake Stall*, (CT12) is combined with *Standing by Pram*, (CT6) on Albion, ½ and 1 pint jugs.

PICNIC THEME – Frank Endersby

PICNIC
Style Two

Design No.:	16 Picnic			
Designer:	Frank Endersby			
Issued:	1995 to the present			

Shape	U.S. $	Can. $	U.K. £	Aust. $
Baby plate, round, small	N/I	46.00	14.00	62.95
Cereal / oatmeal bowl	N/I	33.00	11.00	49.95
Plate, 6 ½"	N/I	25.00	8.00	34.95
Plate, 8"	N/I	35.00	11.00	49.95

Picnic, Style Two (16)

Playing Badminton (17)

PLAYING BADMINTON / RESTING, Style One

Design No.:	Front —17 Playing Badminton
	Reverse — 18 Resting, Style One
Designer:	Frank Endersby
Issued:	1995 to the present

Shape	U.S. $	Can. $	U.K. £	Aust. $
Hug-a-mug, one handle	30.00	33.00	11.00	49.95
Hug-a-mug, two handles	32.50	39.00	12.00	56.95
Money ball	33.75	40.00	15.00	62.95
Stratford straight beaker	15.00	25.00	10.00	25.00
Stratford teacup	7.50	12.00	5.00	12.00

Note: It is unusual to find the Stratford beaker with this design as this shape was officially withdrawn in 1993, two years before this Frank Endersby design was introduced.

Resting (18)

Pillow Fight (SF7)

PILLOW FIGHT
Style One

Design No.:	SF7
Designer:	Barbara Vernon
Issued:	By 1940 - by 1952
Combined with:	*Chicken Pulling a Cart*, SF8

Shape	U.S. $	Can. $	U.K. £	Aust. $
Baby plate, oval, small				
with signature	200.00	275.00	125.00	300.00
without signature	150.00	200.00	95.00	225.00
Casino teapot, 24s				
with signature	375.00	550.00	250.00	600.00
without signature	300.00	450.00	200.00	500.00
Cereal / oatmeal bowl				
with signature	35.00	45.00	20.00	50.00
without signature	25.00	35.00	15.00	40.00
Hot water plate				
with signature	125.00	165.00	80.00	175.00
without signature	100.00	135.00	65.00	150.00
Plate, 6 ½"				
with signature	30.00	40.00	20.00	45.00
without signature	20.00	25.00	12.00	30.00
Plate, 7 ½"				
with signature	65.00	85.00	40.00	95.00
without signature	25.00	35.00	15.00	45.00

PLAYING ON THE RIVER

Design No.:	SF16
Designer:	Walter Hayward after Barbara Vernon
Issued:	By 1952 - by 1998
Combined with:	*Mr. Piggly's Stores*, SF14

Shape	U.S. $	Can. $	U.K. £	Aust. $
Baby plate, round, small				
with signature	30.00	40.00	20.00	50.00
without signature	20.00	27.50	12.50	30.00
Cake stand	150.00	250.00	100.00	300.00
Casino saucer				
with signature	15.00	25.00	10.00	25.00
without signature	7.50	12.00	5.00	12.00
Casino teapot, 30s				
with signature	250.00	375.00	165.00	400.00
without signature	150.00	225.00	100.00	250.00
Cereal / oatmeal bowl				
with signature	25.00	35.00	20.00	40.00
without signature	15.00	20.00	10.00	25.00
Hot water plate				
with signature	100.00	135.00	65.00	150.00
without signature	75.00	100.00	45.00	110.00
Jaffa fruit saucer (plain)				
with signature	25.00	35.00	20.00	40.00
without signature	15.00	20.00	10.00	25.00
Picture plaque, large	20.00	30.00	12.50	30.00
Plate, 6 ½"				
with signature	25.00	35.00	15.00	40.00
without signature	15.00	20.00	10.00	25.00
Plate, 7 ½"				
with signature	30.00	40.00	20.00	45.00
without signature	15.00	20.00	10.00	25.00
Plate, 8"				
with signature	30.00	40.00	20.00	45.00
without signature	15.00	20.00	10.00	25.00

Playing on the River (SF16)

Note: Condition is important. Prices listed are based on nurseryware in mint condition. Items in less than mint condition will command lower prices.

Playing with Cup and Spoon (EC6)

PLAYING WITH CUP AND SPOON

Design No.:	EC6
Designer:	Barbara Vernon
Issued:	1937 to the present
Combined with:	*Bedtime with Dollies*, EC125
	Daisy Chains, HW25
	Drummer, EC2
	Drummer and Bugler, EC126
	Fishing in the Goldfish Bowl, HW3R
	Hikers, EC124
	Hobby Horse, Style Two, EC121
	Holding Hat and Coat, EC4
	Playing with Doll and Pram, EC123
	Raising Hat, Style Two, EC7
	Reading, EC122
	Sheltering Under an Umbrella, EC3
	Sleeping in a Rocking Chair, EC1
	Trumpeter, EC5

Shape	U.S. $	Can. $	U.K. £	Aust. $
Albion sugar bowl	30.00	40.00	17.50	45.00
Beaker cover	40.00	55.00	25.00	60.00
Casino teacup				
with signature	15.00	25.00	10.00	25.00
without signature	7.50	12.00	5.00	12.00
Egg cup				
Style One	30.00	40.00	20.00	45.00
Style Two	40.00	55.00	25.00	60.00
Style Three	N/I	15.00	5.00	19.95
Lid of hot water plate	50.00	65.00	30.00	70.00
Money ball	**33.75**	**40.00**	**15.00**	**62.95**

FINE WHITE CHINA

	U.S. $	Can. $	U.K. £	Aust. $
Night light			Very Rare	
Saucer	300.00	400.00	200.00	425.00
Teacup	300.00	400.00	200.00	425.00

Note: Fine white china prices are indications only due to the scarcity of the shapes. Prices will vary.

PLAYING WITH DOLL AND PRAM

Design No.:	EC123
Designer:	Walter Hayward
Issued:	1959 to the present
Combined with:	*Bedtime with Dollies*, EC125
	Building Sand Castles, HW138
	Dancing with Doll, HW115R
	Drummer, EC2
	Drummer and Bugler, EC126
	Hikers, EC124
	Hobby Horse, Style Two, EC121
	Holding Hat and Coat, EC4
	Playing with Cup and Spoon, EC6
	Playing with Dolls and Prams, HW115
	Reading, EC122
	Sailing Boats, HW138R
	Sheltering Under an Umbrella, EC3
	Sleeping in a Rocking Chair, EC1

Playing with Doll and Pram (EC123)

Shape	U.S. $	Can. $	U.K. £	Aust. $
Albion cream jug	35.00	55.00	20.00	60.00
Albion jug, ½ pint	85.00	115.00	50.00	125.00
Albion jug, 1 pint	100.00	150.00	60.00	165.00
Albion sugar bowl	30.00	40.00	17.50	45.00
Beaker cover	40.00	55.00	25.00	60.00
Egg cup				
Style One	30.00	40.00	20.00	45.00
Style Two	40.00	55.00	25.00	60.00
Style Three	**N/I**	**15.00**	**5.00**	**19.95**
Hug-a-mug, two handles	10.00	15.00	7.50	15.00
Lid of hot water plate	50.00	65.00	30.00	70.00

Playing with Dolls and Prams (HW115)

Dancing with Doll (HW115R)

PLAYING WITH DOLLS AND PRAMS / DANCING WITH DOLL

Design No.:	Front — HW115 Playing with Dolls and Prams
	Reverse — HW115R Dancing with Doll
Designer:	Walter Hayward
Issued:	1959 - by 1998
Combined with:	*Broken Umbrella*, HW27R
	Disturbing Sleeping Father, HW118
	Hikers, EC124
	Ice Cream on the Beach, HW136R
	Lunch Break, HW29R
	Playing with Doll and Pram, EC123
	*Playing with Doll and Teddy, HW120R
	*Roller Skating Arm in Arm, HW137R
	Serving Tea, HW116R
	Trying on Hats, HW28R

Shape	U.S. $	Can. $	U.K. £	Aust. $
Albion cream jug	35.00	55.00	20.00	60.00
Albion jug, ½ pint	85.00	115.00	50.00	125.00
Albion jug, 1 pint	100.00	150.00	60.00	165.00
Albion teapot	50.00	70.00	30.00	75.00
Casino saucer	7.50	12.00	5.00	12.00
Casino teacup	7.50	12.00	5.00	12.00
Divider dish	50.00	75.00	35.00	75.00
Don beaker	25.00	35.00	15.00	40.00
Don beaker, one handle	25.00	35.00	15.00	40.00
Don mug, one handle	10.00	15.00	6.50	18.00
Don mug, two handles	10.00	15.00	6.50	18.00
Egg box				
small	225.00	350.00	150.00	400.00
medium	300.00	450.00	200.00	500.00
large	375.00	550.00	250.00	600.00
Hug-a-mug, one handle	10.00	15.00	7.50	15.00
Hug-a-mug, two handles	10.00	15.00	7.50	15.00
Jaffa fruit saucer (plain)	15.00	20.00	10.00	25.00
Lamp	50.00	75.00	30.00	85.00
Lid of hot water plate	50.00	65.00	30.00	70.00
Money ball	10.00	15.00	7.50	15.00
Picture plaque, small	20.00	30.00	12.50	20.00
Plate, 6 ½"	15.00	20.00	10.00	25.00
Savings book	15.00	22.50	10.00	22.50
Stratford straight beaker	15.00	25.00	10.00	25.00
Stratford teacup	7.50	12.00	5.00	12.00

* Indicates scene on divider dish.

Note: The savings book can have a combined design of *Dancing with Doll* (HW115R) and *Trying on Hats* (HW28R) or *Dancing with Doll* (HW115R) and *Lunch Break* (HW29R).

PLAYTIME THEME — Frank Endersby

SEE-SAW
Style Two

Design No.: 52 See-saw
Designer: Frank Endersby
Issued: 1995 - 2003

Shape	U.S. $	Can. $	U.K. £	Aust. $
Baby plate, round, small	20.00	27.50	12.50	30.00
Plate, 6 ½"	15.00	20.00	10.00	25.00
Plate, 8"	15.00	20.00	10.00	25.00

See-saw, Style Two (52)

Pushing Swing (53)

PUSHING SWING / BUNNY ON SWING

Design No.: Front — 53 Pushing Swing
Reverse — 54 Bunny on Swing
Designer: Frank Endersby
Issued: 1995 - 2003

Shape	U.S. $	Can. $	U.K. £	Aust. $
Hug-a-mug, one handle	10.00	15.00	7.50	15.00
Hug-a-mug, two handles	10.00	15.00	7.50	15.00

Bunny on Swing (54)

Portrait Painter (SF20)

PORTRAIT PAINTER

Design No.:	SF20
Designer:	Walter Hayward
Issued:	1954 - by 1998

Shape	U.S. $	Can. $	U.K. £	Aust. $
Baby plate, round, small				
with signature	30.00	40.00	20.00	50.00
without signature	20.00	27.50	12.50	30.00
Cake stand	150.00	250.00	100.00	300.00
Casino saucer				
with signature	15.00	25.00	10.00	25.00
without signature	7.50	12.00	5.00	12.00
Casino teapot, 30s				
with signature	250.00	375.00	165.00	400.00
without signature	150.00	225.00	100.00	250.00
Cereal / oatmeal bowl				
with signature	25.00	35.00	20.00	40.00
without signature	15.00	20.00	10.00	25.00
Hot water plate				
with signature	100.00	135.00	65.00	150.00
without signature	75.00	100.00	45.00	110.00
Jaffa fruit saucer (plain)				
with signature	25.00	35.00	20.00	40.00
without signature	15.00	20.00	10.00	25.00
Plate, 6 ½"				
with signature	25.00	35.00	15.00	40.00
without signature	15.00	20.00	20.00	25.00
Plate, 7 ½"				
with signature	30.00	40.00	20.00	45.00
without signature	15.00	20.00	10.00	25.00
Plate, 8"	15.00	20.00	10.00	25.00

POST OFFICE THEME — Frank Endersby

POSTING LETTERS

Design No.:	28 Posting Letters	
Designer:	Frank Endersby	
Issued:	1995 to the present	

Shape	U.S. $	Can. $	U.K. £	Aust. $
Cereal bowl	N/I	33.00	11.00	49.95
Money ball	15.00	20.00	10.00	20.00
Plate, 6 ½"	N/I	25.00	8.00	34.95
Plate, 8"	N/I	35.00	11.00	49.95

Posting Letters (28)

Letter Box (29)

LETTER BOX / CARRYING LETTER

Design No.:	Front — 29 Letter Box	
	Reverse — 30 Carrying Letter	
Designer:	Frank Endersby	
Issued:	1995 to the present	
Combined with:	*Playing with Balloons, (33)	
	*Trying on Hat, (12)	

Shape	U.S. $	Can. $	U.K. £	Aust. $
Hug-a-mug, one handle	30.00	33.00	11.00	49.95
Hug-a-mug, two handles	32.50	39.00	12.00	56.95
Divider dish	50.00	75.00	35.00	75.00
Stratford teacup	7.50	12.00	5.00	12.00

* Indicates scene on divider dish.

Carrying Letter (30)

Postman Delivering Letters (HW19)

Writing Letters (HW19R)

POSTMAN DELIVERING LETTERS / WRITING LETTERS

Design No.:	Front — HW19 Postman Delivering Letters
	Reverse — HW19R Writing Letters
Designer:	Walter Hayward after Barbara Vernon
Issued:	By 1952 - 1967

Shape	U.S. $	Can. $	U.K. £	Aust. $
Baby plate, round, small				
with signature	200.00	275.00	125.00	300.00
without signature	150.00	200.00	100.00	225.00
Casino jug, 24s				
with signature	475.00	675.00	300.00	725.00
without signature	400.00	500.00	250.00	600.00
Casino jug, 36s				
with signature	300.00	425.00	190.00	475.00
without signature	275.00	400.00	175.00	450.00
Casino jug, 42s				
with signature	275.00	400.00	175.00	450.00
without signature	200.00	275.00	125.00	300.00
Casino saucer				
with signature	75.00	100.00	50.00	125.00
without signature	50.00	65.00	30.00	75.00
Casino sugar bowl, 30s				
with signature	200.00	275.00	125.00	300.00
without signature	125.00	175.00	80.00	200.00
Casino teacup				
with signature	75.00	100.00	50.00	125.00
without signature	50.00	65.00	30.00	75.00
Casino teapot, 24s				
with signature	375.00	525.00	235.00	575.00
without signature	300.00	425.00	190.00	475.00
Casino teapot, 30s				
with signature	300.00	425.00	190.00	475.00
without signature	225.00	325.00	150.00	375.00
Don beaker				
with signature	150.00	225.00	100.00	250.00
without signature	100.00	150.00	65.00	165.00
Don beaker, one handle				
with signature	150.00	225.00	100.00	250.00
without signature	100.00	150.00	65.00	165.00
Don mug, one handle				
with signature	75.00	100.00	50.00	125.00
without signature	35.00	55.00	20.00	60.00
Don mug, two handles				
with signature	75.00	100.00	50.00	125.00
without signature	35.00	55.00	20.00	60.00
Lid of hot water plate				
with signature	175.00	250.00	110.00	275.00
without signature	125.00	175.00	80.00	200.00
Plate, 6 ½"				
with signature	90.00	125.00	55.00	135.00
without signature	65.00	85.00	40.00	95.00

PRESSING TROUSERS

Pressing Trousers (HW14)

Design No.: HW14
Designer: Barbara Vernon
Issued: By 1937 - 1967
Combined with: *Cycling*, HW15R
Dunce, HW1R
Feeding the Baby, HW13
Fishing in the Gold Fish Bowl, HW3R
Footballer, HW13R
Frightening Spider, SF4

Golfer, HW4R
Leapfrog, HW12R
Netting a Cricket, HW6
Raising Hat, Style One, HW16R
Santa Claus, SF9
Top Hat, HW14R
Watering the Flowers, SF15
Wedding, LFd

Shape	U.S. $	Can. $	U.K. £	Aust. $
Baby plate, round, small				
with signature	50.00	65.00	30.00	70.00
without signature	30.00	40.00	20.00	45.00
Casino jug, 24s				
with signature	400.00	625.00	275.00	650.00
without signature	350.00	550.00	250.00	550.00
Casino jug, 30s				
with signature	300.00	475.00	200.00	475.00
without signature	225.00	325.00	150.00	325.00
Casino saucer				
with signature	75.00	125.00	50.00	125.00
without signature	50.00	75.00	35.00	75.00
Casino teacup				
with signature	75.00	125.00	50.00	125.00
without signature	50.00	75.00	35.00	75.00
Casino teapot, 30s				
with signature	325.00	500.00	225.00	550.00
without signature	250.00	400.00	175.00	450.00
Casino teapot, 36s				
with signature	250.00	375.00	165.00	400.00
without signature	225.00	350.00	150.00	400.00
Don beaker				
with signature	65.00	85.00	40.00	90.00
without signature	35.00	45.00	20.00	50.00
Don beaker, one handle				
with signature	65.00	85.00	40.00	90.00
without signature	35.00	45.00	20.00	50.00

Shape	U.S. $	Can. $	U.K. £	Aust. $
Don mug, one handle				
with signature	50.00	65.00	30.00	75.00
without signature	15.00	20.00	10.00	25.00
Don mug, two handles				
with signature	50.00	65.00	30.00	75.00
without signature	15.00	20.00	10.00	25.00
Jaffa fruit saucer				
plain rim	50.00	65.00	30.00	70.00
wavy rim	75.00	100.00	50.00	125.00
Jam pot	1,500.00	2,000.00	950.00	2,000.00
Lid of hot water plate				
with signature	100.00	135.00	65.00	150.00
without signature	75.00	100.00	50.00	115.00
Plate, 6 ½"				
with signature	30.00	40.00	20.00	45.00
without signature	20.00	25.00	12.00	30.00
FINE WHITE CHINA				
Baby bowl		Very Rare		
Bread and butter plate	800.00	1,000.00	500.00	1,100.00
Cereal/oatmeal bowl		Very Rare		
Coupe		Very Rare		
Plate, 5"	650.00	850.00	400.00	875.00
Rex mug	1,000.00	1,350.00	625.00	1,400.00
Saucer	300.00	400.00	200.00	300.00
Sugar bowl	1,200.00	1,500.00	750.00	1,500.00
Teacup	300.00	400.00	200.00	300.00

Note: The Rex mug combines *Pressing Trousers* (HW14) with *Cycling* (HW15R).

Proposal (HW11)

PROPOSAL

Design No.:	HW11
Designer:	Barbara Vernon
Issued:	By 1937 - by 1967
Combined with:	*Cycling*, HW15R
	Dress Making, HW26
	Dunce, HW1R
	Family at Breakfast, HW12
	Family with Pram, Style One, HW15
	Footballer, HW13R
	Golfer, HW4R
	Holding Hat and Coat, EC4
	Kissing Under the Mistletoe, HW11R
	Leapfrog, HW12R
	Netting a Cricket, HW6
	Playing with Cup and Spoon, EC6
	Pulling on Trousers, HW2
	Raising Hat, Style One, HW16R
	Santa Claus, SF9
	Wedding, LFd

Shape	U.S. $	Can. $	U.K. £	Aust. $
Baby plate, round, small				
with signature	50.00	65.00	30.00	70.00
without signature	30.00	40.00	20.00	45.00
Candle holder	2,000.00	2,500.00	1,250.00	2,500.00
Casino jugs, 36s				
with signature	300.00	475.00	200.00	475.00
without signature	250.00	400.00	175.00	400.00
Casino jug, 42s				
with signature	250.00	400.00	175.00	400.00
without signature	200.00	325.00	150.00	325.00
Casino saucer				
with signature	75.00	125.00	50.00	125.00
without signature	50.00	75.00	35.00	75.00
Casino sugar bowl, 30s				
with signature	200.00	325.00	125.00	350.00
without signature	150.00	225.00	100.00	250.00
Casino sugar bowl, 36s				
with signature	175.00	275.00	125.00	325.00
without signature	125.00	200.00	85.00	225.00
Casino teacup				
with signature	75.00	125.00	50.00	125.00
without signature	50.00	75.00	35.00	75.00
Casino teapot, 24s				
with signature	375.00	550.00	250.00	600.00
without signature	300.00	450.00	200.00	500.00
Casino teapot, 30s				
with signature	325.00	500.00	225.00	550.00
without signature	250.00	400.00	175.00	450.00
Cereal/oatmeal bowl				
with signature	35.00	45.00	20.00	50.00
without signature	25.00	35.00	15.00	40.00

Shape	U.S. $	Can. $	U.K. £	Aust. $
Don beaker				
with signature	65.00	85.00	40.00	90.00
without signature	35.00	45.00	20.00	50.00
Don beaker, one handle				
with signature	65.00	85.00	40.00	90.00
without signature	35.00	45.00	20.00	50.00
Don mug, one handle				
with silver rim	350.00	475.00	225.00	500.00
with signature	50.00	65.00	30.00	75.00
without signature	15.00	20.00	10.00	25.00
Don mug, two handles				
with signature	50.00	65.00	30.00	75.00
without signature	15.00	20.00	10.00	25.00
Jaffa fruit saucer				
plain rim	50.00	65.00	30.00	70.00
wavy rim	75.00	100.00	50.00	125.00
Jam pot	1,500.00	2,000.00	950.00	2,000.00
Lid of hot water plate				
with signature	100.00	135.00	65.00	150.00
without signature	75.00	100.00	50.00	115.00
Plate, 6 ½"				
with signature	30.00	40.00	20.00	45.00
without signature	20.00	25.00	12.00	30.00
FINE WHITE CHINA				
Baby bowl		Very rare		
Beaker	300.00	400.00	200.00	425.00
Plate, 5"	650.00	850.00	400.00	875.00
Rex mug	1,000.00	1,350.00	625.00	1,450.00
Saucer	300.00	400.00	200.00	425.00
Sugar bowl	1,000.00	1,350.00	625.00	1,450.00
Teacup	300.00	400.00	200.00	425.00

Note: 1. On the Rex mugs *Proposal* (HW111) is combined with one of the following: *Dunce* (HW1R), *Golfer* (HW4R) or *Leapfrog* (HW12R).
2. Fine white china prices are indications only due to the scarcity of the shapes. Prices will vary.

PULLING ON TROUSERS

Design No.:	HW2
Designer:	Barbara Vernon
Issued:	By 1937 - by 1952
Combined with:	*Artist*, HW1
	Bedtime in Bunks, SF3
	Family at Breakfast, HW12
	Family with Pram, Style One, HW15
	Feeding the Baby, HW
	Fishing in the Goldfish Bowl, HW3R
	Game of Golf, SF11
	Golfer, HW4R
	Holding Hat and Coat, EC4
	Netting a Cricket, HW6
	Proposal, HW11
	Raising Hat, Style One, HW16R
	Reading the Times, HW2R

Pulling on Trousers (HW2)

Shape	U.S. $	Can. $	U.K. £	Aust. $
Casino jug, 30s				
with signature	300.00	475.00	200.00	475.00
without signature	225.00	325.00	150.00	325.00
Casino jug, 36s				
with signature	300.00	475.00	200.00	475.00
without signature	250.00	400.00	175.00	400.00
Casino jug, 42s				
with signature	250.00	400.00	175.00	400.00
without signature	200.00	325.00	150.00	325.00
Casino saucer				
with signature	75.00	125.00	50.00	75.00
without signature	50.00	75.00	35.00	25.00
Casino sugar bowl, 30s				
with signature	200.00	325.00	125.00	350.00
without signature	150.00	225.00	100.00	250.00
Casino teacup				
with signature	75.00	125.00	50.00	75.00
without signature	50.00	75.00	35.00	25.00
Cup / mug, large			Rare	
Don beaker				
with signature	65.00	85.00	40.00	90.00
without signature	35.00	45.00	20.00	50.00

Shape	U.S. $	Can. $	U.K. £	Aust. $
Don beaker, one handle				
with signature	65.00	85.00	40.00	90.00
without signature	35.00	45.00	20.00	50.00
Don mug, one handle				
with signature	50.00	65.00	30.00	75.00
without signature	15.00	20.00	10.00	25.00
Don mug, two handles				
with signature	50.00	65.00	30.00	75.00
without signature	15.00	20.00	10.00	25.00
Jaffa fruit saucer				
plain rim	50.00	65.00	30.00	70.00
wavy rim	75.00	100.00	50.00	125.00
Jam pot	1,500.00	2,000.00	950.00	2,000.00
Lid of hot water plate				
with signature	100.00	135.00	65.00	150.00
without signature	75.00	100.00	50.00	115.00
Plate, 6 ½"				
with signature	30.00	40.00	20.00	45.00
without signature	20.00	25.00	12.00	30.00
FINE WHITE CHINA				
Teacup			Very rare	

Punch and Judy Show (HW136)

Ice Cream on the Beach (HW136R)

PUNCH AND JUDY SHOW / ICE CREAM ON THE BEACH

Design No.:	Front — HW136 Punch and Judy Show
	Reverse — HW136R Ice Cream on the Beach
Designer:	Walter Hayward
Issued:	1967 - by 1998
Combined with:	*Cowboy on Rocking Horse, HW140R
	Playing with Dolls and Prams, HW115
	*Roller Skating, HW137R
	Sailing Boats, HW138R
	Serving Tea, HW116R
	To the Station, HW17R

Shape	U.S. $	Can. $	U.K. £	Aust. $
Albion cream jug	35.00	55.00	20.00	60.00
Albion jug, ½ pint	85.00	115.00	50.00	125.00
Albion jug, 1 pint	100.00	150.00	60.00	165.00
Albion teapot	50.00	70.00	30.00	75.00
Cake stand	150.00	250.00	100.00	300.00
Casino saucer	7.50	12.00	5.00	12.00
Casino teacup	7.50	12.00	5.00	12.00
Casino teapot, 30s	150.00	225.00	100.00	250.00
Divider dish	50.00	75.00	35.00	75.00
Don beaker	25.00	35.00	15.00	40.00
Don beaker, one handle	25.00	35.00	15.00	40.00
Don mug, one handle	10.00	15.00	6.50	18.00
Don mug, two handles	10.00	15.00	6.50	18.00
Egg box				
small	225.00	350.00	150.00	400.00
medium	300.00	450.00	200.00	500.00
large	375.00	550.00	250.00	600.00
Hug-a-mug, one handle	10.00	15.00	7.50	15.00
Hug-a-mug, two handles	10.00	15.00	7.50	15.00
Jaffa fruit saucer (plain)	15.00	20.00	10.00	25.00
Lamp	50.00	75.00	30.00	85.00
Malvern beaker	15.00	25.00	10.00	25.00
Money ball	10.00	15.00	7.50	15.00
Picture plaque, small	20.00	30.00	12.50	30.00
Savings book	15.00	22.50	10.00	22.50
Stratford straight beaker	15.00	25.00	10.00	25.00
Stratford teacup	7.50	12.00	5.00	12.00

* Indicates scene on divider dish.

QUEEN OF THE MAY — Colin Twinn

First Variation, Small Size

Design No.:	Front — CT7 Queen of the May
	Reverse — CT8 Counting Motif
Designer:	Colin Twinn
Issued:	1988 - 1993
Combined with:	*Picking Daisies*, CT4

Shape	U.S. $	Can. $	U.K. £	Aust. $
Albion cream jug	35.00	55.00	20.00	60.00
Albion jug, ½ pint	85.00	115.00	50.00	125.00
Albion jug, 1 pint	100.00	150.00	60.00	165.00
Baby plate, small, round	20.00	27.50	12.50	30.00
Hug-a-mug, one handle	10.00	15.00	7.50	15.00
Hug-a-mug, two handles	10.00	15.00	7.50	15.00
Picture plaque, small	20.00	30.00	12.50	30.00
Malvern beaker	15.00	25.00	10.00	25.00

Queen of the May, First Variation (CT7)

Note: Two money balls were issued for the U.S. Special Events Tour in 1992. This design was featured on the Spring tour with no special inscription. *Happy Birthday from Bunnykins* (CT60) was featured on the Fall tour. *Queen of the May* (CT17) is combined with *Picking Daisies* (CT4) on a one handled, hug-a-mug, see page 197.

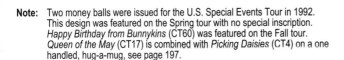

Counting Motif (CT8)

Queen of the May, Second Variation (CT13)

Second Variation, Large Size

Design No.:	CT13 Queen of the May
Designer:	Colin Twinn
Issued:	1989- 1993
Combined with:	*Picking Daisies*, CT13

Shape	U.S. $	Can. $	U.K. £	Aust. $
Albion jug, 1 pint	100.00	150.00	60.00	165.00
Baby plate, round, small	15.00	20.00	10.00	20.00
Cake stand	150.00	250.00	100.00	300.00
Cereal / oatmeal bowl	15.00	20.00	10.00	25.00
Lamp	50.00	75.00	30.00	85.00
Picture plaque, small	20.00	30.00	12.50	30.00
Picture plaque, large	20.00	30.00	12.50	30.00
Plate, 8"	15.00	20.00	10.00	25.00

Raft (SF111)

RAFT

Design No.:	SF111
Designer:	Walter Hayward after Penelope Hollinshead
Issued:	1959 - 2003

Shape	U.S. $	Can. $	U.K. £	Aust. $
Baby plate, round, small	20.00	27.50	12.50	30.00
Casino saucer	7.50	12.00	5.00	12.00
Casino teapot, 30s	150.00	225.00	100.00	250.00
Cereal / oatmeal bowl	15.00	20.00	10.00	25.00
Coupe plate, 6 ¾"		Very Rare		
Hot water plate	75.00	100.00	45.00	110.00
Jaffa fruit saucer (plain)	15.00	20.00	10.00	25.00
Picture plaque, large	20.00	30.00	12.50	30.00
Plate, 6 ½"	15.00	20.00	10.00	25.00
Plate, 7 ½"	15.00	20.00	10.00	25.00
Plate, 8"	15.00	20.00	10.00	25.00

Note: 1. Retirement dates are all approximate. When a design is retired all remaining stocks of the retired litho prints are used until exhausted.
2. Condition is important. Prices listed are based on nurseryware in mint condition. Items in less than mint condition will command lower prices.

RAISING HAT
Style One

Design No.:	HW16R
Designer:	Barbara Vernon
Issued:	By 1937 - by 1952
Combined with:	*Family at Breakfast*, HW12
	Family with Pram, Style One, HW15
	Feeding the Baby, HW13
	Lambeth Walk, HW16
	Pressing Trousers, HW14
	Proposal, HW11
	Pulling on Trousers, HW2
	Sleeping in a Rocking Chair, EC1
	Wedding, LFd

Raising Hat, Style One (HW16R)

Shape	U.S. $	Can. $	U.K. £	Aust. $
Casino jug, 42s				
with signature	250.00	400.00	175.00	400.00
without signature	200.00	325.00	150.00	325.00
Casino teacup				
with signature	75.00	125.00	50.00	125.00
without signature	50.00	75.00	35.00	75.00
Casino teapot, 30s				
with signature	325.00	500.00	225.00	550.00
without signature	250.00	400.00	175.00	450.00
Casino teapot, 36s				
with signature	250.00	375.00	175.00	400.00
without signature	225.00	350.00	150.00	375.00
Don beaker				
with signature	65.00	85.00	40.00	90.00
without signature	35.00	45.00	20.00	50.00
Don beaker, one handle				
with signature	65.00	85.00	40.00	90.00
without signature	35.00	45.00	20.00	50.00
Don mug, one handle				
with signature	50.00	65.00	30.00	75.00
without signature	15.00	20.00	10.00	25.00
Jam pot	1,500.00	2,000.00	950.00	2,000.00
Lid of hot water plate				
with signature	75.00	100.00	45.00	110.00
without signature	50.00	65.00	30.00	70.00

Note: *Raising Hat* (HW16R) is combined with *Family with Pram*, Style One, (HW15) on a large round and an oval baby plate, and also a 7 ½" plate. For an illustration see page 69.

Raising Hat, Style Two (EC7)

RAISING HAT
Style Two

Design No.:	EC7
Designer:	Barbara Vernon
Issued:	1937 to the present
Combined with:	*Bedtime with Dollies*, EC125
	Drummer, EC2
	Drummer and Bugler, EC126
	Engine Pulling a Carriage, HW17
	Family with Pram, Style One, HW15
	Hikers, EC124
	Hobby Horse, Style Two, EC121
	Holding Hat and Coat, EC4
	Playing with Cup and Spoon, EC6
	Playing with Doll and Pram, EC123
	Reading, EC122
	Sheltering Under an Umbrella, EC3
	Sleeping in a Rocking Chair, EC1
	To the Station, HW17R
	Trumpeter, EC5

Shape	U.S. $	Can. $	U.K. £	Aust. $
Albion sugar bowl	30.00	40.00	17.50	45.00
Beaker cover	40.00	55.00	25.00	60.00
Casino sugar bowl, 30s	150.00	225.00	100.00	250.00
Egg cup				
Style One	30.00	40.00	20.00	60.00
Style Two	40.00	55.00	25.00	60.00
Style Three	N/I	15.00	5.00	19.95
Lid of hot water plate	50.00	65.00	30.00	70.00

READING

Design No.:	EC122
Designer:	Walter Hayward
Issued:	1959 to the present
Combined with:	*Bedtime with Dollies*, EC125
	The Doll's House, HW120
	Drummer, EC2
	Drummer and Bugler, EC126
	Hikers, EC124
	Hobby Horse, Style One, HW24R
	Hobby Horse, Style Two, EC121
	Playing with Cup and Spoon, EC6
	Playing with Doll and Pram, EC123
	Raising Hat, Style Two, EC7
	Sheltering Under an Umbrella, EC3
	Sledging, Style One, HW141
	Sleeping in a Rocking Chair, EC1
	Trumpeter, EC5

Shape	U.S. $	Can. $	U.K. £	Aust. $
Albion sugar bowl	30.00	40.00	17.50	45.00
Beaker cover	40.00	55.00	25.00	60.00
Egg cup				
Style One	30.00	40.00	20.00	45.00
Style Two	40.00	55.00	25.00	60.00
Style Three	N/I	15.00	5.00	19.95
Lid of hot water plate	50.00	65.00	30.00	70.00
Money ball	10.00	15.00	7.50	15.00

Reading (EC122)

READING THE TIMES

Design No.:	HW2R
Designer:	Barbara Vernon
Issued:	By 1937 - by 1952
Combined with:	*Cycling*, HW15R
	Footballer, HW13R
	Golfer, HW4R
	Kissing Under the Mistletoe, HW11R
	Netting a Cricket, HW6
	Pulling on Trousers, HW2
	Smoking in the Doorway, SF2

Shape	U.S. $	Can. $	U.K. £	Aust. $
Casino jug, 42s	275.00	400.00	175.00	450.00
Casino teacup	75.00	100.00	50.00	125.00
Cup / mug, large	350.00	475.00	225.00	500.00
Don beaker	150.00	225.00	100.00	250.00
Don beaker, one handle	150.00	225.00	100.00	250.00
Don mug, one handle	75.00	100.00	50.00	125.00
Don mug, two handles	75.00	100.00	50.00	125.00

Note: This design should appear with the Barbara Vernon facsimile signature.

Reading the Times (HW2R)

RING-A-RING O'ROSES

Ring-a-Ring o'Roses (SF21)

Design No.:	SF21
Designer:	Walter Hayward
Issued:	1954 - by 1998

Shape	U.S. $	Can. $	U.K. £	Aust. $
Baby plate, round, small				
with signature	30.00	40.00	20.00	50.00
without signature	20.00	27.50	12.50	30.00
Cake stand	150.00	250.00	100.00	300.00
Casino saucer				
with signature	15.00	25.00	10.00	25.00
without signature	7.50	12.00	5.00	12.00
Casino teapot, 24s				
with signature	275.00	400.00	175.00	450.00
without signature	175.00	275.00	125.00	325.00
Cereal / oatmeal bowl				
with signature	25.00	35.00	20.00	40.00
without signature	15.00	20.00	10.00	25.00
Hot water plate				
with signature	100.00	135.00	65.00	150.00
without signature	75.00	100.00	45.00	110.00
Jaffa fruit saucer (plain)				
with signature	25.00	35.00	20.00	40.00
without signature	15.00	20.00	10.00	25.00
Picture plaque, large	20.00	30.00	12.50	30.00
Plate, 6 ½"				
with signature	25.00	35.00	15.00	40.00
without signature	15.00	20.00	10.00	25.00
Plate, 7 ½"				
with signature	30.00	40.00	20.00	45.00
without signature	15.00	20.00	10.00	25.00
Plate, 8"	15.00	20.00	10.00	25.00

Rocking Horse (HW24)

Hobby Horse (HW24R)

ROCKING HORSE / HOBBY HORSE, Style One

Design No.:	Front — HW24 Rocking Horse
	Reverse — HW24R Hobby Horse
Designer:	Walter Hayward after Barbara Vernon
Issued:	1954 - 1967
Combined with:	*Reading*, EC122
	Trumpeter, EC5

Shape	U.S. $	Can. $	U.K. £	Aust. $
Beaker cover				
with signature	85.00	115.00	55.00	125.00
without signature	75.00	100.00	45.00	110.00
Casino teacup				
with signature	75.00	125.00	50.00	125.00
without signature	50.00	75.00	35.00	75.00
Don beaker				
with signature	65.00	85.00	40.00	90.00
without signature	35.00	45.00	20.00	50.00
Don beaker, one handle				
with signature	65.00	85.00	40.00	90.00
without signature	35.00	45.00	20.00	50.00
Don mug, one handle				
with signature	50.00	65.00	30.00	75.00
without signature	15.00	20.00	10.00	25.00
Don mug, two handles				
with signature	50.00	65.00	30.00	75.00
without signature	15.00	20.00	10.00	25.00
Egg cup, Style Two	50.00	65.00	30.00	75.00
Jaffa fruit saucer (plain)				
with signature	50.00	65.00	30.00	75.00
without signature	30.00	40.00	20.00	45.00
Lamp	50.00	75.00	30.00	85.00
Lid of hot water plate				
with signature	100.00	135.00	65.00	150.00
without signature	75.00	100.00	50.00	115.00
Money ball	10.00	15.00	7.50	15.00
Plate, 6 ½"				
with signature	30.00	40.00	20.00	45.00
without signature	20.00	25.00	12.00	30.00

Note: *Hobby Horse* (HW24R) is combined with *Reading* (EC122) on the Egg cup, style two.

ROLLER SKATING RACE /
ROLLER SKATING ARM IN ARM

Design No.:	Front — HW137 Roller Skating Race
	Reverse — HW137R Roller Skating Arm in Arm
Designer:	Walter Hayward
Issued:	1967 - by 1998
Combined with:	*Building Sand Castles*, HW138
	Dancing with Doll, HW115R
	Playing with Dolls and Prams, HW115
	Sailing Boats, HW138R

Shape	U.S. $	Can. $	U.K. £	Aust. $
Albion cream jug	35.00	55.00	20.00	60.00
Albion jug, 1 pint	100.00	150.00	60.00	165.00
Albion teapot	50.00	70.00	30.00	75.00
Cake stand	150.00	250.00	100.00	300.00
Casino teacup	7.50	12.00	5.00	12.00
Divider dish	50.00	75.00	35.00	75.00
Don beaker	25.00	35.00	15.00	40.00
Don beaker, one handle	25.00	35.00	15.00	40.00
Don mug, one handle	10.00	15.00	6.50	18.00
Don mug, two handles	10.00	15.00	6.50	18.00
Egg box				
small	225.00	350.00	150.00	400.00
medium	300.00	450.00	200.00	500.00
large	375.00	550.00	250.00	600.00
Hug-a-mug, one handle	10.00	15.00	7.50	15.00
Hug-a-mug, two handles	10.00	15.00	7.50	15.00
Jaffa fruit saucer (plain)	15.00	20.00	10.00	25.00
Lamp	50.00	75.00	30.00	85.00
Malvern beaker	15.00	25.00	10.00	25.00
Money ball	10.00	15.00	7.50	15.00
Picture plaque, small	20.00	30.00	12.50	30.00
Plate, 6 ½"	15.00	20.00	10.00	25.00
Savings book	15.00	22.50	10.00	22.50
Stratford straight beaker	15.00	25.00	10.00	25.00
Stratford teacup	7.50	12.00	5.00	12.00

Roller Skating Race (HW137)

Roller Skating Arm in Arm (HW137R)

ROW BOAT / NIPPED BY A CRAB

Row Boat (HW21)

Nipped by a Crab (HW21R)

Design No.: Front — HW21 Row Boat
Reverse — HW21R Nipped by a Crab
Designer: Walter Hayward
Issued: By 1952 - by 1998

Combined with: *Cricketer*, HW22R
Family with Pram, Style One, HW15
Hikers, EC124
Swinging, HW20
Wheelbarrow Race, Style One, HW22

Shape	U.S. $	Can. $	U.K. £	Aust. $
Albion jug, ½ pint	85.00	115.00	50.00	125.00
Albion jug, 1 pint	100.00	150.00	60.00	165.00
Albion teapot	50.00	70.00	30.00	75.00
Casino jug, 36s				
with signature	175.00	275.00	125.00	275.00
without signature	125.00	200.00	85.00	200.00
Casino saucer				
with signature	15.00	25.00	10.00	25.00
without signature	7.50	12.00	5.00	12.00
Casino sugar bowl, 36s				
with signature	150.00	225.00	85.00	250.00
without signature	125.00	175.00	70.00	175.00
Casino teacup				
with signature	15.00	25.00	10.00	25.00
without signature	7.50	12.00	5.00	12.00
Casino teapot, 24s				
with signature	275.00	400.00	175.00	450.00
without signature	175.00	275.00	125.00	325.00
Divider dish	50.00	75.00	35.00	75.00
Don beaker				
with signature	50.00	65.00	30.00	75.00
without signature	25.00	35.00	15.00	40.00
Don beaker, one handle				
with signature	50.00	65.00	30.00	75.00
without signature	25.00	35.00	15.00	40.00
Don mug, one handle				
with signature	40.00	55.00	25.00	60.00
without signature	10.00	15.00	6.50	18.00

Shape	U.S. $	Can. $	U.K. £	Aust. $
Don mug, two handles				
with signature	40.00	55.00	25.00	60.00
without signature	10.00	15.00	6.50	18.00
Egg box				
small	225.00	350.00	150.00	400.00
medium	300.00	450.00	200.00	500.00
large	375.00	550.00	250.00	600.00
Hug-a-mug, one handle	10.00	15.00	7.50	15.00
Hug-a-mug, two handles	10.00	15.00	7.50	15.00
Jaffa fruit saucer (plain)				
with signature	25.00	35.00	20.00	40.00
without signature	15.00	20.00	10.00	25.00
Lamp	50.00	75.00	30.00	85.00
Lid of hot water plate				
with signature	75.00	100.00	45.00	110.00
without signature	50.00	65.00	30.00	70.00
Malvern beaker	15.00	25.00	10.00	25.00
Money ball	10.00	15.00	7.50	15.00
Picture plaque, small	20.00	30.00	12.50	30.00
Plate, 6 ½"				
with signature	25.00	35.00	15.00	40.00
without signature	15.00	20.00	10.00	25.00
Savings book	15.00	22.50	10.00	22.50
Stratford straight beaker	15.00	25.00	10.00	25.00
Stratford teacup	7.50	12.00	5.00	12.00

Note: A Casino jug combines *Rowboat* (HW21), with *Swinging* (HW20).

SANTA BUNNYKINS
CHRISTMAS TREE ORNAMENT

Design No.:	Front — CT68 Santa Bunnykins
	Reverse — CT69 Christmas 1991
Designer:	Colin Twinn
Issued:	1991 - 1991
Series:	Christmas Tree Ornaments

Shape	U.S. $	Can. $	U.K. £	Aust. $
Christmas Tree Ornament	15.00	20.00	10.00	25.00

Note: For other Christmas tree ornaments in this series see pages 40, 42, 78, and 163.

Santa Bunnykins Christmas Tree Ornament (CT68)

Santa Bunnykins Christmas Tree Ornament (CT69)

Santa Claus (SF9)

SANTA CLAUS

Design No.:	SF9
Designer:	Barbara Vernon
Issued:	By 1940 - by 1952
Combined with:	*Feeding the Baby*, HW13
	Pressing Trousers, HW14
	Proposal, HW11

Shape	U.S. $	Can. $	U.K. £	Aust. $
Baby plate, oval, small				
with signature	200.00	275.00	125.00	300.00
without signature	150.00	200.00	95.00	225.00
Baby plate, round, small				
with signature	50.00	65.00	30.00	70.00
without signature	30.00	40.00	20.00	45.00
Candle holder	2,000.00	2,500.00	1,250.00	2,500.00
Casino jug, 36s				
with signature	250.00	400.00	175.00	425.00
without signature	175.00	275.00	125.00	300.00
Casino teapot, 30s				
with signature	325.00	500.00	225.00	550.00
without signature	250.00	400.00	175.00	450.00
Cereal / oatmeal bowl				
with signature	35.00	45.00	20.00	50.00
without signature	25.00	35.00	15.00	40.00
Hot water plate				
with signature	125.00	165.00	80.00	175.00
without signature	100.00	135.00	65.00	150.00
Jaffa fruit saucer				
plain rim	50.00	65.00	30.00	70.00
wavy rim	75.00	100.00	50.00	125.00
Plate, 6 ½"				
with signature	30.00	40.00	20.00	45.00
without signature	20.00	25.00	12.00	30.00
Plate, 7"				
with signature	65.00	85.00	40.00	95.00
without signature	25.00	35.00	15.00	45.00
Plate, 7 ½"				
with signature	65.00	85.00	40.00	95.00
without signature	25.00	35.00	15.00	45.00
Plate, 8 ½"				
with signature	75.00	100.00	45.00	115.00
without signature	25.00	35.00	15.00	45.00
FINE WHITE CHINA				
Cereal bowl	350.00	475.00	225.00	500.00
Plate, 5"	650.00	850.00	400.00	875.00
Plate, 7"	650.00	850.00	400.00	875.00

Note: Fine white china prices are indications only due to the scarcity of the shapes. Prices will vary.

SCHOOL THEME – Frank Endersby

MATHS LESSON

Design No.:   25 Maths Lesson
Designer: Frank Endersby
Issued: 1995 to the present

Shape	U.S. $	Can. $	U.K. £	Aust. $
Baby plate, round, small	N/I	46.00	14.00	62.95
Plate, 6 ½"	N/I	25.00	8.00	34.95
Plate, 8"	N/I	35.00	11.00	49.95

Maths Lesson ((25)

Teacher Scolding (26)

TEACHER SCOLDING / BUNNY WITH BAG

Design No.:   Front — 26 Teacher Scolding
                 Reverse — 27 Bunny with Bag
Designer: Frank Endersby
Issued: 1995 to the present
Combined with: *Carrying Letter, (30)

Shape	U.S. $	Can. $	U.K. £	Aust. $
Hug-a-mug, one handle	30.00	33.00	11.00	49.95
Hug-a-mug, two handles	32.50	39.00	12.00	56.95
Divider dish	50.00	75.00	35.00	75.00

* Indicates scene on divider dish.

Bunny with Bag (27)

SCHOOL DINNER THEME — Colin Twinn

School Dinner, First Variation (CT17)

First Variation, Small Size

Design No.:   CT17 School Dinner
Designer: Colin Twinn
Issued: 1990 - 1993

Shape	U.S. $	Can. $	U.K. £	Aust. $
Albion jug, 1 pint	100.00	150.00	60.00	165.00
Baby plate, round, small	20.00	27.50	12.50	30.00
Cake stand	150.00	250.00	100.00	300.00
Cereal / oatmeal bowl	15.00	20.00	10.00	25.00
Jaffa fruit saucer (plain)	15.00	20.00	10.00	25.00
Plate, 8"	15.00	20.00	10.00	25.00

School Dinner, Second Variation (CT30)

Second Variation, Large Size / COOK AND BUNNY

Design No.:   Front — CT30 School Dinner
               Reverse — CT31 Cook and Bunny
Designer: Colin Twinn
Issued: 1990 - 1993

Shape	U.S. $	Can. $	U.K. £	Aust. $
Albion cream jug	35.00	55.00	20.00	60.00
Albion jug, 1 pint	100.00	150.00	60.00	165.00
Albion teapot	50.00	70.00	30.00	75.00
Hug-a-mug, one handle	10.00	15.00	7.50	15.00
Hug-a-mug, two handles	10.00	15.00	7.50	15.00
Lamp	50.00	75.00	30.00	85.00
Malvern beaker	15.00	25.00	10.00	25.00
Money ball	10.00	15.00	7.50	15.00
Savings book	15.00	22.50	10.00	22.50
Stratford teacup	7.50	12.00	5.00	12.00

Cook and Bunny (CT31)

SCHOOL GATES THEME — Colin Twinn

First Variation, Large Size

Design No.:   CT20 School Gates
Designer: Colin Twinn
Issued: 1991 - 1993

Shape	U.S. $	Can. $	U.K. £	Aust. $
Albion jug, 1 pint	100.00	150.00	60.00	165.00
Cereal / oatmeal bowl	15.00	20.00	10.00	25.00
Lamp	50.00	75.00	30.00	85.00
Picture plaque, large	20.00	30.00	12.50	30.00
Plate, 6"	15.00	20.00	10.00	25.00
Plate, 8"	15.00	20.00	10.00	25.00

School Gates, First Variation (CT20)

School Gates, Second Variation (CT22)

SCHOOL GATES
Second Variation, Small Size / BUNNY ON TRIKE

Design No.:   Front — CT22 School Gates
Designer: Reverse — CT23 Bunny on Trike
Issued: 1991 - 1993
Combined with: *Bathtime Scene*, Style Two, Second Variation, CT24
                 Bunnies in the Bath, First Version, CT25
                 Classrooom Scene, Style Two, Second Version, CT16
                 Ice Cream Seller, Second Variation, CT11

Shape	U.S. $	Can. $	U.K. £	Aust. $
Albion jug, ½ pint	85.00	115.00	50.00	125.00
Albion teapot	50.00	70.00	30.00	75.00
Hug-a-mug, one handle	10.00	15.00	7.50	15.00
Hug-a-mug, two handles	10.00	15.00	7.50	15.00
Lamp	50.00	75.00	30.00	85.00
Money ball	10.00	15.00	7.50	15.00
Picture plaque, small	20.00	30.00	12.50	30.00
Stratford straight beaker	15.00	25.00	10.00	25.00

Bunny on Trike (CT23)

See-saw, Style One (SF17)

SEE-SAW
Style One

Design No.:	SF17
Designer:	Walter Hayward
Issued:	By 1952 - by 1998
Combined with:	*Engine Pulling a Carriage*, HW17
	Mr. Piggly's Stores, SF14
	To the Station, HW17R

Shape	U.S. $	Can. $	U.K. £	Aust. $
Albion jug, ½ pint	85.00	115.00	50.00	125.00
Albion jug, 1 pint	100.00	150.00	60.00	165.00
Baby plate, round, small				
with signature	30.00	40.00	20.00	50.00
without signature	20.00	27.50	12.50	30.00
Cake stand	150.00	250.00	100.00	300.00
Casino sugar bowl, 36s				
with signature	150.00	225.00	85.00	250.00
without signature	125.00	175.00	70.00	175.00
Cereal / oatmeal bowl				
with signature	25.00	35.00	20.00	40.00
without signature	15.00	20.00	10.00	25.00
Coupe plate, 6 ¾"		Very Rare		
Hot water plate				
with signature	100.00	135.00	65.00	150.00
without signature	75.00	100.00	45.00	110.00
Jaffa fruit saucer (plain)				
with signature	25.00	35.00	20.00	40.00
without signature	15.00	20.00	10.00	25.00
Picture plaque, large	20.00	30.00	12.50	30.00
Plate, 6 ½"				
with signature	25.00	35.00	15.00	40.00
without signature	15.00	20.00	10.00	25.00
Plate, 7 ½"				
with signature	30.00	40.00	20.00	45.00
without signature	15.00	20.00	10.00	25.00
Plate, 8"	15.00	20.00	10.00	25.00

Note: 1. Casino sugar bowl combines *See-Saw* (SF17) and *To The Station* (HW17R).
2. Condition is important. Prices listed are based on nurseryware in mint condition. Items in less than mint condition will command lower prices.

SHELTERING UNDER AN UMBRELLA

Design No.:	EC3
Designer:	Barbara Vernon
Issued:	1937 to the present
Combined with:	*Afternoon Tea*, HW116
	Bedtime with Dollies, EC125
	Drummer, EC2
	Family Going Out on Washing Day, HW8
	Fishing in the Goldfish Bowl, HW3R
	Hikers, EC124
	Hobby Horse, Style Two, EC121
	Holding Hat and Coat, EC4
	Playing with Cup and Spoon, EC6
	Playing with Doll and Pram, EC123
	Raising Hat, Style Two, EC7
	Reading, EC122
	Serving Tea, HW116R
	Sleeping in a Rocking Chair, EC1
	Trumpeter, EC5
	Washing Day, HW8R

Sheltering Under an Umbrella (EC3)

Shape	U.S. $	Can. $	U.K. £	Aust. $
Albion sugar bowl	30.00	40.00	17.50	45.00
Beaker cover				
with signature	50.00	65.00	30.00	70.00
without signature	40.00	55.00	25.00	60.00
Casino sugar bowl, 30s				
with signature	150.00	225.00	100.00	250.00
without signature	125.00	200.00	85.00	225.00
Casino sugar bowl, 36s				
with signature	125.00	200.00	85.00	225.00
without signature	100.00	150.00	65.00	175.00
Egg cup				
Style One				
with signature	40.00	55.00	25.00	60.00
without signature	30.00	40.00	20.00	45.00
Style Two	40.00	55.00	25.00	60.00
Style Three	N/I	15.00	5.00	19.95
Lid of hot water plate				
with signature	75.00	100.00	45.00	110.00
without signature	50.00	65.00	30.00	70.00

FINE WHITE CHINA

Teacup	Very rare

SHOPPING THEME — Frank Endersby

Shopping (1)

SHOPPING

Design No.: 1 Shopping
Designer: Frank Endersby
Issued: 1995 to the present

Shape	U.S. $	Can. $	U.K. £	Aust. $
Baby plate, round, small	20.00	27.50	12.50	30.00
Jaffa fruit saucer	15.00	20.00	10.00	25.00
Plate, 6 ½"	N/I	25.00	8.00	34.95
Plate, 8"	N/I	35.00	11.00	49.95

Vegetable Stall (2)

VEGETABLE STALL / EATING APPLES

Design No.: Front — 2 Vegetable Stall
Reverse — 3 Eating Apples
Designer: Frank Endersby
Issued: 1995 to the present
Combined with: *Resting*, Style Two, (21)

Shape	U.S. $	Can. $	U.K. £	Aust. $
Hug-a-mug, one handle	**30.00**	**33.00**	**11.00**	**49.95**
Hug-a-mug, two handles	**32.50**	**39.00**	**12.00**	**56.95**
Divider dish	50.00	75.00	35.00	75.00
Stratford teacup	7.50	12.00	5.00	12.00

* Indicates scene on divider dish.

Note: 1. Bold type in the listing tables indicate a current design on a current shape.
2. N/I, Not issued individually. The item(s) will be found only in boxed sets in that market.

Eating Apples (3)

SLEDGING, Style One
/ SNOWBALL FIGHT

Design No.:	Front — HW141 Sledging
	Reverse — HW141R Snowball Fight
Designer:	Walter Hayward
Issued:	1967 - by 1998
Combined with:	*Engine Pulling a Carriage*, HW17
	Pea Shooter, HW118R
	Reading, EC122
	Serving Tea, HW116R

Shape	U.S. $	Can. $	U.K. £	Aust. $
Albion cream jug	35.00	55.00	20.00	60.00
Albion jug, ½ pint	85.00	115.00	50.00	125.00
Albion jug, 1 pint	100.00	150.00	60.00	165.00
Albion teapot	50.00	70.00	30.00	75.00
Casino teacup	7.50	12.00	5.00	12.00
Divider dish	50.00	75.00	35.00	75.00
Don beaker	25.00	35.00	15.00	40.00
Don beaker, one handle	25.00	35.00	15.00	40.00
Don mug, one handle	10.00	15.00	6.50	18.00
Don mug, two handles	10.00	15.00	6.50	18.00
Egg box				
small	225.00	350.00	150.00	400.00
medium	300.00	450.00	200.00	500.00
large	375.00	550.00	250.00	600.00
Hug-a-mug, one handle				
Christmas 1988 - 1991	10.00	15.00	7.50	15.00
regular issue	10.00	15.00	7.50	15.00
Hug-a-mug, two handles				
Christmas 1988 - 1991	10.00	15.00	7.50	15.00
regular issue	10.00	15.00	7.50	15.00
Jaffa fruit saucer (plain)	15.00	20.00	10.00	25.00
Lamp	50.00	75.00	30.00	85.00
Malvern beaker	15.00	25.00	10.00	25.00
Money ball	10.00	15.00	7.50	15.00
Picture plaque, small	20.00	30.00	12.50	30.00
Savings book	15.00	22.50	10.00	22.50
Stratford straight beaker	15.00	25.00	10.00	25.00
Stratford teacup	7.50	12.00	5.00	12.00

* Indicates scene on divider dish.

Sledging, Style One (HW141)

Snowball Fight (HW141R)

Note: A Merry Christmas from Bunnykins was added to the hug-a-mugs as part of the Christmas set issued between 1988 - 1991. *Sledging*, Style One (HW141) was combined with *Reading* (EC122) on a money ball and *Engine Pulling a Carriage* (HW17) is combined with *Snowball Fight* (HW141R) on a Don mug with two handles.

Sleeping in a Rocking Chair (EC1)

SLEEPING IN A ROCKING CHAIR

Design No.:	EC1
Designer:	Barbara Vernon
Issued:	1937 to the present
Combined with:	*Bugler with Toy Donkey*, HW26R
	Dress Making, HW26
	Drummer, EC2
	Drummer and Bugler, EC126
	Feeding the Baby, HW13
	Footballer, HW13R
	Haymaking, HW29
	Hikers, EC124
	Hobby Horse, Style Two, EC121
	Lambeth Walk, Second Version, HW16
	Lunch Break, HW29R
	Playing with Cup and Spoon, EC6
	Playing with Doll and Pram, EC123
	Raising Hat, Style One, HW16R
	Raising Hat, Style Two, EC7
	Reading, EC122
	Sheltering Under an Umbrella, EC3
	Skipping, HW20R
	Swinging, HW20
	Trumpeter, EC5

Shape	U.S. $	Can. $	U.K. £	Aust. $
Albion sugar bowl	30.00	40.00	17.50	45.00
Beaker cover				
with signature	50.00	65.00	30.00	70.00
without signature	40.00	55.00	25.00	60.00
Casino sugar bowl, 30s				
with signature	150.00	225.00	100.00	250.00
without signature	125.00	200.00	85.00	225.00
Egg cup				
Style One				
with signature	40.00	55.00	25.00	60.00
without signature	30.00	40.00	20.00	45.00
Style Two	40.00	55.00	25.00	60.00
Style Three	N/I	15.00	5.00	19.95
Lid of hot water plate				
with signature	75.00	100.00	45.00	110.00
without signature	50.00	65.00	30.00	70.00

SMOKING IN THE DOORWAY

Design No.:	SF2
Designer:	Barbara Vernon
Issued:	1937 - by 1952
Combined with:	*Family at Breakfast*, HW12
	Fixing Braces, HW3
	Pulling on Trousers, HW2
	Reading the Times, HW2R

Smoking in the Doorway (SF2)

Shape	U.S. $	Can. $	U.K. £	Aust. $
Baby plate, oval, small	350.00	450.00	225.00	475.00
Baby plate, round, small	200.00	275.00	125.00	300.00
Candle holder	2,000.00	2,500.00	1,250.00	2,500.00
Casino jug, 24s	475.00	675.00	300.00	725.00
Casino saucer	75.00	100.00	50.00	125.00
Casino teapot, 30s	300.00	425.00	190.00	475.00
Cereal / oatmeal bowl	100.00	135.00	65.00	150.00
Don beaker, one handle	150.00	225.00	100.00	250.00
Hot water plate	200.00	275.00	125.00	300.00
Jaffa fruit saucer				
plain rim	95.00	135.00	60.00	150.00
wavy rim	125.00	175.00	80.00	200.00
Plate, 6 ½"	90.00	125.00	55.00	135.00
Plate, 7 ½"	100.00	135.00	65.00	145.00
Porridge plate	125.00	175.00	80.00	185.00

FINE WHITE CHINA

	U.S. $	Can. $	U.K. £	Aust. $
Plate, 7"	650.00	850.00	400.00	875.00

Note: This design should appear with the Barbara Vernon facsimile signature.

A very rare combination of a Bunnykins design
on a Series Ware shape.

SNOW SCENES THEME — Frank Endersby

Snow Scene, First Version (58)

SNOW SCENE

Design No.:   58 Snow Scene
Designer: Frank Endersby
Issued: 1995 - 2003

Shape	U.S. $	Can. $	U.K. £	Aust. $
Jaffa fruit saucer	15.00	20.00	10.00	25.00
Plate, 6 ½"	15.00	20.00	10.00	25.00
Plate, 8"	15.00	20.00	10.00	25.00

Building Snowman (59)

BUILDING SNOWMAN / SLEDGING, STYLE TWO

Design No.:   Front — 59 Building Snowman
                   Reverse — 60 Sledging
Designer: Frank Endersby
Issued: 1995 - 2003
Combined with: *Resting in Wheelbarrow*, (57)

Shape	U.S. $	Can. $	U.K. £	Aust. $
Hug-a-mug, one handle	10.00	15.00	7.50	15.00
Hug-a-mug, two handles	10.00	15.00	7.50	15.00
Divider dish	50.00	75.00	35.00	75.00
Malvern beaker	15.00	25.00	10.00	25.00
Money ball	10.00	15.00	7.50	15.00
Stratford teacup	7.50	12.00	5.00	12.00

* Indicates scene on divider dish.

Sledging, Style Two (60)

Note: **1.** Bold type in the listing tables indicate a current design on a current shape.
       2. N/I, Not issued individually. The item(s) will be found only in boxed sets in that market.

SOLDIERS MARCHING TO THE MUSIC /
SOLDIER MARCHING

Design No.:   Front — HW18 Soldiers Marching to the Music
                 Reverse — HW18R Soldier Marching
Designer: Walter Hayward after Barbara Vernon
Issued: By 1952 - 1967
Combined with: *Convalescing*, SF5
                 Lambeth Walk, Second Version, HW16

Shape	U.S. $	Can. $	U.K. £	Aust. $
Casino jug, 30s				
with signature	300.00	475.00	200.00	475.00
without signature	200.00	325.00	150.00	325.00
Casino saucer				
with signature	75.00	125.00	50.00	125.00
without signature	50.00	75.00	35.00	75.00
Casino teacup				
with signature	75.00	125.00	50.00	125.00
without signature	50.00	75.00	35.00	75.00
Casino teapot, 36s				
with signature	250.00	375.00	165.00	400.00
without signature	225.00	350.00	150.00	400.00
Don beaker				
with signature	65.00	85.00	40.00	90.00
without signature	35.00	45.00	20.00	50.00
Don beaker, one handle				
with signature	65.00	85.00	40.00	90.00
without signature	35.00	45.00	20.00	50.00
Don mug, one handle				
with signature	50.00	65.00	30.00	75.00
without signature	15.00	20.00	10.00	25.00
Don mug, two handles				
with signature	50.00	65.00	30.00	75.00
without signature	15.00	20.00	10.00	25.00
Jaffa fruit saucer (plain)				
with signature	50.00	65.00	30.00	70.00
without signature	30.00	40.00	20.00	45.00
Lid of hot water plate				
with signature	100.00	135.00	65.00	150.00
without signature	75.00	100.00	50.00	115.00
Plate, 6 ½"				
with signature	30.00	40.00	20.00	45.00
without signature	20.00	25.00	12.00	30.00

Soldiers Marching to the Music (HW18)

Soldier Marching (HW18R)

Space Rocket Launch (SF132)

SPACE ROCKET LAUNCH

Design No.:	SF132
Designer:	Walter Hayward
Issued:	1967 - by 1998

Shape	U.S. $	Can. $	U.K. £	Aust. $
Albion cream jug	35.00	55.00	20.00	60.00
Albion jug, 1 pint	100.00	150.00	60.00	165.00
Baby plate, round, small	20.00	27.50	12.50	30.00
Cake stand	150.00	250.00	100.00	300.00
Casino saucer	7.50	12.00	5.00	12.00
Cereal / oatmeal bowl	15.00	20.00	10.00	25.00
Hot water plate	75.00	100.00	45.00	110.00
Jaffa fruit saucer (plain)	15.00	20.00	10.00	25.00
Picture plaque, large	20.00	30.00	12.50	30.00
Plate 6 ½"	15.00	20.00	10.00	25.00
Plate 7 ½"	15.00	20.00	10.00	25.00
Plate 8"	15.00	20.00	10.00	25.00

SPRING CLEANING

Design No.:	LF14
Designer:	Walter Hayward
Issued:	By 1952 - 1970

Shape	U.S. $	Can. $	U.K. £	Aust. $
Baby plate, oval, large				
with signature	200.00	275.00	125.00	300.00
without signature	150.00	200.00	95.00	225.00
Baby plate, round, large				
with signature	100.00	135.00	65.00	150.00
without signature	75.00	100.00	50.00	125.00
Bread and butter plate				
with signature	250.00	400.00	175.00	400.00
without signature	200.00	325.00	150.00	325.00
Cereal / oatmeal bowl				
with signature	35.00	45.00	20.00	50.00
without signature	25.00	35.00	15.00	40.00
Hot water plate				
with signature	125.00	165.00	80.00	175.00
without signature	100.00	135.00	65.00	150.00
Plate, 8 ½"				
with signature	75.00	100.00	45.00	115.00
without signature	25.00	35.00	15.00	45.00
Porridge plate				
with signature	110.00	175.00	70.00	200.00
without signature	85.00	125.00	55.00	150.00

Spring Cleaning (LF14)

SPRING CLEANING THEME — Frank Endersby

DUSTING

Design No.:	19 Dusting
Designer:	Frank Endersby
Issued:	1995 to the present

Shape	U.S. $	Can. $	U.K. £	Aust. $
Baby plate, round, small	N/I	46.00	14.00	62.95
Plate, 6 ½"	N/I	25.00	8.00	34.95
Plate, 8"	N/I	35.00	11.00	49.95

Beating Carpet (20)

BEATING CARPET / RESTING, Style Two

Design No.:	Front — 20 Beating Carpet
	Reverse — 21 Resting, Style Two
Designer:	Frank Endersby
Issued:	1995 to the present
Combined with:	*Eating Apples, (3)

Shape	U.S. $	Can. $	U.K. £	Aust. $
Hug-a-mug, one handle	30.00	33.00	11.00	49.95
Hug-a-mug, two handles	32.50	39.00	12.00	56.95
Divider dish	50.00	75.00	35.00	75.00

* Indicates scene on divider dish.

Resting (21)

Note: 1. Bold type in the listing tables indicate a current design on a current shape.
2. N/I, Not issued individually. The item(s) will be found only in boxed sets in that market.

Storytime (SF110)

STORYTIME

Design No.: SF110
Designer: Walter Hayward
Issued: 1959 - 1967

Shape	U.S. $	Can. $	U.K. £	Aust. $
Baby plate, round, small	150.00	200.00	100.00	225.00
Casino Jug, 36s	275.00	400.00	175.00	450.00
Casino saucer	50.00	65.00	30.00	75.00
Cereal / oatmeal bowl	90.00	125.00	55.00	135.00
Hot water plate	150.00	200.00	100.00	225.00
Plate 6 ½"	65.00	85.00	40.00	95.00
Plate 7 ½"	75.00	100.00	45.00	110.00
Plate 8"	75.00	100.00	45.00	110.00

Casino Cup, *Fishing in the Goldfish Bowl* (HW3R)

SWINGING / SKIPPING

Design No.:	Front — HW20 Swinging
	Reverse — HW20R Skipping
Designer:	Walter Hayward
Issued:	By 1952 - 1967
Combined with:	*Dress Making*, HW26
	Holding Hat and Coat, EC4
	Mr. Piggly's Store, SF14
	Nipped by a Crab, HW22R
	Row Boat, HW21
	Sleeping in a Rocking Chair, EC1

Swinging (HW20)

Shape	U.S. $	Can. $	U.K. £	Aust. $
Casino jug, 36s				
with signature	250.00	400.00	175.00	425.00
without signature	175.00	275.00	125.00	300.00
Casino saucer				
with signature	75.00	125.00	50.00	125.00
without signature	50.00	75.00	35.00	75.00
Casino sugar bowl, 36s				
with signature	175.00	275.00	125.00	325.00
without signature	125.00	200.00	85.00	225.00
Casino teacup				
with signature	75.00	125.00	50.00	125.00
without signature	50.00	75.00	35.00	75.00
Casino teapot, 36s				
with signature	250.00	375.00	165.00	400.00
without signature	225.00	350.00	150.00	375.00
Divider dish	50.00	75.00	35.00	75.00
Don beaker				
with signature	65.00	85.00	40.00	90.00
without signature	35.00	45.00	20.00	50.00
Don beaker, one handle				
with signature	65.00	85.00	40.00	90.00
without signature	35.00	45.00	20.00	50.00
Don mug, one handle				
with signature	50.00	65.00	30.00	75.00
without signature	15.00	20.00	10.00	25.00
Don mug, two handles				
with signature	50.00	65.00	30.00	75.00
without signature	15.00	20.00	10.00	25.00
Egg box				
small	225.00	350.00	150.00	400.00
Jaffa fruit saucer (plain)				
with signature	50.00	65.00	30.00	70.00
without signature	30.00	40.00	20.00	45.00
Lid of hot water plate				
with signature	100.00	135.00	65.00	150.00
without signature	75.00	100.00	50.00	115.00
Plate, 6 ½"				
with signature	30.00	40.00	20.00	45.00
without signature	20.00	25.00	12.00	30.00

Skipping (HW20R)
Casino cup, *Fishing in the Goldfish Bowl* (HW3R)

Note: A Casino jug combines *Swinging*, (HW20) with *Rowboat* (HW21).

Television Time (SF112)

TELEVISION TIME

Design No.:   SF112
Designer: Walter Hayward
Issued: 1959 - by 1998

Shape	U.S. $	Can. $	U.K. £	Aust. $
Baby plate, round, small	20.00	27.50	12.50	30.00
Cake stand	150.00	250.00	100.00	300.00
Casino saucer	7.50	12.00	5.00	12.00
Cereal / oatmeal bowl	15.00	20.00	10.00	25.00
Hot water plate	75.00	100.00	45.00	110.00
Jaffa fruit saucer				
plain	15.00	20.00	10.00	25.00
wavy	35.00	55.00	20.00	60.00
Picture plaque, large	20.00	30.00	12.50	30.00
Plate, 6 ½"	15.00	20.00	10.00	25.00
Plate, 7 ½"	15.00	20.00	10.00	25.00

TENNIS

A boxed Bunnykins for Grown Ups Set containing a cereal bowl and a hug-a-mug with one handle with the *Aerobics/Jogging* design, a 6" plate with the *Aeroplane* design, an 8" plate with the *Breakfast Time* design and a cereal bowl with the *Tennis* design was distributed mainly in the U.S.A.

Design No.:   None
Designer: Walter Hayward
Issued: 1986 - 1988
Series: Bunnykins for Grown-Ups

Shape	U.S. $	Can. $	U.K. £	Aust. $
Cereal / oatmeal bowl	40.00	60.00	25.00	60.00
Complete set (M.I.B.)	200.00	300.00	100.00	300.00

Tennis

Note: See also *Aerobics / Jogging* and *Aeroplane* page 12 and *Breakfast Time* page *30*.

TICKET QUEUE

Design No.:	SF109
Designer:	Walter Hayward
Issued:	1959 - by 1998

Shape	U.S. $	Can. $	U.K. £	Aust. $
Baby plate, round, small	20.00	27.50	12.50	30.00
Casino saucer	7.50	12.00	5.00	12.00
Cereal / oatmeal bowl	15.00	20.00	10.00	25.00
Hot water plate	75.00	100.00	45.00	110.00
Picture plaque, large	20.00	30.00	12.50	30.00
Plate, 6 ½"	15.00	20.00	10.00	25.00
Plate, 7 ½"	15.00	20.00	10.00	25.00
Plate, 8"	15.00	20.00	10.00	25.00
Plate, 10 ½"	20.00	25.00	12.00	30.00

Ticket Queue (SF109)

Toast for Tea Today (SF23)

TOAST FOR TEA TODAY

Design No.:	SF23
Designer:	Walter Hayward
Issued:	1954 - 1967
Combined with:	*Dress Making*, HW26
	Dressing Up, First Version, SF22
	Haymaking, HW29
	Mr. Piggly's Stores, SF14
	Windy Day, HW27

Shape	U.S. $	Can. $	U.K. £	Aust. $
Baby plate, round, small				
with signature	50.00	65.00	30.00	70.00
without signature	30.00	45.00	20.00	45.00
Casino saucer				
with signature	75.00	125.00	50.00	125.00
without signature	50.00	80.00	35.00	80.00
Casino teapot, 24s				
with signature	375.00	550.00	250.00	600.00
without signature	300.00	450.00	200.00	500.00
Casino teapot, 30s				
with signature	325.00	500.00	225.00	550.00
without signature	250.00	400.00	175.00	450.00
Cereal / oatmeal bowl				
with signature	35.00	45.00	20.00	50.00
without signature	25.00	35.00	15.00	40.00
Hot water plate				
with signature	125.00	165.00	80.00	175.00
without signature	100.00	135.00	65.00	150.00
Jaffa fruit saucer (plain)				
with signature	50.00	65.00	30.00	70.00
without signature	30.00	40.00	20.00	45.00
Plate, 6 ½"				
with signature	30.00	40.00	20.00	45.00
without signature	20.00	25.00	12.00	30.00
Porridge Bowl	85.00	125.00	55.00	150.00

Top Hat (HW14R)

TOP HAT

Design No.:	HW14R
Designer:	Barbara Vernon
Issued:	By 1937 - 1967
Combined with:	*Embracing at a Window*, HW5
	Feeding the Baby, HW13
	Lambeth Walk, HW16
	Pressing Trousers, HW14

Shape	U.S. $	Can. $	U.K. £	Aust. $
Casino jug, 36s				
with signature	150.00	225.00	100.00	225.00
without signature	125.00	200.00	85.00	200.00
Casino jug, 42s				
with signature	125.00	200.00	90.00	200.00
without signature	100.00	150.00	70.00	150.00
Casino teacup				
with signature	15.00	25.00	10.00	25.00
without signature	7.50	12.00	5.00	12.00
Don beaker				
with signature	50.00	65.00	30.00	75.00
without signature	25.00	35.00	15.00	40.00
Don beaker, one handle				
with signature	50.00	65.00	30.00	75.00
without signature	25.00	35.00	15.00	40.00
Don mug, one handle				
with signature	40.00	55.00	25.00	60.00
without signature	10.00	15.00	6.50	18.00
Don mug, two handles				
with signature	40.00	55.00	25.00	60.00
without signature	10.00	15.00	6.50	18.00
FINE WHITE CHINA				
Saucer	300.00	400.00	200.00	425.00
Teacup	300.00	400.00	200.00	425.00

TOPPLING THE FRUIT CART

Design No.:	SF134
Designer:	Walter Hayward
Issued:	1967 - by 1998

Shape	U.S. $	Can. $	U.K. £	Aust. $
Albion jug, 1 pint	100.00	150.00	60.00	165.00
Baby plate, round, small	20.00	27.50	12.50	30.00
Cake stand	150.00	250.00	100.00	300.00
Casino saucer	7.50	12.00	5.00	12.00
Cereal / oatmeal bowl	15.00	20.00	10.00	25.00
Hot water plate	75.00	100.00	45.00	110.00
Jaffa fruit saucer (plain)	15.00	20.00	10.00	25.00
Picture plaque, large	20.00	30.00	12.50	30.00
Plate, 6 ½"	15.00	20.00	10.00	25.00
Plate, 7 ½"	15.00	20.00	10.00	25.00
Plate, 8"	15.00	20.00	10.00	25.00

Toppling the Fruit Cart (SF134)

TOY SHOP

Design No.:	SF114
Designer:	Walter Hayward after Barbara Vernon
Issued:	1959 - 1967

Shape	U.S. $	Can. $	U.K. £	Aust. $
Baby plate, round, small	30.00	40.00	20.00	45.00
Casino saucer	50.00	75.00	35.00	75.00
Cereal / oatmeal bowl	25.00	35.00	15.00	40.00
Hot water plate	100.00	135.00	65.00	150.00
Jaffa fruit saucer (plain)	30.00	40.00	20.00	45.00
Plate, 6 ½"	20.00	25.00	12.00	30.00
Plate, 7 ½"	25.00	35.00	15.00	45.00

Toy Shop (SF114)

A busy Hug-a-mug

TRAIN STATION THEME — Frank Endersby

WAITING FOR TRAIN

Design No.:   49 Waiting for Train
Designer: Frank Endersby
Issued: 1995 - 2003

Shape	U.S. $	Can. $	U.K. £	Aust. $
Baby plate, round, small	20.00	27.50	12.50	30.00
Jaffa fruit saucer	15.00	20.00	10.00	25.00
Plate, 6 ½"	15.00	20.00	10.00	25.00
Plate, 8"	15.00	20.00	10.00	25.00

Ticket Office (50)

TICKET OFFICE / SITTING ON SUITCASE

Design No.:   Front — 50 Ticket Office
                Reverse — 51 Sitting on Suitcase
Designer: Frank Endersby
Issued: 1995 - 2003

Shape	U.S. $	Can. $	U.K. £	Aust. $
Hug-a-mug, one handle	10.00	15.00	7.50	15.00
Hug-a-mug, two handles	10.00	15.00	7.50	15.00

Note: 1. Bold type in the listing tables indicate a current design on a current shape.
       2. N/I, Not issued individually. The item(s) will be found only in boxed sets in that market.

Sitting on Suitcase (51)

TRIMMING THE TREE
CHRISTMAS TREE ORNAMENT

Design No.:	Front — CT80 Trimming the Tree
	Reverse — CT81 Christmas 1994
Designer:	Colin Twinn
Issued:	1994 - 1994
Series:	Christmas Tree Ornaments

Shape	U.S. $	Can. $	U.K. £	Aust. $
Christmas tree ornaments	15.00	25.00	10.00	30.00

Trimming the Tree (CT80)

Note: For other Christmas tree ornaments in this series see pages 40, 42, 78 and 141.

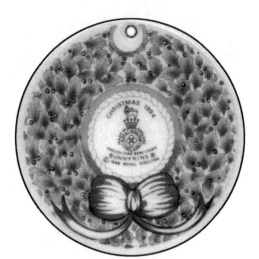

Trimming the Tree (CT81)

Trumpeter (EC5)

TRUMPETER

Design No.:	EC5
Designer:	Barbara Vernon
Issued:	1937 to the present
Combined with:	*Bedtime with Dollies*, EC125
	Drummer, EC2
	Drummer and Bugler, EC126
	Family Going out on Washing Day, HW8
	Feeding the Baby, HW13
	Hat Shop, HW28
	Hikers, EC124
	Hobby Horse, Style One, HW24R
	Hobby Horse, Style Two, EC121
	Holding Hat and Coat, EC4
	Playing with Cup and Spoon, EC6
	Raising Hat, Style Two, EC7
	Reading, EC122
	Rocking Horse, HW24
	Sheltering Under an Umbrella, EC3
	Sleeping in a Rocking Chair, EC1
	Washing Day, HW8R

Shape	U.S. $	Can. $	U.K. £	Aust. $
Albion sugar bowl	30.00	40.00	17.50	45.00
Beaker cover				
with signature	50.00	65.00	30.00	70.00
without signature	40.00	55.00	25.00	60.00
Casino sugar bowl, 36s				
with signature	100.00	150.00	65.00	175.00
without signature	80.00	115.00	50.00	125.00
Egg cup				
Style One				
with signature	40.00	55.00	25.00	60.00
without signature	30.00	40.00	20.00	45.00

Shape	U.S. $	Can. $	U.K. £	Aust. $
Egg cup				
Style Two				
with signature	50.00	65.00	30.00	70.00
without signature	40.00	55.00	25.00	60.00
Style Three	N/I	15.00	5.00	20.00
Lid of hot water plate				
with signature	75.00	100.00	45.00	110.00
without signature	50.00	65.00	30.00	70.00
Money ball	35.00	40.00	15.00	65.00

TUG OF WAR

Design No.:	LF1
Designer:	Barbara Vernon
Issued:	By 1937 - by 1952

Shape	U.S. $	Can. $	U.K. £	Aust. $
Bread / butter plate, handles				
with signature	500.00	650.00	300.00	675.00
without signature	400.00	525.00	250.00	550.00
Plate, 8 ½"				
with signature	225.00	300.00	150.00	325.00
without signature	175.00	225.00	115.00	250.00
Porridge plate				
with signature	300.00	400.00	200.00	425.00
without signature	250.00	325.00	150.00	350.00
FINE WHITE CHINA				
Bread and butter plate	800.00	1,000.00	500.00	1,100.00

Tug of War (LF1)

UNRAVELLING THE KNITTING / TRYING ON KNITTING

Design No.:	Front — HW119 Unravelling the Knitting
	Reverse — HW119R Trying on Knitting
Designer:	Walter Hayward
Issued:	1959 - 1992
Combined with:	*Bedtime with Dollies*, EC125
	Broken Umbrella, HW27R
	Windy Day, HW27

Shape	U.S. $	Can. $	U.K. £	Aust. $
Albion cream jug	35.00	55.00	20.00	60.00
Albion jug, ½ pint	85.00	115.00	50.00	125.00
Albion jug, 1 pint	100.00	150.00	60.00	165.00
Albion teapot	50.00	70.00	30.00	75.00
Cake stand	150.00	250.00	100.00	300.00
Casino jug, 30s	150.00	250.00	100.00	275.00
Casino jug, 36s	125.00	200.00	85.00	225.00
Casino jug, 42s	100.00	150.00	70.00	175.00
Casino saucer	7.50	12.00	5.00	12.00
Casino sugar bowl, 36s	100.00	150.00	65.00	175.00
Casino teacup	7.50	12.00	5.00	12.00
Casino teapot, 30s	150.00	225.00	100.00	250.00
Don beaker	25.00	35.00	15.00	40.00
Don beaker, one handle	25.00	35.00	15.00	40.00
Don mug, one handle	10.00	15.00	6.50	18.00
Don mug, two handles	10.00	15.00	6.50	18.00
Egg box				
small	225.00	350.00	150.00	400.00
medium	300.00	450.00	200.00	500.00
large	375.00	550.00	250.00	600.00
Hug-a-mug, one handle	10.00	15.00	7.50	15.00
Hug-a-mug, two handles	10.00	15.00	7.50	15.00
Jaffa fruit saucer (plain)	15.00	20.00	10.00	25.00
Lamp	50.00	75.00	30.00	85.00
Lid of hot water plate	50.00	65.00	30.00	70.00
Malvern beaker / mug	15.00	25.00	10.00	25.00
Money ball	10.00	15.00	7.50	15.00
Picture plaque, small	20.00	30.00	12.50	30.00
Plate, 6 ½"	15.00	20.00	10.00	25.00
Savings book	15.00	22.50	10.00	22.50
Stratford straight beaker	15.00	25.00	10.00	25.00
Stratford teacup	7.50	12.00	5.00	12.00

Unravelling the Knitting (HW119)

Trying on Knitting (HW119R)

Note: Retirement dates are all approximate. When a design is retired all remaining stocks of retired litho prints are used until exhausted.

Visiting the Cottage, First Version (SF6a)

VISITING THE COTTAGE
First Version

Design No.: SF6a
Designer: Barbara Vernon
Issued: By 1940 - c.1949

Shape	U.S. $	Can. $	U.K. £	Aust. $
Baby plate, round, small	350.00	450.00	225.00	475.00
Baby plate, round, large	400.00	525.00	250.00	550.00
Bread and butter plate	500.00	650.00	300.00	675.00
Hot water plate	375.00	500.00	250.00	550.00
Plate, 6 ½"	225.00	300.00	150.00	325.00
Plate, 7 ½"	225.00	300.00	150.00	325.00
Plate, 8 ½"	225.00	300.00	150.00	325.00
Porridge plate	300.00	400.00	200.00	425.00

Note: This design should appear with the Barbara Vernon facsimile signature.

VISITING THE COTTAGE
Second Version

Design No.: SF6b
Designer: Barbara Vernon
Issued: c.1949 - 1952

Shape	U.S. $	Can. $	U.K. £	Aust. $
Baby plate, round, small	200.00	275.00	125.00	300.00
Baby plate, round, large	250.00	325.00	150.00	350.00
Bread / butter plate	400.00	525.00	250.00	550.00
Casino saucer	75.00	100.00	50.00	125.00
Casino jug, 24s	475.00	675.00	300.00	725.00
Cereal / oatmeal bowl	100.00	135.00	65.00	150.00
Jaffa fruit saucer				
plain rim	95.00	135.00	65.00	150.00
wavy rim	125.00	175.00	80.00	185.00
Plate, 6 ½"	90.00	125.00	55.00	135.00
Plate, 7 ½"	100.00	135.00	65.00	145.00
Plate, 8 ½"	100.00	135.00	65.00	145.00
Porridge plate	125.00	175.00	80.00	185.00

Visiting the Cottage, Second Version (SF6b)

Note: This design should appear with the Barbara Vernon facsimile signature.

WASHING DAY

Design No.:	HW8R
Designer:	Barbara Vernon
Issued:	By 1937 - by 1967
Combined with:	*Family at Breakfast*, HW12
	Family Going out on Washing Day, HW8
	Sheltering Under an Umbrella, EC3
	Trumpeter, EC5

Washing Day (HW8R)

Shape	U.S. $	Can. $	U.K. £	Aust. $
Casino sugar bowl, 36s				
with signature	175.00	275.00	125.00	325.00
without signature	125.00	200.00	85.00	225.00
Casino teacup				
with signature	75.00	125.00	50.00	125.00
without signature	50.00	75.00	35.00	25.00
Casino teapot, 30s				
with signature	325.00	500.00	225.00	550.00
without signature	250.00	400.00	175.00	450.00
Casino teapot, 36s				
with signature	250.00	375.00	165.00	400.00
without signature	225.00	350.00	150.00	375.00
Don beaker, one handle				
with signature	65.00	85.00	40.00	90.00
without signature	35.00	45.00	20.00	50.00
Don mug, one handle				
with signature	50.00	65.00	30.00	75.00
without signature	15.00	20.00	10.00	25.00
Don mug, two handles				
with signature	50.00	65.00	30.00	75.00
without signature	15.00	20.00	10.00	25.00

Washing in the Open Air (HW10R)

WASHING IN THE OPEN AIR

Design No.:	HW10R
Designer:	Barbara Vernon
Issued:	By 1937 - by 1967
Combined with:	*Asleep in the Open Air*, HW10
	Convalescing, SF5
	Family with Pram, Style One, HW15
	Feeding the Baby, HW13
	Gardening, Style One, HW9
	Leapfrog, HW12R

Shape	U.S. $	Can. $	U.K. £	Aust. $
Casino jug, 30s				
with signature	375.00	525.00	235.00	575.00
without signature	300.00	425.00	190.00	475.00
Casino jug, 36s				
with signature	300.00	425.00	190.00	475.00
without signature	275.00	400.00	175.00	450.00
Casino sugar bowl, 30s				
with signature	200.00	275.00	125.00	300.00
without signature	125.00	175.00	80.00	200.00
Casino teacup				
with signature	75.00	100.00	50.00	125.00
without signature	50.00	65.00	30.00	75.00
Don beaker, one handle				
with signature	150.00	225.00	65.00	250.00
without signature	100.00	150.00	50.00	165.00
Don mug, one handle				
with signature	75.00	100.00	50.00	125.00
without signature	35.00	55.00	20.00	60.00
Don mug, two handles				
with signature	75.00	100.00	50.00	125.00
without signature	35.00	55.00	20.00	60.00

WASHING UP THEME – Colin Twinn

First Variation, Large Size

Design No.:	CT15 Washing Up
Designer:	Colin Twinn
Issued:	1990 - 1993

Shape	U.S. $	Can. $	U.K. £	Aust. $
Albion jug, 1 pint	100.00	150.00	60.00	165.00
Baby bowl, round, small	20.00	27.50	12.50	30.00
Cake stand	150.00	250.00	100.00	300.00
Picture plaque, large	20.00	30.00	12.50	30.00
Plate, 6½"	15.00	20.00	10.00	25.00
Plate, 8"	15.00	20.00	10.00	25.00

Washing Up, First Variation (CT15)

Washing Up, Second Variation (CT32)

Second Variation, Small Size / SPLASHING AT SINK

Design No.:	Front — CT32 Washing Up
	Reverse — CT33 Splashing at Sink
Designer:	Colin Twinn
Issued:	1990 - 1993
Combined with:	*Ice Cream Seller*, First Variation, CT5
	Pushing the Wheelbarrow, CT3

Shape	U.S. $	Can. $	U.K. £	Aust. $
Albion teapot	50.00	70.00	30.00	75.00
Divider dish	75.00	125.00	50.00	125.00
Hug-a-mug, two handles	10.00	15.00	7.50	15.00
Lamp	50.00	75.00	30.00	85.00
Malvern beaker	15.00	25.00	10.00	25.00
Money ball	10.00	15.00	7.50	15.00
Savings book	15.00	22.50	10.00	22.50

Splashing at Sink (CT33)

Watering the Flowers (SF15)

WATERING THE FLOWERS

Design No.:	SF15
Designer:	Walter Hayward after Barbara Vernon
Issued:	By 1952 - 1967
Combined with:	*Pressing Trousers*, HW14
	Lasso Games, HW117

Shape	U.S. $	Can. $	U.K. £	Aust. $
Baby plate, round, small				
with signature	50.00	65.00	30.00	70.00
without signature	30.00	40.00	20.00	45.00
Casino jug, 30s				
with signature	300.00	475.00	200.00	475.00
without signature	225.00	325.00	150.00	325.00
Casino saucer				
with signature	75.00	125.00	50.00	125.00
without signature	50.00	75.00	35.00	75.00
Casino teapot, 24s				
with signature	375.00	550.00	250.00	600.00
without signature	300.00	450.00	200.00	500.00
Casino teapot, 30s				
with signature	325.00	500.00	225.00	550.00
without signature	250.00	400.00	175.00	450.00
Cereal / oatmeal bowl				
with signature	35.00	45.00	20.00	50.00
without signature	25.00	35.00	15.00	40.00
Hot water plate				
with signature	125.00	165.00	80.00	175.00
without signature	100.00	135.00	65.00	150.00
Jaffa fruit saucer (plain)				
with signature	50.00	65.00	30.00	70.00
without signature	30.00	40.00	20.00	45.00
Plate, 6 ½				
with signature	30.00	40.00	20.00	45.00
without signature	20.00	25.00	12.00	30.00
Plate, 7 ½"				
with signature	65.00	85.00	40.00	95.00
without signature	25.00	35.00	15.00	45.00

WEDDING

Design No.:	LFd
Designer:	Barbara Vernon
Issued:	1937 - by 1952
Combined with:	*Family at Breakfast,* HW12
	Pressing Trousers, HW14
	Proposal, HW11
	Raising Hat, Style One, HW16R

Shape	U.S. $	Can. $	U.K. £	Aust. $
Baby plate, oval, small	350.00	450.00	225.00	475.00
Baby plate, round, large	400.00	525.00	250.00	550.00
Casino teapot, 24s	600.00	8000.00	375.00	850.00
Casino teapot, 36s	450.00	600.00	275.00	650.00
Hot water plate	375.00	500.00	250.00	550.00
Plate, 7 ½"	375.00	500.00	250.00	550.00
Plate, 8 ½"	225.00	300.00	150.00	325.00
Porridge plate	250.00	325.00	150.00	350.00
FINE WHITE CHINA				
Plate, 5"	650.00	850.00	400.00	875.00
Plate 7"	650.00	850.00	400.00	875.00

Wedding (LFd)

Note: This design should appear with the Barbara Vernon facsimile signature.

The Casino teapot (24s), combining *Proposal* (HW11) and *Wedding* (LFd), exists with a silver rimmed lid and a crackle finish, this is considered extremely rare.

WHEELBARROW RACE , Style One / CRICKETER

Wheelbarrow Race, Style One (HW22)

Cricketer (HW22R)

Design No.:   Front — HW22 Wheelbarrow Race
              Reverse — HW22R Cricketer
Designer: Walter Hayward
Issued: By 1952 - by 1998
Combined with: *Asleep in the Open Air*, HW10
              Baking, SF19

Bedtime with Dollies, EC125
Drummer, EC2
Holding Hat and Coat, EC4
Nipped by a Crab, HW121R
Pea Shooter, HW118R
Row Boat, HW21

Shape	U.S. $	Can. $	U.K. £	Aust. $
Albion cream jug	35.00	55.00	20.00	60.00
Albion jug, ½ pint	85.00	115.00	50.00	125.00
Albion jug, 1 pint	100.00	150.00	60.00	165.00
Albion teapot	50.00	70.00	30.00	75.00
Casino jug, 24s				
with signature	300.00	475.00	200.00	475.00
without signature	175.00	275.00	125.00	300.00
Casino jug, 30s				
with signature	250.00	400.00	175.00	425.00
without signature	150.00	250.00	100.00	250.00
Casino jug, 42s				
with signature	150.00	225.00	100.00	225.00
without signature	100.00	150.00	70.00	150.00
Casino saucer				
with signature	15.00	25.00	10.00	25.00
without signature	7.50	12.00	5.00	12.00
Casino sugar bowl, 30s				
with signature	150.00	225.00	100.00	250.00
without signature	125.00	200.00	85.00	225.00
Casino teacup				
with signature	15.00	25.00	10.00	25.00
without signature	7.50	12.00	5.00	12.00
Casino teapot, 30s				
with signature	250.00	375.00	165.00	400.00
without signature	150.00	225.00	100.00	250.00
Casino teapot, 36s				
with signature	250.00	375.00	165.00	400.00
without signature	150.00	225.00	100.00	250.00
Divider dish	50.00	75.00	35.00	75.00

Shape	U.S. $	Can. $	U.K. £	Aust. $
Don beaker				
with signature	50.00	65.00	30.00	75.00
without signature	25.00	35.00	15.00	40.00
Don beaker, one handle				
with signature	50.00	65.00	30.00	75.00
without signature	25.00	35.00	15.00	40.00
Don mug, one handle				
with signature	40.00	55.00	25.00	60.00
without signature	10.00	15.00	6.50	18.00
Don mug, two handles				
with signature	40.00	55.00	25.00	60.00
without signature	10.00	15.00	6.50	18.00
Egg box				
small	225.00	350.00	150.00	400.00
medium	300.00	450.00	200.00	500.00
large	375.00	550.00	250.00	600.00
Hug-a-mug, one handle	10.00	15.00	7.50	15.00
Hug-a-mug, two handles	10.00	15.00	7.50	15.00
Jaffa fruit saucer (plain)	15.00	20.00	10.00	25.00
Lamp	50.00	75.00	30.00	85.00
Lid of hot water plate	50.00	65.00	30.00	70.00
Malvern beaker	15.00	25.00	10.00	25.00
Money ball	10.00	15.00	7.50	15.00
Picture plaque, small	20.00	30.00	12.50	30.00
Plate, 6 ½"				
with signature	25.00	35.00	15.00	40.00
without signature	15.00	20.00	10.00	25.00
Savings book	15.00	22.50	10.00	22.50
Stratford teacup	7.50	12.00	5.00	12.00

WHEELBARROW RACE
Style Two

Design No.:	CT1
Designer:	Colin Twinn
Issued:	1988 - 1993
Combined with:	*Pushing the Wheelbarrow*, CT3

Shape	U.S. $	Can. $	U.K. £	Aust. $
Albion jug, ½ jug	85.00	115.00	50.00	125.00
Albion jug, 1 pint	100.00	150.00	60.00	165.00
Baby plate, round, small	20.00	27.50	12.50	30.00
Cake stand	150.00	250.00	100.00	300.00
Cereal / oatmeal bowl	15.00	20.00	10.00	25.00
Jaffa fruit saucer	15.00	20.00	10.00	25.00
Picture plaque, large	20.00	30.00	12.50	30.00
Plate, 6 ½"	15.00	20.00	10.00	15.00
Plate, 8"	15.00	20.00	10.00	15.00

Wheelbarrow Race, Style Two (CT1)

PUSHING THE WHEELBARROW

Design No.:	CT3
Designer:	Colin Twinn
Issued:	1988 - 1993
Combined with:	*Bunnies in the Bath*, Second Version, CT34
	Ice Cream Seller, First Variation, CT5
	Picking Daisies, CT4
	Splashing at Sink, CT33
	Washing Up, CT32
	Wheelbarrow Race, Style Two, CT1

Shape	U.S. $	Can. $	U.K. £	Aust. $
Albion sugar bowl	30.00	40.00	17.50	45.00
Albion teapot	50.00	70.00	30.00	75.00
Egg cup				
Style Three	10.00	15.00	7.50	18.00
Hug-a-mug, one handle	10.00	15.00	7.50	15.00
Hug-a-mug, two handles	10.00	15.00	7.50	15.00
Lamp	50.00	75.00	30.00	85.00
Malvern beaker	15.00	25.00	10.00	25.00
Stratford teacup	7.50	12.00	5.00	12.00

Pushing the Wheelbarrow (CT3)

WINDY DAY / BROKEN UMBRELLA

Windy Day (HW27)

Broken Umbrella (HW27R)

Design No.:	Front — HW27 Windy Day
	Reverse — HW27R Broken Umbrella
Designer:	Walter Hayward
Issued:	1952 - by 1998
Combined with:	*Apple Picking,* SF25
	Dress Making, HW26

Drummer, EC2
Toast for Tea Today, SF23
Trying on Knitting, HW119R
Playing with Doll and Teddy, HW120R
Unravelling the Knitting, HW119

Shape	U.S. $	Can. $	U.K. £	Aust. $
Albion cream jug	35.00	55.00	20.00	60.00
Albion jug, 1 pint	100.00	150.00	60.00	165.00
Albion jug, ½ pint	85.00	115.00	50.00	125.00
Albion teapot	50.00	70.00	30.00	75.00
Casino jug, 36s				
with signature	175.00	275.00	125.00	275.00
without signature	125.00	200.00	85.00	200.00
Casino jug, 42s				
with signature	150.00	225.00	100.00	225.00
without signature	100.00	150.00	70.00	150.00
Casino saucer				
with signature	15.00	25.00	10.00	25.00
without signature	7.50	12.00	5.00	12.00
Casino teacup				
with signature	15.00	25.00	10.00	25.00
without signature	7.50	12.00	5.00	12.00
Casino teapot, 24s				
with signature	275.00	400.00	175.00	450.00
without signature	175.00	275.00	125.00	325.00
Casino teapot, 36s				
with signature	250.00	375.00	165.00	400.00
without signature	150.00	225.00	100.00	225.00
Divider dish	50.00	75.00	35.00	75.00
Don beaker				
with signature	50.00	65.00	30.00	75.00
without signature	25.00	35.00	15.00	40.00
Don beaker, one handle				
with signature	50.00	65.00	30.00	75.00

Shape	U.S. $	Can. $	U.K. £	Aust. $
Don Beaker, One handle				
without signature	25.00	35.00	15.00	40.00
Don mug, one handle				
with signature	40.00	55.00	25.00	60.00
without signature	10.00	15.00	6.50	18.00
Don mug, two handles				
with signature	40.00	55.00	25.00	60.00
without signature	1o.00	15.00	6.50	18.00
Egg box				
small	225.00	350.00	150.00	400.00
medium	300.00	450.00	200.00	500.00
large	375.00	550.00	250.00	600.00
Hug-a-mug, one handle	10.00	15.00	7.50	15.00
Hug-a-mug, two handles	10.00	15.00	7.50	15.00
Jaffa fruit saucer (plain)				
with signature	25.00	35.00	20.00	40.00
without signature	15.00	20.00	10.00	25.00
Lamp	50.00	75.00	30.00	85.00
Lid of hot water plate	50.00	65.00	30.00	70.00
Malvern beaker	15.00	25.00	10.00	25.00
Money ball	10.00	15.00	7.50	15.00
Picture plaque, small	20.00	30.00	12.50	30.00
Plate, 6 ½"				
with signature	25.00	35.00	15.00	40.00
without signature	15.00	20.00	10.00	25.00
Savings book	15.00	22.50	10.00	22.50
Stratford straight beaker	15.00	25.00	10.00	25.00
Stratford teacup	7.50	12.00	5.00	12.00

Note: *Toast for Tea Today* (SF23) and *Dress Making* (HW25) are combined with *Windy Day* (HW27) on the Casino teapot.

WINNING POST

Design No.:	LF106			
Designer:	Walter Hayward after Barbara Vernon			
Issued:	1959 - 1970			

Shape	U.S. $	Can. $	U.K. £	Aust. $
Baby plate, round, small	150.00	200.00	100.00	225.00
Baby plate, round, large	200.00	275.00	125.00	300.00
Plate, 8 ½"	75.00	100.00	45.00	110.00
Porridge plate	100.00	135.00	65.00	145.00

Winning Post (LF106)

Xmas Menu (LF8)

XMAS MENU

Design No.:	LF8			
Designer:	Barbara Vernon			
Issued:	1940 - by 1952			

Shape	U.S. $	Can. $	U.K. £	Aust. $
Baby plate, oval , large				
with signature	500.00	650.00	320.00	675.00
without signature	450.00	600.00	275.00	625.00
Baby plate, round, large				
with signature	400.00	525.00	250.00	550.00
without signature	350.00	450.00	225.00	475.00
Bread and butter plate				
with signature	500.00	650.00	300.00	675.00
without signature	400.00	525.00	250.00	550.00
Cereal / oatmeal bowl				
with signature	200.00	275.00	125.00	300.00
without signature	175.00	225.00	110.00	250.00
Plate, 8 ½"				
with signature	225.00	300.00	150.00	325.00
without signature	175.00	225.00	110.00	250.00
Porridge plate				
with signature	300.00	400.00	200.00	425.00
without signature	250.00	325.00	150.00	350.00

FINE WHITE CHINA

Shape	U.S. $	Can. $	U.K. £	Aust. $
Bread and butter plate	800.00	1,000.00	500.00	1,100.00

Casino Teapot, *Mr. Piggly's Store*, (SF14)

Casino Teapot, *Dress Making*, (HW26)

BUNNYKINS BREAKFAST SET

Issues of 1939 - 1945

D6010
TEAPOT

Designer: Charles Noke
Height: 4 ¾", 12.1 cm
Colour: Brown rabbit; green leaves
Issued: 1939 - by 1945

Doulton	Price			
Number	U.S. $	Can. $	U.K. £	Aust. $
D6010	1,200.00	1,800.00	750.00	2,000.00

D6034
EGG CUP
Style One

Designer: Charles Noke
Height: 1 ¾", 4.5 cm
Colour: Brown rabbit
Issued: 1939 - by 1939

Doulton	Price			
Number	U.S. $	Can. $	U.K. £	Aust. $
D6034	2,250.00	3,000.00	1,500.00	3,500.00

D6040
SUGAR SIFTER

Designer: Charles Noke
Height: 2 ¾", 7.0 cm
Colour: Brown rabbit, blue sweater , red trousers
Issued: 1939 - by 1945

Doulton	Price			
Number	U.S. $	Can. $	U.K. £	Aust. $
D6040	6,000.00	9,000.00	4,000.00	10,000.00

Note: Designed by Charles Noke in 1939, this breakfast set comprises six pieces.
Production started in 1940 but was soon halted due to wartime needs.

D6056
SUGAR BOWL

Designer: Charles Noke
Height: 1 ¾", 4.5 cm
Colour: Brown rabbit; green leaves
Issued: 1939 - by 1945

Doulton		Price		
Number	U.S. $	Can. $	U.K. £	Aust. $
D6056	1,000.00	1,500.00	650.00	1,750.00

D6057
CREAM JUG

Designer: Charles Noke
Height: 2 ¾", 7.0 cm
Colour: Brown rabbit; green leaves
Issued: 1939 - by 1945

Doulton		Price		
Number	U.S. $	Can. $	U.K. £	Aust. $
D6057	3,000.00	4,500.00	2,000.00	5,000.00

Note: The pieces comprising the Bunnykins Breakfast Set, due to the short production period, are scarce items and thus prices may vary. Prices listed above should be treated as indications only.

BUNNYKINS TEAPOTS
Issues of 1994 - 1998

D6966A
LONDON CITY GENT
BUNNYKINS TEAPOT

Designer:	Unknown
Modeller:	Martyn Alcock
Height:	8", 20.3 cm
Colour:	Brown and black
Issued:	1994 in a special edition of 2,500
Series:	Bunnykins Teapots of the World

Doulton	Price			
Number	U.S. $	Can. $	U.K. £	Aust. $
D6966	100.00	135.00	60.00	150.00

D6996B
U.S.A. PRESIDENT BUNNYKINS TEAPOT

Designer:	Unknown
Modeller:	Shane Ridge
Height:	8", 20.3 cm
Colour:	Red, white and blue
Issued:	1995 in a special edition of 2,500
Series:	Bunnykins Teapots of the World

Doulton	Price			
Number	U.S. $	Can. $	U.K. £	Aust. $
D6996	100.00	135.00	60.00	150.00

D7027
AUSSIE EXPLORER BUNNYKINS TEAPOT

Designer:	Unknown
Modeller:	Shane Ridge
Height:	7 ¾", 19.7 cm
Colour:	Brown bunny, yellow waistcoat, green hat, orange boomerang
Issued:	1996 in a special edition of 2,500
Series:	Bunnykins Teapots of the World

Photograph not available at press time

Doulton Number	Price			
	U.S. $	Can. $	U.K. £	Aust. $
D7027	100.00	135.00	60.00	150.00

D7126
JAPANESE BUNNYKINS TEAPOT
GEISHA GIRL

Designer:	Caroline Dadd
Modeller:	Martyn Alcock
Height:	7 ¾", 19.7 cm
Colour:	Brown bunny, lilac kimono with green and yellow sash, black hat, cream fan with red flowers
Issued:	1998 in a special edition of 2,500
Series:	Bunnykins Teapots of the World. The last of four.

Doulton Number	Price			
	U.S. $	Can. $	U.K. £	Aust. $
D7126	100.00	135.00	60.00	150.00

BUNNYKINS TEA SET
Issues of 1998 - 2001

COOKIE JAR

Designer:	Unknown
Modeller:	Unknown
Height:	13 ½", 34.3 cm
Colour:	Brown bunny, blue dress, white collar and apron, pink hat, red flowers in basquet
Issued:	1998 - 2001

	Price			
Description	U.S. $	Can. $	U.K. £	Aust. $
Cookie jar	20.00	30.00	15.00	30.00

CREAMER

Designer:	Unknown
Modeller:	Unknown
Height:	4 ½", 11.9 cm
Colour:	Girl bunny - white dress with blue polka dots
	Boy bunny - deep pink jacket, pale pink jumper, brown trousers; white cow with black markings
Issued:	1998 - 2001

	Price			
Description	U.S. $	Can. $	U.K. £	Aust. $
Creamer	35.00	50.00	25.00	50.00

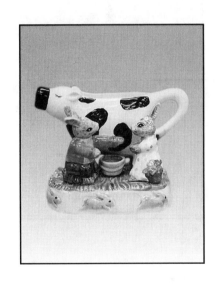

SALT AND PEPPER SET

Designer:	Unknown
Modeller:	Unknown
Height:	Salt — 5 ¾", 14.6 cm
	Pepper — 6", 15.0 cm
Colour:	Salt — Girl bunny wearing white dress with blue polka dots
	Pepper — Boy bunny wearing deep pink jacket, pink jumper
	brown trousers
Issued:	1998 - 2001

	Price			
Description	U.S. $	Can. $	U.K. £	Aust. $
Salt and pepper set	35.00	50.00	25.00	50.00

SUGAR DISH

Designer:	Unknown
Modeller:	Unknown
Height:	5 ½", 14.0 cm
Colour:	Brown bunny, blue dress, white collar and apron;
	brown sugar dish with white lid and spoon
Issued:	1998 - 2001

	Price			
Description	U.S. $	Can. $	U.K. £	Aust. $
Sugar dish	20.00	30.00	15.00	30.00

TEAPOT

Designer:	Unknown
Modeller:	Unknown
Height:	9 ½", 24.0 cm
Colour:	Brown bunny, green jacket, yellow shirt, deep pink bow tie,
	black belt and spectacles
Issued:	1998 - 2001

	Price			
Description	U.S. $	Can. $	U.K. £	Aust. $
Teapot	20.00	30.00	15.00	30.00

Note: This set was released through Royal Doulton stores in the U.S.A.

COUNTRY MANOR TEA SET
Issues of 2003

DBD1
LORD OF THE MANOR
COFFEE POT

Designer:	Shane Ridge
Modeller:	Shane Ridge
Height:	7 ½", 19.1 cm
Colour:	Olive green, black, brown, white, tan and silver
Issued:	2003 in a limited edition of 1,500
Series:	Country Manor Teaset

		Price		
Description	U.S. $	Can. $	U.K. £	Aust. $
Coffee pot	N/I	N/I	165.00	N/I

DBD2
LADY OF THE MANOR
TEAPOT

Designer:	Shane Ridge
Modeller:	Shane Ridge
Height:	6 ¾", 17.2 cm
Colour:	Yellow, white, brown, peach, green and black
Issued:	2003 in a limited edition of 1,500
Series:	Country Manor Teaset

		Price		
Description	U.S. $	Can. $	U.K. £	Aust. $
Teapot	N/I	N/I	165.00	N/I

DBD3
MASTER OF THE MANOR
CUP AND SAUCER

Designer:	Shane Ridge
Modeller:	Shane Ridge
Height:	4 ¼", 11.0 cm
Colour:	Cup: Grey, brown, white and black
	Figure: Brown, yellow, blue, red,
	white and purple
Issued:	2003 in a limited edition of 1,500
Series:	Country Manor Teaset

		Price		
Description	U.S. $	Can. $	U.K. £	Aust. $
Cup and saucer	N/I	N/I	150.00	N/I

DBD4
MISS OF THE MANOR
CUP AND SAUCER

Designer:	Shane Ridge
Modeller:	Shane Ridge
Height:	4 ¼", 11.0 cm
Colour:	Cup: Brown, black, white and blue
	Figure: Red, green, yellow, blue, white
	brown and pink
Issued:	2003 in a limited edition of 1,500
Series:	Country Manor Teaset

		Price		
Description	U.S. $	Can. $	U.K. £	Aust. $
Cup and saucer	N/I	N/I	150.00	N/I

DBD5
COUNTRY MANOR BUTLER
CREAM JUG

Designer:	Shane Ridge
Modeller:	Shane Ridge
Height:	4 ¼", 11.0 cm
Colour:	Black, white, grey, gold,
	red and brown
Issued:	2003 in a limited edition of 1,500
Series:	Country Manor Teaset

		Price		
Description	U.S. $	Can. $	U.K. £	Aust. $
Cream jug	N/I	N/I	75.00	N/I

DBD6
COUNTRY MANOR MAID
COVERED SUGAR

Designer:	Shane Ridge
Modeller:	Shane Ridge
Height:	4 ¼", 11.0 cm
Colour:	Black, white, yellow and brown
Issued:	2003 in a limited edition of 1,500
Series:	Country Manor Teaset

		Price		
Description	U.S. $	Can. $	U.K. £	Aust. $
Covered sugar	N/I	N/I	75.00	N/I

DBD7
COUNTRY MANOR CHEF
CANDY BOX

Designer:	Shane Ridge
Modeller:	Shane Ridge
Height:	5", 12.5 cm
Colour:	Red, white, brown and orange
Issued:	2003 in a limited edition of 1,500
Series:	Country Manor Teaset

		Price		
Description	U.S. $	Can. $	U.K. £	Aust. $
Candy box	N/I	N/I	99.00	N/I

BUNNYKINS TOBY JUGS
Issues of 1999 - 2003

D7157
FORTUNE TELLER BUNNYKINS™

Designer:	Kimberley Curtis
Modeller:	Warren Platt
Height:	5 ½", 14.0 cm
Colour:	Black, blue, brown, mauve, pink, white and yellow
Issued:	1999 in a limited edition of 1,500
Series:	Bunnykins Toby Jugs

Back Stamp	Price			
	U.S. $	Can. $	U.K. £	Aust. $
D-7157-Special	200.00	350.00	125.00	400.00

D7160
PARTY TIME BUNNYKINS™

Designer:	Caroline Dadd
Modeller:	Warren Platt
Height:	6", 15 cm
Colour:	Blue pants; yellow shirt; red hat and balloons
Issued:	2000 in a limited edition of 1,500
Series:	Bunnykins Toby Jugs

Back Stamp	Price			
	U.S. $	Can. $	U.K. £	Aust. $
D-7160-Special	200.00	350.00	125.00	400.00

Photograph not available at press time

D7166
WITCHING TIME BUNNYKINS™

Designer:	Caroline Dadd
Modeller:	Warren Platt
Height:	6", 15 cm
Colour:	Black, yellow and red
Issued:	2001 in a limited edition of 1,500
Series:	Bunnykins Toby Jugs

Back Stamp	Price			
	U.S. $	Can. $	U.K. £	Aust. $
D-7166-Special	200.00	350.00	125.00	400.00

D7185
TOY SOLDIER BUNNYKINS ™

Designer:	Caroline Dadd
Modeller:	Warren Platt
Height:	6 ¼", 15.9 cm
Colour:	Red, blue, brown, yellow, white and grey
Issued:	2003 in a limited edition of 1,500
Series:	Bunnykins Toby Jugs

Backstamp not
available
at press time

Back Stamp	Price			
	U.S. $	Can. $	U.K. £	Aust. $
D7185-Special	N/I	N/I	175.00	N/I

Game of Golf (SF11) by Casa Gessel of Argentina

PART TWO

BUNNYKINS BANKS
Issues of 1967 - 1981

BUNNYKINS COMMEMORATIVES
Issues of 1982 - 2003

BUNNYKINS ENAMEL BOXES
Issues of 1999

Pillar Box; *Letterbox*, SF13, front; *Holding Hat and Coat*, EC4, back
From the Royal Doulton Archives.

BUNNYKINS BANKS
Issues of 1967 - 1981

D6615A
BUNNYBANK
First Version

Designer:	Unknown
Modeller:	John Bromley and David Biggs
Height:	8 ½", 21.6 cm
Colour:	Grey rabbit, green coat and hat, maroon drum
Issued:	1967 - 1977

Doulton Number	Price U.S. $	Can. $	U.K. £	Aust. $
D6615A	200.00	275.00	125.00	300.00

D6615B
BUNNYBANK
Second Version

Designer:	Unknown
Modeller:	John Bromley and David Biggs
Height:	9 ¼", 23.5 cm
Colour:	Brown rabbit, green coat and hat, maroon drum
Issued:	1979 - 1981

Doulton Number	Price U.S. $	Can. $	U.K. £	Aust. $
D6615B	200.00	275.00	125.00	300.00

Note: 1. The second versionl is ¾" taller and the coin slot is altered. Also known as Soldier Bunny
2. Pillar Boxes which are also banks are illustrated opposite and listed on page 202.
3. A prototype Bunny Bank designed by John Bromley is known.

BUNNYKINS COMMEMORATIVES
Issues 1982 - 2002

Birth of the First Child of
T.R.H. The Prince and Princess of Wales 1982

TO CELEBRATE THE BIRTH OF THE FIRST CHILD OF
T.R.H. THE PRINCE AND PRINCESS OF WALES 1982

The following is a list of designs known to appear on these shapes;
more may exist.

Design No.: HW17, HW17R, HW21, HW21R, HW22, HW22R, HW23,
HW23R, HW26, HW26R, HW27R, HW28R, HW29R,
HW119, HW119R, HW136, HW136R, HW137, HW137R,
HW139, HW139R, HW141, HW141R, EC1, EC3, EC4,
EC6, EC121, EC123, EC124, EC125, EC126

Issued: 1982

Shape	U.S. $	Can. $	U.K. £	Aust. $
Hug-a-mug, one handle	50.00	65.00	30.00	70.00
Hug-a-mug, two handles	50.00	65.00	30.00	70.00
Money ball	50.00	65.00	30.00	70.00
Savings book	50.00	65.00	30.00	70.00

TO T.R.H. THE PRINCE AND PRINCESS OF WALES
A SECOND CHILD 1984 IN JOYFUL CELEBRATION

The following is a list of designs known to appear on these
shapes, more may exist.

Design No.: HW22, HW22R, HW23, HW27, HW27R, HW29, HW29R,
HW120R

Issued: 1984

Shape	U.S. $	Can. $	U.K. £	Aust. $
Hug-a-mug, one handle	25.00	35.00	15.00	40.00
Hug-a-mug, two handles	25.00	35.00	15.00	40.00
Savings book	50.00	65.00	30.00	70.00

To T.R.H. The Prince and Princess of Wales
A Second Child 1984

BUNNYKINS CELEBRATE THEIR GOLDEN JUBILEE 1934 - 1984

Birthday Cake

Design No.: SF140 — Birthday Cake
Designer: Walter Hayward
Issued: 1984 - 1984
Backstamp: Golden Jubilee Celebration

Shape	U.S. $	Can. $	U.K. £	Aust. $
Baby plate, round, small				
with inscription	50.00	65.00	30.00	70.00
without inscription	30.00	40.00	20.00	45.00
Cereal bowl				
with inscription	50.00	65.00	30.00	70.00
without inscription	30.00	40.00	20.00	45.00
Plate, 8"				
with inscription	50.00	65.00	30.00	70.00
without inscription	30.00	40.00	20.00	45.00

Note: The inscription was removed from the design after the Jubilee and the design was sold on baby plates, cereal bowls and the 8" plate.

Birthday Cake (SF140)

Chicken Pulling a Cart (SF141)

Chicken Pulling A Cart

This scene was first issued in 1940 and discontinued by 1952. It was reissued in 1984 to commemorate the fiftieth anniversary of Bunnykins and was issued in two variations, with and without the inscription.

Design No.: SF141 — Chicken Pulling a Cart
Designer: After a design by Barbara Vernon (SF8)
Issued: 1984 - 1984
Backstamp: Golden Jubilee Celebration.

Shape	U.S. $	Can. $	U.K. £	Aust. $
Plate, 8"				
with inscription	80.00	100.00	50.00	110.00
without inscription	60.00	80.00	35.00	85.00

Note: For the complete listing on SF141 see page 41.

Marriage of the Prince Andrew
with Miss Sarah Ferguson

TO CELEBRATE THE MARRIAGE OF THE PRINCE ANDREW WITH MISS SARAH FERGUSON WESTMINSTER ABBEY, WEDNESDAY, 23RD JULY 1986

The following is a list of designs known to appear on these shapes; more may exist.

Design No.:	HW26, HW26R, HW27, HW29, HW29R, HW115, HW115R, HW116, HW116R, HW118, HW118R, HW119, HW119R, HW120, HW136, HW136R, HW139, HW139R
Issued:	1986

Shape	U.S. $	Can. $	U.K. £	Aust. $
Hug-a-mug, one handle.	50.00	65.00	30.00	70.00
Money ball	50.00	65.00	30.00	70.00

TO CELEBRATE AUSTRALIA'S BICENTENARY 1788-1988

Design No.:	None
Designer:	Walter Hayward
Issued:	1987 - 1988
Backstamp:	The Australian Bicentenary 1788-1988

Shape	U.S. $	Can. $	U.K. £	Aust. $
Plate, 8"	60.00	80.00	35.00	85.00

Bunnykins Celebrate Australia's
Bicentenary 1788 - 1988

To COMMEMORATE BUNNYKINS 60th ANNIVERSARY 1994

Dancing in the Moonlight
Second Version, First Variation, Large Size

Design No.:	Front — CT91 Dancing in the Moonlight
Designer:	Justin Clarke based on a design by Barbara Vernon
Issued:	1994 - 1994
Backstamp:	Dancing in the Moonlight Bunnykins 60th Anniversary

Shape	U.S. $	Can. $	U.K. £	Aust. $
Baby plate, round, small	25.00	35.00	15.00	40.00
Plate, 8"	25.00	35.00	15.00	40.00

Note: See also *Dancing in the Moonlight*, Style One, page 51.

Dancing in the Moonlight, Second Version,
First Variation (CT91)

Dancing in the Moonlight, Second Version,
Second Variation (CT92)

Dancing in the Moonlight
Second Version, Second Variation, Small Size

Design No.:	Front — CT92 Dancing in the Moonlight Reverse — CT93 Bunnykins 60th Anniversary inscription
Designer:	Justin Clarke based on a design by Barbara Vernon
Issued:	1994 - 1994

Shape	U.S. $	Can. $	U.K. £	Aust. $
Hug-a-mug, one handle	15.00	20.00	10.00	20.00
Money ball	40.00	50.00	25.00	55.00

Bunnykins 60th Anniversary Inscription (CT93)

1990 U.S. SPECIAL EVENTS TOUR

An 8" plate was issued for the 'U.S. Special Events Tour, 1990.' The year 1990 was incorporated under the design. The reverse is inscribed 'To' and 'From' to be completed by customer, and 'Special Events Tour 1990.'

Designer:	Walter Hayward
Diameter:	8", 20.3 cm
Colour:	Cream / multicoloured print
Issued:	1990
Scene:	*Apple Picking* (SF25)

Shape	Issue Price	U.S. $	Can. $	U.K. £	Aust. $
Plate, 8"	Not known	30.00	40.00	20.00	45.00

1992 U.S. SPECIAL EVENTS TOUR

Two money balls were issued for the U.S. Special Events Tour in 1992. This design was featured on the Spring tour with no special inscription. "Happy Birthday from Bunnykins" (CT60) was featured on the Fall tour.

ITEM	Money Ball
Designer:	Colin Twinn
Height:	3", 7.6 cm
Colour:	Cream / multicoloured print
Issued:	1992
Scenes:	Spring: *Queen of the May* (CT7)
	Fall: *Happy Birthday Bunnykins*, Style Two, Second Version (CT60)

Description	Issue Price	U.S. $	Can. $	U.K. £	Aust. $
Spring: *Queen of the May*	Not known	15.00	20.00	10.00	25.00
Fall: *Happy Birthday Bunnykins*		15.00	20.00	10.00	25.00

1993 U.S. SPECIAL EVENTS TOUR

A Hug-a-mug (two handles) was issued for the U.S. Special Event Tour in 1993. The front illustrates *Daisy Chains* (HW25), and the back *Hikers* (EC124) with the words 'U.S. Special Events Tour 1993.'

ITEM   **Hug-A-Mug**
Designer: Walter Hayward
Height: 3", 7.6 cm
Colour: Cream / multicoloured print
Issued: 1993
Scenes: *Daisy Chains* (HW25)
              Hikers (EC124)

Shape	Issue Price	U.S. $	Can. $	U.K. £	Aust. $
Hug-a-mug	Not known	10.00	15.00	7.50	15.00

1994 U.S. SPECIAL EVENTS TOUR

A savings book was issued for the U.S. Special Events Tour 1994. The front features *Skipping Game* (HW139R) and the reverse is inscribed 'To' and 'From' for the customer to complete and 'U.S. Special Events Tour 1994.'

ITEM	**Savings Bank**
Designer:	Walter Hayward
Height:	4 ¼", 10.8 cm
Colour:	Cream / multicoloured print
Issued:	1994
Scene:	*Skipping Game* (HW139R)

Shape	Issue Price	U.S .$	Can. $	U.K. £	Aust. $
Savings Bank	Not known	15.00	20.00	10.00	25.00

TO CELEBRATE THE MILLENNIUM EXHIBITION HELD APRIL 15TH TO MAY 31ST, 2000
AT THE ROYAL DOULTON VISITOR CENTRE

| Display sign - Tug of War | Key fob - Tug of War | Desk clock - Sleeping in a Rocking Chair |

ITEM:	Display Sign	Key Fob	Desk Clock	Desk Clock Scenes:
Designer:	Unknown	Unknown	Unknown	*Drummer, EC2*
Modeller:	Unknown	Unknown	Unknown	*Drummer and Bugler, EC126*
Height:	2 ¼", 6 cm	2½" x 2", 6.4 x5.0 cm	4 ¼", 11 cm	*Hikers, EC124*
Colour:	Multicoloured	Multicoloured	Multicoloured	*Hobby Horse, EC121*
	print	print	print	*Playing with Cup and Spoon, EC6*
Issue:	1,250	1,250	1,000	*Playing with Doll and Pram, EC123*
				Raising Hat, EC7
				Reading, EC122
				Sheltering Under an Umbrella, EC3
				Sleeping in a Rocking Chair, EC1
				Trumpeter, EC5

Shape	Issue Price U.K. £	U.S. $	Can. $	U.K. £	Aust. $
Desk clock	45.00	70.00	90.00	45.00	95.00
Display sign	15.00	25.00	35.00	15.00	40.00
Key Fob	5.00	10.00	15.00	5.00	15.00

Note: Please see DB200 which was also part of the exhibition (page 279).

TO COMMEMORATE THE AUSTRALIAN TOUR, 2000

ITEM:	Scenes:	Designer:	Height:	Colour:
Key Fob	*Trumpeter*, EC4	Barbara Vernon	2½" x 2", 6.4 x 5.0 cm	Cream/multicoloured print
Key Fob	*Drummer*, EC2	Barbara Vernon	2½" x 2", 6.4 x 5.0 cm	Cream/multicoloured print
Key Fob	*Drummer and Bugler*, EC126	Walter Hayward	2½" x 2", 6.4 c 5.0 cm	Cream/multicoloured print

Shape	Issue Price Aust. $	U.S. $	Can. $	U.K. £	Aust. $
Key fobs, set of three	30.00	60.00	100.00	40.00	100.00

ROYAL DOULTON BUNNYKINS EXTRAVAGANZA FAIR, OCTOBER 2001

Mantle clock   Pillar Money Box   Commemorative tray 2001

ITEM:	Mantle Clock	Piller Money Box	Commemorative Tray 2001
Designer:	Unknown	Unknown	Unknown
Height/diameter:	4", 10.1 cm	5 ½", 14 cm	5 ¼", 13.5 cm
Colour:	Multicoloured print	Multicoloured print	Multicoloured print
Issue:	1,000	1,000	300
Scenes:	144 different combinations of 14 designs	*Posting Letters*, (28) *Sitting on Oil Drum*, (39)	*Letter Box*, (29)

Shape	Issue Price U.K. £	U.S. $	Can. $	U.K. £	Aust. $
Mantle clock	45.00	65.00	100.00	45.00	125.00
Pillar Money Box	45.00	65.00	100.00	45.00	125.00
Commemorative Tray	10.00	15.00	25.00	10.00	30.00

TO COMMEMORATE THE 65TH ANNIVERSARY OF NURSERY WARES AND 30TH ANNIVERSARY OF DB NUMBERS
HELD AT THE ROYAL DOULTON VISITOR CENTRE, APRIL 2002

Rex mug

Commemorative tray 2002

30th Anniversary of DB Numbers Key Fob

ITEM:	Rex Mug	Commemorative Tray	Key Fob
Designer:	Unknown	Unknown	Unknown
Height/Diameter:	3", 7.5 cm	5 ¼", 13.5 cm	2 ½" x 2", 6.4 x 5.0 cm
Colour:	Multicoloured print	Multicoloured print	Multicoloured print
Issue:	325	700	Unknown
Scenes:	Unknown	*Beating Carpet*, (20)	30th Anniversary Crest

Shape	Issus Price U.K. £	U.S. $	Can. $	U.K. £	Aust. $
Rex mug	25.00	40.00	60.00	25.00	60.00
Commemorative tray	15.00	25.00	40.00	15.00	40.00
Key Fob	5.00	10.00	15.00	5.00	15.00

TO COMMEMORATE THE GOLDEN JUBILEE OF QUEEN ELIZABETH II, 1953 - 2003
DOULTON, BESWICK COLLECTORS FAIR OCTOBER 20TH, 2002.

Designer:　　Frank Endersby
Diameter:　　10 ½", 26.7 cm
Colour:　　　Cream/multicoloured print
Issued:　　　2002 in a limited edition of 50 (in presentation box)
Scenes:　　　*Swinging,* HW138R
　　　　　　　(Other scenes may be available)

Shape	Issue Price U.K. £	U.S. $	Can. $	U.K. £	Aust. $
Plate, 10"	150.00	300.00	450.00	200.00	500.00

ROYAL DOULTON BUNNYKINS EXTRAVAGANZA, MAY 10TH AND 11TH, 2003

The May event was held at the Royal Doulton Visitor Centre in Burslem.

Designer:	Colin Twinn
Diameter:	6 ½", 16.5 cm
Colour:	Cream/multicoloured print
Issued:	2003 in a limited edition of 200
Scenes:	*ABCDEF*, CT94

Shape	Issue Price U.K. £	U.S. $	Can. $	U.K. £	Aust. $
Plate, 6 ½"	10.00	26.00	35.00	15.00	45.00

BUNNYKINS ENAMEL BOXES

THE BUNNYKINS™ MILLENNIUM BOX

Hand crafted and painted rectangular enamelled, commemorative box which shows the Bunnykin Family gathering at the fireside as the grandfather clock strikes the arrival of the new millennium.

Modeller:	Unknown
Size:	2 ½" x 2" x 1", 6.4 x 5.0 x 2.5 cm
Colour:	Cream, multicoloured print
Issued:	1999 in a limited edition of 500
Comm. by:	Lawleys by Post

Description	U.S. $	Can. $	U.K. £	Aust. $
Millenium box	325.00	425.00	200.00	450.00

THE BUNNYKINS FAMILY™

Lawleys by Post issued a specially commissioned set of five enamelled boxes depicting each of the Bunnykins Family. Father, sitting in the garden; Mother, picking vegetables; Polly, smelling the flowers; William, playing with an aeroplane and Baby sleeping. The hand made metal boxes are hand painted and come in a special edition of 500, with matching numbers, in a presentation box.

Modeller:	Unknown
Size:	1. Father/Mother; 1 ¾", 4.5 cm
	2. Polly/William; 1", 2.5 cm
	3. Baby; ¾", 1.9 cm
Colour:	Cream, multicoloured print
Issued:	1999 in a limited edition of 500
Comm. by:	Lawleys by Post

Description	U.S. $	Can. $	U.K. £	Aust. $
Father	90.00	125.00	55.00	135.00
Mother	90.00	125.00	55.00	135.00
Polly	60.00	80.00	35.00	85.00
William	60.00	80.00	35.00	85.00
Baby	50.00	65.00	30.00	70.00
Set of five boxes	300.00	400.00	195.00	425.00

PART THREE

BUNNYKINS FIGURINES— EARTHENWARE
Issues of 1939 - 1940
Issues of 1972 - 2004

BUNNYKINS FIGURINE BASES
Issues of 2002 - 2004

BUNNYKINS FIGURINES – RESIN
Issues of 1996 - 1997

BUNNYKINS FIGURINE BACKSTAMPS

The Bunnykins backstamps have been reclassified due to design changes over the last three years. The stamps are whole numbers in the order of their appearance. They are then subdivided into "Standard" and "Modified." A "Standard" and "Special" stamp are the same except the "Special" serves to indicate a Limited Edition, Event, etc. A "Modified" backstamp is the "Standard" altered so it may be adapted to the base of the particular model to which it is to be applied. Flexibility must be allowed in dating by use of backstamps due to the over or under use of the backstamp lithos. Royal Doulton consumed all inventories of lithos before changing to a new style.

Not Seen

BK-1. Standard 1972 - 1975
Doulton & Co. Limited

BK-1 Modified

Not Seen

BK-2 Standard 1976 - 1983
Doulton Tableware Ltd.

BK-2 Modified

Not Seen

BK-3 Standard 1984
Golden Jubilee Celebration

BK-3 Modified

BK-4 Standard 1985 - 1986
Royal Doulton (U.K.)

BK-4a Modified

BK-5 Standard 1987 - 1997
Royal Doulton 1987 - 1997

BK-5a Modified 1987 - 1997

BK-5 Special

BK-5a Special

BK-6 Standard 1998

BK-6a Modified 1998

BK-6 Special

BK-6a Special

Royal Doulton Crown and Lion logo with the 1998 folded umbrella date cypher.

BUNNYKINS FIGURINE BACKSTAMPS

BK-7 Standard 1999   **BK-7a Modified 1999**   **BK-7 Special 1999**   **BK-7a Special 1999**
Royal Doulton, Crown and Lion logo with 1999 Top Hay cypher.

BK-8 Standard 2000   **BK-8a Modified 2000**   **BK-8a Modified 2000**   **BK-8 Special 2000**
Royal Doulton, Crown and Lion logo with Millennium 2000 stamp and different date cyphers.

BK-9 Standard 2000   **BK-9 Modified 2000**   **BK-9 Special 2000**   **BK-9a Special 2000**
Royal Doulton, Crown and Lion logo with 2000 Fob Watch cypher.

BK-10 Stsandard 2000   **BK-10a Modified 2000**   **BK-10 Special 2000**   **BK-10a Special 2000**
Royal Doulton, oval backstamp designs with 2000 Fob Watch cypher.

BUNNYKINS FIGURINE BACKSTAMPS

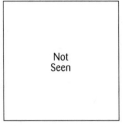

BK-11 Standard 2001   **BK-11a Modified 2001**   **BK-11 Special 2001**   **BK-11a Special 2001**
Royal Doulton, oval backstamp with 2001 Vest cypher.

BK-12 Standard 2002   **BK12a Modified 2002**   **BK-12 Special 2002**   **BK-12a Special 2002**
Royal Doulton, round backstamp with 2002 Boot cypher.

BK-13 Standard 2003   **BK-13a Modified 2003**   **BK-13 Special 2003**   **BK-13a Special 2003**
Royal Doulton, round backstamp with 2003 Gloves cypher.

BK-14 Standard   **BK-14a Modified**   **BK-14 Special**   **BK-14a Special**
Royal Doulton, Running Bunny / Bunnykins logo, 2003 - 2004.

BUNNYKINS FIGURINES BY SERIES

If you collect it is always a good idea to do so with a purpose or an objective in mind, only well thought out collections will have balance, allowing you to display your figurines with pride. You may decide to acquire the complete range, maybe only the marching bands, or build a collection around a theme which Bunnykins figurines may only be a part of, for example, the Olympics. It is with this in mind that the following listing by Series may be of assistance to you.

AMERICAN HERITAGE

American Firefighter Bunnykins, third variation	DB268
Betsy Ross Bunnykins	DB313
Liberty Bell Bunnykins	DB257
Pilgrim Bunnykins	DB212
Statue of Liberty Bunnykins	DB198
Uncle Sam Bunnykins, second variation	DB175

ARTHURIAN LEGENDS

King Arthur Bunnykins	DB304
Merlin Bunnykins	DB303
Queen Guinevere Bunnykins	DB302
Sir Galahad Bunnykins	DB299
Sir Gawain Bunnykins	DB300
Sir Lancelot Bunnykins	DB301

AUSTRALIAN HERITAGE

Captain Cook Bunnykins	DB251
Digger Bunnykins	DB248
Federation Bunnykins	DB224
Sydney Bunnykins	DB195
Waltzing Matilda Bunnykins	DB236

BUNNYKINS FAMILY

Billy Bunnykin	D6001
Farmer Bunnykin	D6003
Father Bunnykins, Style Two	DB227
Freddie Bunnykin	D6024
Mary Bunnykin	D6002
Mother Bunnykin	D6004
Mother and Baby Bunnykins, Style Two	DB226
Reggie Bunnykin	D6025

BUNNYKINS GAMES

Basketball Bunnykins	DB208
Gymnast Bunnykins	DB207
Runner Bunnykins	DB205
Soccer Bunnykins	DB209
Swimmer Bunnykins	DB206

BUNNYKINS OF THE YEAR

1996 Father Bunnykins, Style One	DB154
1997 Sailor Bunnykins	DB166
1998 Seaside Bunnykins	DB177
1999 Mother Bunnykins	DB189
2000 Sundial Bunnykins	DB213
2001 Sands of Time Bunnykins	DB229
2002 Stop Watch Bunnykins	DB253
2003 Eskimo Bunnykins	DB275
2004 Winter Lapland Bunnykins	DB297

BUNNYKINS OF THE WORLD

Mandarin Bunnykins DB252

CRICKET

Batsman Bunnykins	DB144
Bowler Bunnykins	DB145
Out For a Duck Bunnykins	DB160
Test Century Bunnykins	DB272
Wicketkeeper Bunnykins	DB150

DANCERS OF THE WORLD

Flamenco Bunnykins	DB256
Morris Dancer Bunnykins	DB204
Tyrolean Dancer Bunnykins	DB242

FAIRY TALES

Cinderella Bunnykins	DB231
Little Red Riding Hood Bunnykins	DB230

FOOTBALLER / GOALKEEPER BUNNYKINS
First Variation

Footballer Bunnykins	DB117
Goalkeeper Bunnykins	DB116

Second Variation

Footballer Bunnykins	DB119
Goalkeeper Bunnykins	DB118

Third Variation

Footballer Bunnykins	DB121
Goalkeeper Bunnykins	DB120

Fourth Variation

Goalkeeper Bunnykins	DB122
Soccer Player Bunnykins	DB123

HOLIDAY OUTING

Father Bunnykins, Style One	DB154
Mother Bunnykins	DB189
Sailor Bunnykins	DB166
Seaside Bunnykins	DB177
Tourist Bunnykins	DB190

INTERNATIONAL COLLECTORS CLUB
ICC Members Exclusives

1987 Collector Bunnykins	DB54
1992 Master Potter Bunnykins	DB131
1995 Partners in Collecting	DB151
1999 Tourist Bunnykins	DB190
2000 Sightseer Bunnykins	DB215
2001 Choir Singer Bunnykins	DB223
2002 Cinderella Bunnykins	DB231
2003 Romeo Bunnykins	DB284
2004 Tutankhamun Bunnykins	DB296

ICC Membership Gift

1999 Judge Bunnykins	DB188
2000 Lawyer Bunnykins	DB214
2002 Vicar Bunnykins	DB254
2003 Juliet Bunnykins	DB283
2004 Ankehesenamun Bunnykins	DB295

JAZZ BAND

Banjo Player Bunnykins	DB182
Clarinet Player Bunnykins	DB184
Double Bass Player Bunnykins	DB185
Drummer Player Bunnykins, Style Two	DB250
Saxaphone Player Bunnykins	DB186
Trumpet Player Bunnykins	DB210

MUSIC BOXES

Astro Bunnykins 'Rocket Man'	DB35
Carol Singer	DB53
Happy Birthday Bunnykins	DB36
Jogging Bunnykins	DB37
Mr. Bunnybeat Strumming	DB38
Mrs. Bunnykins At the Easter Parade	DB39
Santa Bunnykins	DB34
Tally Ho! Bunnykins, First Variation	DB33A
Tally Ho! Bunnykins, Second Variation	DB33B

NURSERY RHYME

Jack and Jill Bunnykins	DB222
Little Bo Peep Bunnykins	DB220
Little Boy Blue Bunnykins	DB239
Little Jack Horner Bunnykins	DB221
Little Miss Muffet Bunnykins	DB240
Mary Mary Quite Contrary Bunnykins	DB247
Wee Willie Winkie Bunnykins	DB270

OCCASIONS COLLECTION

Birthday Girl Bunnykins	DB290
Christmas Morning Bunnykins	DB285
Congratulations Bunnykins	DB291
Easter Parade Bunnykins	DB292
Easter Treat Bunnykins	DB289
Graduation Day Bunnykins	DB286
Love Heart Bunnykins	DB288
Wedding Day Bunnykins	DB287

OOMPAH BANDS

First Variation - Red Band

Cymbals Bunnykins	DB25
Drum-major Bunnykins	DB27
Drummer Bunnykins, 50th Anniversary	DB26A
Drummer Bunnykins, Oompah Band	DB26B
Sousaphone Bunnykins	DB23
Trumpeter Bunnykins	DB24

Second Variation - Blue Band

Cymbals Bunnykins	DB88
Drum-major Bunnykins	DB90
Drummer Bunnykins	DB89
Sousaphone Bunnykins	DB86
Trumpeter Bunnykins	DB87

Third Variation - Green Band

Cymbals Bunnykins	DB107
Drum-major Bunnykins	DB109
Drummer Bunnykins	DB108
Sousaphone Bunnykins	DB105
Trumpeter Bunnykins	DB106

PUNCH AND JUDY

Judy Bunnykins	DB235
Mr. Punch Bunnykins	DB234

ROBIN HOOD

Friar Tuck Bunnykins	DB246
King Richard Bunnykins	DB258
Little John Bunnykins	DB243
Maid Marion Bunnykins	DB245
Prince John Bunnykins	DB266
Robin Hood Bunnykins	DB244
Sheriff of Nottingham Bunnykins	DB265
Will Scarlett Bunnykins	DB264

ROMAN EMPIRE COLLECTION

Centurian Bunnykins	DB294
Emperor Bunnykins	DB312

ROYAL FAMILY

First Variation

Harry the Herald	DB49
King John	DB45
Prince Frederick	DB48
Princess Beatrice	DB47
Queen Sophie	DB46

Second Variation

Harry the Herald	DB95
King John	DB91
Prince Frederick	DB94
Princess Beatrice	DB93
Queen Sophie	DB92

Third Variation

Harry the Herald	DB115

SPECIAL EVENTS

1986 Mrs. Bunnykins At the Easter Parade, Second Variation	DB52
1987 Storytime Bunnykins, Second Variation	DB59
1988 Family Photograph Bunnykins, Second Variation	DB67
1989 Billie & Buntie Bunnykins Sleigh Ride, Second Variation	DB81
1991 Bedtime Bunnykins, Fourth Variation	DB103
2000 Morris Dancer Bunnykins	DB204
2001 Little Red Riding Hood Bunnykins	DB230
2001 Tyrolean Dancer Bunnykins	DB242
2002 Flamenco Bunnykins	DB256
2003 Hornpiper Bunnykins	DB261
2004 Summer Lapland Bunnykins	DB298

TIME

Sands of Time Bunnykins	DB229
Sundial Bunnykins	DB213
Stop Watch Bunnykins D	B253

TOUCHDOWN BUNNYKINS

Touchdown Bunnykins	DB29A
Boston College	DB29B
Cincinnati Bengals	DB98
Notre Dame College	DB99
Ohio State University	DB96
University of Indiana	DB100
University of Michigan	DB97

TRAVEL SERIES

Chocs Away Bunnykins	DB267
Day Trip Bunnykins	DB260
Dodgem Bunnykins	DB249
Ship Ahoy Bunnykins	DB279

TUDOR COLLECTION

Anne Boleyn	DB307
Anne of Cleves	DB309
Catherine of Aragon	DB306
Catherine Parr	DB311
Henry VIII	DB305
Jane Seymour	DB308
Kathryn Howard	DB310

TABLEAU

Bath Night Bunnykins	DB241
Merry Christmas Bunnykins	DB194
Sandcastle Money Box	DB228

EARTHENWARE ISSUES
1939 - 1940

D6001
BILLY BUNNYKIN™

Designer: Charles Noke
Height: 4 ½", 11.9 cm
Colour: Red trousers, blue jacket,
white bow tie with blue spots
Issued: 1939-c.1940

Doulton	Price			
Number	U.S. $	Can. $	U.K. £	Aust. $
D6001	2,000.00	2,800.00	1,200.00	3,000.00

D6002
MARY BUNNYKIN™

Designer: Charles Noke
Height: 6 ½", 16.5 cm
Colour: Red bodice, dark blue collar;
pale blue skirt, white apron
Issued: 1939-c.1940

Doulton	Price			
Number	U.S. $	Can. $	U.K. £	Aust. $
D6002	2,000.00	2,800.00	1,200.00	3,000.00

D6003
FARMER BUNNYKIN™

Designer: Charles Noke
Height: 7 ½", 19.1 cm
Colour: Green coat, blue and white smock,
yellow bow tie, red handkerchief with
white dots
Issued: 1939-c.1940

Doulton	Price			
Number	U.S. $	Can. $	U.K. £	Aust. $
D6003	2,000.00	2,800.00	1,200.00	3,000.00

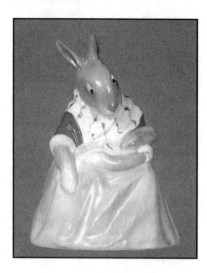

D6004
MOTHER BUNNYKIN™

Designer:	Charles Noke
Height:	7", 17.8 cm
Colour:	Blue skirt, red jacket, white shawl with blue stripes
Issued:	1939-c.1940

Doulton	Price			
Number	U.S. $	Can. $	U.K. £	Aust. $
D6004	2,500.00	3,250.00	1,500.00	3,500.00

D6024
FREDDIE BUNNYKIN™

Designer:	Charles Noke
Height:	3 ¾", 9.5 cm
Colour:	Green trousers, red jacket and yellow bow tie
Issued:	1939-c.1940

Doulton	Price			
Number	U.S. $	Can. $	U.K. £	Aust. $
D6024	3,500.00	5,000.00	2,000.00	5,000.00

D6025
REGGIE BUNNYKIN™

Designer:	Charles Noke
Height:	3 ¾", 9.5 cm
Colour:	Blue smock; red bow tie
Issued:	1939-c.1940

Doulton	Price			
Number	U.S. $	Can. $	U.K. £	Aust. $
D6025	3,500.00	5,000.00	2,000.00	5,000.00

EARTHENWARE ISSUES

1972 to 2004

DB1
FAMILY PHOTOGRAPH BUNNYKINS™
First Variation

Designer:	Based on a design by Walter Hayward
Modeller:	Albert Hallam
Height:	4 ½", 11.9 cm
Colour:	Blue, white, burgundy and grey
Issued:	1972 - 1988
Varieties:	DB67; also called Father, Mother and Victoria Bunnykins, DB68

Back Stamp	Price			
	U.S. $	Can. $	U.K. £	Aust. $
BK-1 to BK-5	135.00	185.00	85.00	185.00

DB2
BUNTIE BUNNYKINS HELPING MOTHER™

Designer:	Based on a design by Walter Hayward
Modeller:	Albert Hallam
Height:	3 ½", 8.9 cm
Colour:	Rose-pink and yellow
Issued:	1972 - 1993

Back Stamp	Price			
	U.S. $	Can. $	U.K. £	Aust. $
BK-1 to BK-5	80.00	115.00	55.00	125.00

DB3
BILLIE BUNNYKINS COOLING OFF™

Designer:	Based on a design by Walter Hayward
Modeller:	Albert Hallam
Height:	3 ¾", 9.5 cm
Colour:	Burgundy, yellow and green-grey
Issued:	1972 - 1987

Back Stamp	Price			
	U.S. $	Can. $	U.K. £	Aust. $
BK-1 to BK-5	200.00	300.00	125.00	300.00

Note: A colourway variation exists with white boots.

DB4
BILLIE & BUNTIE BUNNYKINS
SLEIGH RIDE™
First Variation

Designer:	Based on a design by Walter Hayward
Modeller:	Albert Hallam
Height:	3 ¼", 8.3 cm
Colour:	Blue, maroon and yellow
Issued:	1972 - 1997
Varieties:	DB81

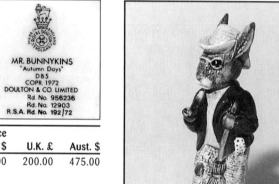

Back Stamp	Price			
	U.S. $	Can. $	U.K. £	Aust. $
BK-1 to BK-5	50.00	65.00	30.00	75.00

Note: Colour variations exist in Buntie's dress.

DB5
MR. BUNNYKINS AUTUMN DAYS™

Designer:	Based on a design by Walter Hayward
Modeller:	Albert Hallam
Height:	4", 10.1 cm
Colour:	Maroon, yellow and blue
Issued:	1972 - 1982

Back Stamp	Price			
	U.S. $	Can. $	U.K. £	Aust. $
BK-1 to BK-2	350.00	450.00	200.00	475.00

DB6
MRS. BUNNYKINS CLEAN SWEEP™

Designer:	Based on a design by Walter Hayward
Modeller:	Albert Hallam
Height:	4", 10.1 cm
Colour:	Blue and white
Issued:	1972 - 1991

Back Stamp	Price			
	U.S. $	Can. $	U.K. £	Aust. $
BK-1 to BK-5	100.00	135.00	65.00	150.00

DB7
DAISIE BUNNYKINS SPRING TIME™

Designer:	Based on a design by Walter Hayward	
Modeller:	Albert Hallam	
Height:	3 ½", 8.9 cm	
Colour:	Blue, white and yellow	
Issued:	1972 - 1983	

Back Stamp	Price			
	U.S. $	Can. $	U.K. £	Aust. $
BK-1 to BK-2	325.00	425.00	200.00	450.00

DB8
DOLLIE BUNNYKINS PLAYTIME™
First Variation

Designer:	Based on a design by Walter Hayward
Modeller:	Albert Hallam
Height:	4", 10.1 cm
Colour:	White dress with pink design, blue dress
Issued:	1972 - 1993
Varieties:	DB80

Back Stamp	Price			
	U.S. $	Can. $	U.K. £	Aust. $
BK-1 to BK-5	80.00	110.00	50.00	125.00

DB9
STORYTIME BUNNYKINS™
First Variation

Designer:	Based on a design by Walter Hayward
Modeller:	Albert Hallam
Height:	3", 7.6 cm
Colour:	White dress with blue design, pink dress
Issued:	1972 - 1997
Varieties:	DB59; also called Partners in Collecting, DB151

Back Stamp	Price			
	U.S. $	Can. $	U.K. £	Aust. $
BK-1 to BK-5	50.00	75.00	30.00	80.00

DB10
BUSY NEEDLES BUNNYKINS™

Designer:	Based on a design by Walter Hayward
Modeller:	Albert Hallam
Height:	3 ¼", 8.3 cm
Colour:	White, green and maroon
Issued:	1973 - 1988
Varieties:	Also called Susan Bunnykins, DB70

Back Stamp	Price			
	U.S. $	Can. $	U.K. £	Aust. $
BK-1 to BK-5	85.00	150.00	60.00	165.00

DB11
RISE AND SHINE BUNNYKINS™

Designer:	Based on a design by Walter Hayward
Modeller:	Albert Hallam
Height:	3 ¾", 9.5 cm
Colour:	Maroon, yellow and blue
Issued:	1973 - 1988

Back Stamp	Price			
	U.S. $	Can. $	U.K. £	Aust. $
BK-1 to BK-5	125.00	175.00	80.00	200.00

DB12
TALLY HO! BUNNYKINS™
First Variation

Designer:	Based on a design by Walter Hayward
Modeller:	Albert Hallam
Height:	3 ¾", 9.5 cm
Colour:	Burgundy, yellow, blue, white and green
Issued:	1973 - 1988
Varieties:	DB78; also called William Bunnykins, DB69

Back Stamp	Price			
	U.S. $	Can. $	U.K. £	Aust. $
BK-1 to BK-5	125.00	175.00	75.00	200.00

Note: A colourway variation exists with a white jacket and black trousers.

DB13
THE ARTIST BUNNYKINS™

Designer:	Based on a design by Walter Hayward
Modeller:	Alan Maslankowski
Height:	3 ¾", 9.5 cm
Colour:	Burgundy, yellow and blue
Issued:	1975 - 1982

Back Stamp	Price			
	U.S. $	Can. $	U.K. £	Aust. $
BK-1 to BK-3	325.00	450.00	200.00	500.00

DB14
GRANDPA'S STORY BUNNYKINS™

Designer:	Based on a design by Walter Hayward
Modeller:	Alan Maslankowski
Height:	4", 10.1 cm
Colour:	Burgundy, grey, yellow blue and green
Issued:	1975 - 1983

Back Stamp	Price			
	U.S. $	Can. $	U.K. £	Aust. $
BK-1 to BK-3	325.00	450.00	200.00	500.00

DB15
SLEEPYTIME BUNNYKINS™

Designer:	Based on a design by Walter Hayward
Modeller:	Alan Maslankowski
Height:	1 ¾", 4.7 cm
Colour:	Brown, white, yellow, blue and red
Issued:	1975 - 1993

Back Stamp	Price			
	U.S. $	Can. $	U.K. £	Aust. $
BK-1 to BK-5	65.00	95.00	45.00	100.00

DB16
MR. BUNNYBEAT STRUMMING™

Designer:	Harry Sales
Modeller:	David Lyttleton
Height:	4 ½", 11.9 cm
Colour:	Pink and yellow coat, blue and white stripped trousers, white with blue polka-dot neck bow
Issued:	1982 - 1988
Varieties:	Also called Rock and Roll Bunnykins, DB124

Back Stamp	Price			
	U.S. $	Can. $	U.K. £	Aust. $
BK-2 to BK-5	225.00	275.00	160.00	300.00

DB17
SANTA BUNNYKINS HAPPY CHRISTMAS™

Designer:	Harry Sales
Modeller:	David Lyttleton
Height:	4 ½", 11.9 cm
Colour:	Red, white and brown
Issued:	1981 - 1996

Back Stamp	Price			
	U.S. $	Can. $	U.K. £	Aust. $
BK-2 to BK-5	50.00	75.00	35.00	80.00

DB18
MR. BUNNYKINS
AT THE EASTER PARADE™
First Variation

Designer:	Harry Sales
Modeller:	David Lyttleton
Height:	5", 12.7 cm
Colour:	Red, yellow, brown and yellow ribbon
Issued:	1982 - 1993
Varieties:	DB51

Back Stamp	Price			
	U.S. $	Can. $	U.K. £	Aust. $
BK-2 to BK-5	95.00	125.00	60.00	135.00

DB19
MRS. BUNNYKINS
AT THE EASTER PARADE™
First Variation

Designer:	Harry Sales
Modeller:	David Lyttleton
Height:	4 ½", 11.9 cm
Colour:	Pale blue and maroon
Issued:	1982 - 1996
Varieties:	DB52

Back Stamp	Price			
	U.S. $	Can. $	U.K. £	Aust. $
BK-2 to BK-5	65.00	90.00	40.00	95.00

DB20
ASTRO BUNNYKINS ROCKET MAN™

Designer:	Harry Sales
Modeller:	David Lyttleton
Height:	4 ¼", 10.8 cm
Colour:	White, red, blue and yellow
Issued:	1983 - 1988

Back Stamp	Price			
	U.S. $	Can. $	U.K. £	Aust. $
BK-2 to BK-5	150.00	225.00	100.00	225.00

DB21
HAPPY BIRTHDAY BUNNYKINS™

Designer:	Harry Sales
Modeller:	Graham Tongue
Height:	3 ¾", 9.5 cm
Colour:	Red and blue
Issued:	1983 - 1997

Back Stamp	Price			
	U.S. $	Can. $	U.K. £	Aust. $
BK-2 to BK-5	50.00	75.00	30.00	80.00

DB22
JOGGING BUNNYKINS™

Designer:	Harry Sales
Modeller:	David Lyttleton
Height:	2 ½", 6.4 cm
Colour:	Yellow, blue and white
Issued:	1983 - 1989

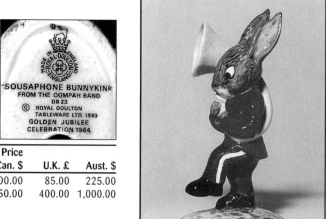

Back Stamp	Price			
	U.S. $	Can. $	U.K. £	Aust. $
BK-2 to BK-5	125.00	175.00	80.00	200.00

DB23
SOUSAPHONE BUNNYKINS™
First Variation

Designer:	Harry Sales
Modeller:	David Lyttleton
Height:	3 ½", 8.9 cm
Colour:	Red, blue and yellow
Issued:	1984 - 1990
Varieties:	DB86, DB105
Series:	Bunnykins Oompah Band

Back Stamp	Price			
	U.S. $	Can. $	U.K. £	Aust. $
BK-2 to BK-5	135.00	200.00	85.00	225.00
Set DB23 - 27 (5pcs.)	675.00	950.00	400.00	1,000.00

DB24
TRUMPETER BUNNYKINS™
First Variation

Designer:	Harry Sales
Modeller:	David Lyttleton
Height:	3 ½", 8.9 cm
Colour:	Red, blue and yellow
Issued:	1984 - 1990
Varieties:	DB87, DB106
Series:	Bunnykins Oompah Band

Back Stamp	Price			
	U.S. $	Can. $	U.K. £	Aust. $
BK-2 to BK-5	135.00	200.00	85.00	225.00

DB25
CYMBALS BUNNYKINS™
First Variation

Designer:	Harry Sales
Modeller:	David Lyttleton
Height:	3 ½", 8.9 cm
Colour:	Red, blue and yellow
Issued:	1984 - 1990
Varieties:	DB88, DB107
Series:	Bunnykins Oompah Band

Back Stamp	Price			
	U.S. $	Can. $	U.K. £	Aust. $
BK-2 to BK-5	135.00	200.00	85.00	225.00

DB26A
DRUMMER BUNNYKINS™
Style One, First Variation, 50th Anniversary Edition

Designer:	Harry Sales
Modeller:	David Lyttleton
Height:	3 ½", 8.9 cm
Colour:	Blue, yellow, red and cream
Issued:	1984 - 1984
Series:	Bunnykins Oompah Band

Back Stamp	Price			
	U.S. $	Can. $	U.K. £	Aust. $
BK-3	175.00	250.00	115.00	275.00

DB26B
DRUMMER BUNNYKINS™
Style One, Second Variation

Designer:	Harry Sales
Modeller:	David Lyttleton
Height:	3 ¾", 9.5 cm
Colour:	Blue, yellow, red and cream
Issued:	1984 - 1990
Varieties:	DB89, DB108
Series:	Bunnykins Oompah Band

Back Stamp	Price			
	U.S. $	Can. $	U.K. £	Aust. $
BK-2 to BK-5	135.00	200.00	85.00	225.00

DB27
DRUM-MAJOR BUNNYKINS™
First Variation

Designer:	Harry Sales
Modeller:	David Lyttleton
Height:	3 ½", 8.9 cm
Colour:	Red, blue and yellow
Issued:	1984 - 1990
Varieties:	DB90, DB109
Series:	Bunnykins Oompah Band

Back Stamp	Price			
	U.S. $	Can. $	U.K. £	Aust. $
BK-2 to BK-5	135.00	200.00	85.00	225.00

DB28A
OLYMPIC BUNNYKINS™
First Variation

Designer:	Harry Sales
Modeller:	David Lyttleton
Height:	3 ¾", 9.5 cm
Colour:	White and blue
Issued:	1984 - 1988

Back Stamp	Price			
	U.S. $	Can. $	U.K. £	Aust. $
BK-2 to BK-5	175.00	250.00	100.00	275.00

DB28B
OLYMPIC BUNNYKINS™
Second Variation

Designer:	Harry Sales
Modeller:	David Lyttleton
Height:	3 ½", 8.9 cm
Colour:	Gold and green
Issued:	1984 - 1984

Back Stamp	Price			
	U.S. $	Can. $	U.K. £	Aust. $
BK-3 Special	350.00	500.00	200.00	600.00

DB29A
TOUCHDOWN BUNNYKINS™
First Variation

Designer:	Harry Sales
Modeller:	David Lyttleton
Height:	3 ¼", 8.3 cm
Colour:	Blue and white
Issued:	1985 - 1988
Varieties:	DB29B, DB96, DB97, DB98, DB99, DB100

Back Stamp	Price			
	U.S. $	Can. $	U.K. £	Aust. $
BK-3 to BK-5	150.00	200.00	95.00	225.00

DB29B
TOUCHDOWN BUNNYKINS™
Second Variation (Boston College)

Designer:	Harry Sales
Modeller:	David Lyttleton
Height:	3 ¼", 8.3 cm
Colour:	Maroon and gold
Issued:	1985 in a limited edition of 50
Varieties:	DB29A, DB96, DB97, DB98, DB99, DB100

Back Stamp	Price			
	U.S. $	Can. $	U.K. £	Aust. $
BK-2	2,000.00	2,750.00	1,250.00	2,750.00

DB30
KNOCKOUT BUNNYKINS™

Designer:	Harry Sales
Modeller:	David Lyttleton
Height:	4", 10.1 cm
Colour:	Yellow, green and white
Issued:	1984 - 1988

Back Stamp	Price			
	U.S. $	Can. $	U.K. £	Aust. $
BK-3 to BK-5	250.00	350.00	160.00	375.00

DB31
DOWNHILL BUNNYKINS™

Designer:	Harry Sales	
Modeller:	Graham Tongue	
Height:	2 ½", 6.4 cm	
Colour:	Yellow, green, maroon and grey	
Issued:	1985 - 1988	

Back Stamp	Price			
	U.S. $	Can. $	U.K. £	Aust. $
BK-3 to BK-5	200.00	300.00	125.00	325.00

DB32
BOGEY BUNNYKINS™

Designer:	Harry Sales
Modeller:	David Lyttleton
Height:	4", 10.1 cm
Colour:	Green, brown and yellow
Issued:	1984 - 1992

Back Stamp	Price			
	U.S. $	Can. $	U.K. £	Aust. $
BK-2 to BK-5	125.00	200.00	75.00	200.00

DB33A
TALLY HO!™
Music Box
First Variation, Tally-Ho! Figurine

Designer:	Based on a design by Walter Hayward
Modeller:	Albert Hallam
Height:	7", 17.8 cm
Colour:	Red coat, yellow jumper
Issued:	1984 - 1993
Tune:	Rock A Bye Baby

Back Stamp	Price			
	U.S. $	Can. $	U.K. £	Aust. $
BKT-8a to BKT-10a	225.00	300.00	135.00	325.00

DB33B
TALLY HO!™
Music Box
Second Variation, William Bunnykins Figurine

Designer:	Based on a design by Walter Hayward
Modeller:	Albert Hallam
Height:	7", 17.8 cm
Colour:	Brown trousers, red coat and maroon tie
Issued:	1988 - 1991
Tune:	'Rock A Bye Baby'

Back Stamp	Price			
	U.S. $	Can. $	U.K. £	Aust. $
BKT-8a to BKT-10a	250.00	325.00	150.00	350.00

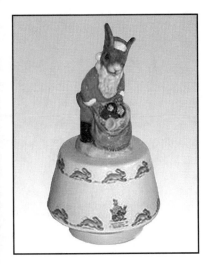

DB34
SANTA BUNNYKINS™
Music Box

Designer:	Harry Sales
Modeller:	David Lyttleton
Height:	7 ¼", 18.4 cm
Colour:	Red, white and brown
Issued:	1984 - 1991
Tune:	'White Christmas'

Back Stamp	Price			
	U.S. $	Can. $	U.K. £	Aust. $
BKT-8a to BKT-10a	200.00	275.00	125.00	300.00

DB35
ASTRO BUNNYKINS ROCKET MAN™
Music Box

Designer:	Harry Sales
Modeller:	David Lyttleton
Height:	7", 17.8 cm
Colour:	White, red and blue
Issued:	1984 - 1989
Tune:	'Fly Me To The Moon'

Back Stamp	Price			
	U.S. $	Can. $	U.K. £	Aust. $
BKT-8a to BKT-10a	250.00	325.00	150.00	350.00

DB36
HAPPY BIRTHDAY BUNNYKINS™
Music Box

Designer:	Harry Sales
Modeller:	Graham Tongue
Height:	7", 17.8 cm
Colour:	Red and white
Issued:	1984 - 1991
Tune:	'Happy Birthday To You'

Backstamp not available at press time

Back Stamp	Price			
	U.S. $	Can. $	U.K. £	Aust. $
BKT-8a to BKT-10a	200.00	275.00	125.00	300.00

DB37
JOGGING BUNNYKINS™
Music Box

Designer:	Harry Sales
Modeller:	David Lyttleton
Height:	5 ½", 14.0 cm
Colour:	Yellow and blue
Issued:	1987 - 1989
Tune:	'King of the Road'

Backstamp not available at press time

Back Stamp	Price			
	U.S. $	Can. $	U.K. £	Aust. $
BKT-8a to BKT-10a	200.00	275.00	125.00	300.00

DB38
MR. BUNNYBEAT STRUMMING™
Music Box

Designer:	Harry Sales
Modeller:	David Lyttleton
Height:	7 ½", 19.1 cm
Colour:	Pink, white and yellow
Issued:	1987 - 1989
Tune:	'Hey Jude'

Backstamp not available at press time

Back Stamp	Price			
	U.S. $	Can. $	U.K. £	Aust. $
BKT-8a to BKT-10a	250.00	350.00	175.00	375.00

BUNNYKINS

DB198 – Statue of Liberty
Bunnykins

DB199 – Airman Bunnykins

DB200 - Happy Millennium Bunnykins Tableau

DB201 - Cowboy Bunnykins

DB202 – Indian Bunnykins

DB203 – Businessman Bunnykins

DB204 – Morris Dancer
Bunnykins

DB205 – Runner Bunnykins

DB206 – Swimmer Bunnykins

DB207 – Gymnast Bunnykins

DB208 – Basketball Bunnykins
Style One

BUNNYKINS

DB209 – Soccer Bunnykins

DB210 – Trumpet Player
Bunnykins

DB211 – Minstrel Bunnykins

DB212 – Pilgrim Bunnykins

DB213 – Sundal Bunnykins

DB214 – Lawyer Bunnykins

DB215 – Sightseer Bunnykins

DB216A – England Athlete Bunnykins
Sydney 2000, *First Variation*

DB216B – England Athlete
Bunnykins Sydney 2000
Second Variation

DB217 – Old Balloon Seller
Bunnykins

DB218 – Fortune Teller
Bunnykins

DB219 – Britannia Bunnykins

BUNNYKINS

DB220 – Little Bo Peep
Bunnykins

DB221 – Little Jack Horner
Bunnykins

DB222 – Jack and Jill Bunnykins

DB223 – Choir Singer
Bunnykins

DB224 – Federation Bunnykins

DB225 – Easter Surprise
Bunnykins

DB226 – Mother and Baby Bunnykins
Style Two (Large Size)

DB227 – Father Bunnykins
Style Two (Large Size)

DB228 – Sandcastle Money Box

DB229 – Sands of Time
Bunnykins

DB230 – Little Red Riding Hood
Bunnykins

BUNNYKINS

DB231 – Cinderella Bunnykins

DB233 – Shopper Bunnykins

DB234 – Mr. Punch
Bunnykins

DB235 – Judy Bunnykins

DB236 – Waltzing Matilda
Bunnykins

DB237 – Father Christmas
Bunnykins

DB238 – On Line Bunnykins

DB239 – Little Boy Blue Bunnykins

DB240 – Little Miss Muffet
Bunnykins

DB241 – Bath Night Bunnykins

Note: DB232 not issued

BUNNYKINS

DB242 – Tyrolean Dancer
Bunnykins

DB243 – Little John Bunnykins

DB244 – Robin Hood Bunnykins

DB245 – Maid Marion
Bunnykins

DB246 – Friar Tuck Bunnykins

DB247 – Mary Mary Quite
Contrary Bunnykins

DB248 – Digger Bunnykins

DB249 – Dodgem Bunnykins

DB250 – Drummer Bunnykins
Style Two

DB251 – Captain Cook Bunnykins

DB252 – Mandarin Bunnykins

DB253 – Stop Watch
Bunnykins

BUNNYKINS

DB254 – Vicar Bunnykins

DB255 – Golfer Bunnykins

DB256 – Flamenco Bunnykins

DB257 – Liberty Bell Bunnykins

DB258 – King Richard Bunnykins

DB259 – Town Crier Bunnykins

DB260 – Day Trip Bunnykins

DB261 – Hornpiper Bunnykins

DB262 – Basketball Bunnykins
Style Two

DB263 – Mermaid Bunnykins

DB264 – Will Scarlet
Bunnykins

DB265 – Sheriff of Nottingham
Bunnykins

BUNNYKINS

DB266 – Prince John Bunnykins

DB267 – Chocs Away Bunnykins

DB268 – American Firefighter Bunnykins

DB269 – With Love Bunnykins

DB270 – Wee Willie Winkle Bunnykins

DB271 – Caddie Bunnykins

DB272 – Test Century Bunnykins

DB273 – Deep Sea Diver Bunnykins

DB274 – Dutch Bunnykins

DB275 – Eskimo Bunnykins

DB276 – Sweet Dreams Baby Bunny

BUNNYKINS

DB277 – Strawberries Bunnykins

DB278 – Tennis Bunnykins

DB279 – Ship Ahoy Bunnykins

DB280 – Samurai Bunnykins

DB281 – Matador Bunnykins

DB282 – Ice Hockey Bunnykins

DB283 – Juliet Bunnykins

DB284 – Romeo Bunnykins

DB285 – Christmas Morning Bunnykins

DB286 – Graduation Day Bunnykins

DB287 – Wedding Day Bunnykins

DB39
MRS. BUNNYKINS
AT THE EASTER PARADE™
Music Box

Designer:	Harry Sales
Modeller:	David Lyttleton
Height:	7", 17.8 cm
Colour:	Blue, yellow and maroon
Issued:	1987 - 1991
Tune:	'Easter Parade'

Back Stamp	Price			
	U.S. $	Can. $	U.K. £	Aust. $
BKT-8a to BKT-10a	200.00	275.00	125.00	300.00

DB40
AEROBIC BUNNYKINS™

Designer:	Harry Sales
Modeller:	David Lyttleton
Height:	2 ¾", 7.0 cm
Colour:	Yellow and pale blue
Issued:	1985 - 1988

Back Stamp	Price			
	U.S. $	Can. $	U.K. £	Aust. $
BK-4 to BK-5	200.00	275.00	125.00	275.00

DB41
FREEFALL BUNNYKINS™

Designer:	Harry Sales
Modeller:	David Lyttleton
Height:	2 ¼", 5.7 cm
Colour:	Grey, yellow and white
Issued:	1988 - 1989

Back Stamp	Price			
	U.S. $	Can. $	U.K. £	Aust. $
BK-4 to BK-5	325.00	475.00	200.00	550.00

Note: Different colourway variations exist, dark grey to light grey suits.

DB42
ACE BUNNYKINS™

Designer:	Harry Sales
Modeller:	David Lyttleton
Height:	3 ¾", 9.5 cm
Colour:	White and blue
Issued:	1986 - 1989

Back Stamp	Price			
	U.S. $	Can. $	U.K. £	Aust. $
BK-4 to BK-5	225.00	325.00	150.00	350.00

DB43
HOME RUN BUNNYKINS™
(1 on Back of Jersey)

Designer:	Harry Sales
Modeller:	David Lyttleton
Height:	4", 10.1 cm
Colour:	Blue, yellow and white
Issued:	1986 - 1993

Back Stamp	Price			
	U.S. $	Can. $	U.K. £	Aust. $
BK-4 to BK-5	100.00	150.00	65.00	165.00

DB44: ASSIGNED TO BALLET BUNNYKINS BUT NOT ISSUED.

DB45
KING JOHN™
First Variation

Designer:	Harry Sales
Modeller:	David Lyttleton
Height:	4", 10.1 cm
Colour:	Red, yellow and blue
Issued:	1986 - 1990
Varieties:	DB91
Series:	Bunnykins Royal Family

Back Stamp	Price			
	U.S. $	Can. $	U.K. £	Aust. $
BK-4 to BK-5	125.00	150.00	65.00	175.00
Set DB45 - 49 (5pcs.)	500.00	750.00	325.00	850.00

DB46
QUEEN SOPHIE™
First Variation

Designer:	Harry Sales
Modeller:	David Lyttleton
Height:	4 ½", 11.9 cm
Colour:	Blue and red
Issued:	1986 - 1990
Varieties:	DB92
Series:	Bunnykins Royal Family

Back Stamp	Price			
	U.S. $	Can. $	U.K. £	Aust. $
BK-4 to 5	125.00	165.00	75.00	165.00

DB47
PRINCESS BEATRICE™
First Variation

Designer:	Harry Sales
Modeller:	David Lyttleton
Height:	3 ½", 8.9 cm
Colour:	Pale green
Issued:	1986 - 1990
Varieties:	DB93
Series:	Bunnykins Royal Family

Back Stamp	Price			
	U.S. $	Can. $	U.K. £	Aust. $
BK-4a to BK-5a	125.00	165.00	75.00	165.00

DB48
PRINCE FREDERICK™
First Variation

Designer:	Harry Sales
Modeller:	David Lyttleton
Height:	3 ½", 8.9 cm
Colour:	Groon, white and rod
Issued:	1986 - 1990
Varieties:	DB94
Series:	Bunnykins Royal Family

Back Stamp	Price			
	U.S. $	Can. $	U.K. £	Aust. $
BK-4a to BK-5a	125.00	165.00	75.00	165.00

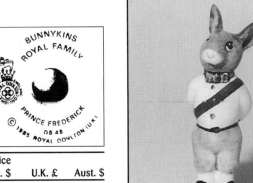

DB49
HARRY THE HERALD™
First Variation

Designer:	Harry Sales
Modeller:	David Lyttleton
Height:	3 ½", 8.9 cm
Colour:	Maroon, white and tan
Issued:	1986 - 1990
Varieties:	DB95, DB115
Series:	Bunnykins Royal Family

Back Stamp	Price			
	U.S. $	Can. $	U.K. £	Aust. $
BK-4a to BK-5a	135.00	175.00	100.00	200.00

DB50
UNCLE SAM BUNNYKINS™
First Variation

Designer:	Harry Sales
Modeller:	David Lyttleton
Height:	4 ½", 11.9 cm
Colour:	Blue, red and white
Issued:	1986 - 2001
Varieties:	DB175

Back Stamp	Price			
	U.S. $	Can. $	U.K. £	Aust. $
BK-4a to BK-5a	65.00	100.00	40.00	100.00

Note: Prototype exists with yellow bowtie; and a colourway variation exists with a dark blue jacket, an all white model is also known.

DB51
MR. BUNNYKINS AT THE EASTER PARADE™
Second Variation

Designer:	Harry Sales
Modeller:	David Lyttleton
Height:	5", 12.7 cm
Colour:	Blue tie and hat band, maroon coat, light grey trousers, pink ribbon on package
Issued:	1986 - 1986
Varieties:	DB18

Back Stamp	Price			
	U.S. $	Can. $	U.K. £	Aust. $
BK-4	1,200.00	1,800.00	700.00	2,000.00

DB52
MRS. BUNNYKINS AT THE EASTER PARADE™
Second Variation

Designer:	Harry Sales
Modeller:	David Lyttleton
Height:	4 ½", 11.9 cm
Colour:	Maroon dress, white collar, blue bow on bonnet, multicoloured bows on packages
Issued:	1986 - 1986
Varieties:	DB19
Series:	Special Events 1986

Back Stamp	Price			
	U.S. $	Can. $	U.K. £	Aust. $
BK-4	900.00	1,250.00	600.00	1,350.00

DB53
CAROL SINGER BUNNYKINS™
Music Box

Designer:	Harry Sales
Modeller:	David Lyttleton
Height:	7", 17.8 cm
Colour:	Red, yellow and green
Issued:	1986 - 1990
Tune:	'Silent Night'

Backstamp not
available
at press time

Back Stamp	Price			
	U.S. $	Can. $	U.K. £	Aust. $
BK-9a to BK-10a	400.00	550.00	250.00	600.00

DB54
COLLECTOR BUNNYKINS™

Designer:	Harry Sales
Modeller:	David Lyttleton
Height:	4 ¼", 10.8 cm
Colour:	Brown, blue and grey
Issued:	1987 - 1987
Series:	ICC Members Exclusive

Back Stamp	Price			
	U.S. $	Can. $	U.K. £	Aust. $
BK-5 Special	525.00	750.00	325.00	800.00

DB55
BEDTIME BUNNYKINS™
First Variation

Designer:	Graham Tongue
Modeller:	David Lyttleton
Height:	3 ¼", 8.3 cm
Colour:	Blue and white stripped pyjamas, brown teddy bear
Issued:	1987 - 1998
Varieties:	DB63, DB79, DB103

Back	Price			
Stamp	U.S. $	Can. $	U.K. £	Aust. $
BK-5a	45.00	65.00	30.00	75.00

Note: A colourway variation exists with a white bear.

DB56
BE PREPARED BUNNYKINS™

Designer:	Graham Tongue
Modeller:	David Lyttleton
Height:	4", 10.1 cm
Colour:	Dark green and grey
Issued:	1987 - 1996

Back	Price			
Stamp	U.S. $	Can. $	U.K. £	Aust. $
BK-5a	75.00	100.00	50.00	100.00

DB57
SCHOOLDAYS BUNNYKINS™

Designer:	Graham Tongue
Modeller:	David Lyttleton
Height:	3 ½", 8.9 cm
Colour:	Dark green, white and yellow
Issued:	1987 - 1994

Back	Price			
Stamp	U.S. $	Can. $	U.K. £	Aust. $
BK-5a	150.00	200.00	100.00	200.00

DB58
AUSTRALIAN BUNNYKINS™

Designer:	Harry Sales
Modeller:	Warren Platt
Height:	4", 10.1 cm
Colour:	Gold and green
Issued:	1988 - 1988

Back Stamp	Price			
	U.S. $	Can. $	U.K. £	Aust. $
BK-5a Special	375.00	525.00	250.00	550.00

DB59
STORYTIME BUNNYKINS™
Second Variation

Designer:	Based on a design by Walter Hayward
Modeller:	Albert Hallam
Height:	3", 7.6 cm
Colour:	Left - green polka dots on white dress, yellow shoes
	Right - yellow dress, green shoes
Issued:	1987 - 1987
Varieties:	DB9; also called Partners in Collecting, DB151
Series:	Special Events 1987

Back Stamp	Price			
	U.S. $	Can. $	U.K. £	Aust. $
BK-5	300.00	475.00	200.00	500.00

DB60
SCHOOLMASTER BUNNYKINS™

Designer:	Graham Tongue
Modeller:	Warren Platt
Height:	4", 10.1 cm
Colour:	Black, green and white
Issued:	1987 - 1996

Back Stamp	Price			
	U.S. $	Can. $	U.K. £	Aust. $
BK-5a	90.00	125.00	60.00	135.00

DB61
BROWNIE BUNNYKINS™

Designer:	Graham Tongue
Modeller:	Warren Platt
Height:	4", 10.1 cm
Colour:	Brown uniform, yellow neck-tie
Issued:	1987 - 1993

Back Stamp	Price			
	U.S. $	Can. $	U.K. £	Aust. $
BK-5a	150.00	200.00	90.00	225.00

Note: Models with unpainted belts exist.

DB62
SANTA BUNNYKINS HAPPY CHRISTMAS™
Christmas Tree Ornament

Designer:	Harry Sales
Modeller:	David Lyttleton
Height:	3 ¾", 9.5 cm
Colour:	Red and white
Issued:	1987 in a limited edition of 1,551

Back Stamp	Price			
	U.S. $	Can. $	U.K. £	Aust. $
BK-5	800.00	1,200.00	500.00	1,250.00

Note: A colourway variation exists with a white jacket and trousers.

DB63
BEDTIME BUNNYKINS™
Second Variation

Designer:	Graham Tongue
Modeller:	David Lyttleton
Height:	3 ¼", 8.3 cm
Colour:	Red and white stripped pyjamas, white teddy bear
Issued:	1987 - 1987
Varieties:	DB55, DB79, DB103

Back Stamp	Price			
	U.S. $	Can. $	U.K. £	Aust. $
BK-5a Special	300.00	450.00	200.00	500.00

DB64
POLICEMAN BUNNYKINS™

Designer:	Graham Tongue	
Modeller:	Martyn Alcock	
Height:	4 ¼", 10.8 cm	
Colour:	Dark blue uniform	
Issued:	1988 - 2000	

Back Stamp	Price U.S. $	Can. $	U.K. £	Aust. $
BK-5a to BK-8a	50.00	65.00	30.00	75.00

DB65
LOLLIPOPMAN BUNNYKINS™

Designer:	Graham Tongue	
Modeller:	Martyn Alcock	
Height:	3 ¾", 9.5cm	
Colour:	White and yellow	
Issued:	1988 - 1991	

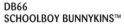

Back Stamp	Price U.S. $	Can. $	U.K. £	Aust. $
BK-5a	250.00	350.00	150.00	350.00

Note: Two colourway variations in the sign exist, one with a red rim and the other with a white rim.

DB66
SCHOOLBOY BUNNYKINS™

Designer:	Graham Tongue	
Modeller:	Martyn Alcock	
Height:	4", 10.1 cm	
Colour:	Blue, white and grey	
Issued:	1988 - 1991	

Back Stamp	Price U.S. $	Can. $	U.K. £	Aust. $
BK-5a	275.00	250.00	175.00	350.00

DB67
FAMILY PHOTOGRAPH BUNNYKINS™
Second Variation

Designer:	Based on a design by Walter Hayward
Modeller:	Albert Hallam
Height:	4 ½", 11.9 cm
Colour:	Pink, black and white
Issued:	1988 - 1988
Varieties:	DB1; also called Father, Mother and Victoria Bunnykins, DB68
Series:	Special Events 1988

Back Stamp	Price			
	U.S. $	Can. $	U.K. £	Aust. $
BK-5 Special	250.00	350.00	165.00	375.00

DB68
FATHER, MOTHER & VICTORIA BUNNYKINS™

Designer:	Based on design Family Photograph by Walter Hayward
Modeller:	Martyn Alcock
Height:	4 ½", 11.9 cm
Colour:	Blue, grey, maroon and yellow
Issued:	1988 - 1996
Varieties:	Also called Family Photograph Bunnykins, DB1, DB67

Back Stamp	Price			
	U.S. $	Can. $	U.K. £	Aust. $
BK-5	75.00	100.00	50.00	110.00

DB69
WILLIAM BUNNYKINS™

Designer:	Based on a design by Walter Hayward
Modeller:	Martyn Alcock
Height:	4", 10.1 cm
Colour:	Red and white
Issued:	1988 - 1993
Varieties:	Also called Tally Ho! Bunnykins, DB12, DB78

Back Stamp	Price			
	U.S. $	Can. $	U.K. £	Aust. $
BK-5	125.00	165.00	75.00	165.00

DB70
SUSAN BUNNYKINS™

Designer:	Based on the design Busy Needles by Walter Hayward
Modeller:	Martyn Alcock
Height:	3 ¼", 8.3 cm
Colour:	White, blue and yellow
Issued:	1988 - 1993
Varieties:	Also called Busy Needles Bunnykins, DB10

Back Stamp	Price			
	U.S. $	Can. $	U.K. £	Aust. $
BK-5a	150.00	200.00	90.00	200.00

DB71
POLLY BUNNYKINS™

Designer:	Graham Tongue
Modeller:	Martyn Alcock
Height:	3 ½", 8.9 cm
Colour:	Pink
Issued:	1988 - 1993

Back Stamp	Price			
	U.S. $	Can. $	U.K. £	Aust. $
BK-5a	125.00	165.00	75.00	165.00

DB72
TOM BUNNYKINS™

Designer:	Graham Tongue
Modeller:	Martyn Alcock
Height:	3", 7.6 cm
Colour:	Browns, white and blue
Issued:	1988 - 1993

Back Stamp	Price			
	U.S. $	Can. $	U.K. £	Aust. $
BK-5a	125.00	165.00	75.00	165.00

DB73
HARRY BUNNYKINS™

Designer:	Graham Tongue
Modeller:	Martyn Alcock
Height:	3", 7.9 cm
Colour:	Blue, brown, white and yellow
Issued:	1988 - 1993

Back Stamp	Price			
	U.S. $	Can. $	U.K. £	Aust. $
BK-5a	95.00	135.00	60.00	145.00

DB74A
NURSE BUNNYKINS™
First Variation (Red Cross)

Designer:	Graham Tongue
Modeller:	Martyn Alcock
Height:	4 ¼", 10.8 cm
Colour:	Dark and light blue and white, red cross
Issued:	1989 - 1994
Varieties:	DB74B

Back Stamp	Price			
	U.S. $	Can. $	U.K. £	Aust. $
BK-5a	250.00	325.00	150.00	350.00

DB74B
NURSE BUNNYKINS™
Second Variation (Green Cross)

Designer:	Graham Tongue
Modeller:	Martyn Alcock
Height:	4 ¼", 10.8 cm
Colour:	Dark and light blue and white, green cross
Issued:	1994 - 2000
Varieties:	DB74A

Back Stamp	Price			
	U.S. $	Can. $	U.K. £	Aust. $
BK-5a to BK-8a	50.00	65.00	30.00	75.00

DB75
FIREMAN BUNNYKINS™
First Variation

Designer:	Graham Tongue
Modeller:	Martyn Alcock
Height:	4 ¼", 10.8 cm
Colour:	Dark blue and yellow
Issued:	1989 - 2001
Varieties:	DB183; Also called American Firefighter Bunnykins, DB268

Back Stamp	Price			
	U.S. $	Can. $	U.K. £	Aust. $
BK-5 to BK-10	50.00	65.00	30.00	75.00

DB76
POSTMAN BUNNYKINS™

Designer:	Graham Tongue
Modeller:	Martyn Alcock
Height:	4 ½", 11.9 cm
Colour:	Dark blue and red
Issued:	1989 - 1993

Back Stamp	Price			
	U.S. $	Can. $	U.K. £	Aust. $
BK-5	150.00	200.00	100.00	225.00

DB77
PAPERBOY BUNNYKINS™

Designer:	Graham Tongue
Modeller:	Martyn Alcock
Height:	4", 10.1 cm
Colour:	Green, yellow, red and white
Issued:	1989 - 1993

Back Stamp	Price			
	U.S. $	Can. $	U.K. £	Aust. $
BK-5	150.00	200.00	90.00	225.00

DB78
TALLY HO! BUNNYKINS™
Second Variation

Designer:	Based on a design by Walter Hayward
Modeller:	Albert Hallam
Height:	4", 10.1 cm
Colour:	Light blue coat and white rocking horse, yellow sweater
Issued:	1988 - 1988
Varieties:	DB12; also called William Bunnykins, DB69

Back Stamp	Price			
	U.S. $	Can. $	U.K. £	Aust. $
BK-5 Special	200.00	300.00	125.00	325.00

DB79
BEDTIME BUNNYKINS™
Third Variation

Designer:	Graham Tonge
Modeller:	David Lyttleton
Height:	3 ¼", 8.3 cm
Colour:	Light blue and white
Issued:	1988 - 1988
Varieties:	DB55, DB63, DB103

Back Stamp	Price			
	U.S. $	Can. $	U.K. £	Aust. $
BK-5 Special	500.00	750.00	350.00	800.00

Note: This was a limited colourway commissioned by Belk's Department Stores.

DB80
DOLLIE BUNNYKINS PLAYTIME™
Second Variation

Designer:	Based on a design by Walter Hayward
Modeller:	Albert Hallam
Height:	4", 10.1 cm
Colour:	White and yellow
Issued:	1988 in a limited edition of 250
Varieties:	DB8

Back Stamp	Store	Price			
		U.S. $	Can. $	U.K. £	Aust. $
BK-5 Special	Higbee	150.00	225.00	100.00	275.00
BK-5 Special	Holmes	150.00	225.00	100.00	275.00
BK-5 Special	Hornes	150.00	225.00	100.00	275.00
BK-5 Special	Strawbridge	150.00	225.00	100.00	275.00

DB81
BILLIE & BUNTIE BUNNYKINS
SLEIGH RIDE™
Second Variation

Designer:	Based on a design by Walter Hayward
Modeller:	Albert Hallam
Height:	3 ½", 8.9 cm
Colour:	Green, yellow and red
Issued:	1989 - 1989
Varieties:	DB4
Series:	Special Events 1989

Back Stamp	Price			
	U.S. $	Can. $	U.K. £	Aust. $
BK-5 Special	200.00	300.00	125.00	325.00

DB82
ICE CREAM BUNNYKINS™

Designer:	Graham Tongue
Modeller:	Warren Platt
Height:	4 ½", 11.9 cm
Colour:	White, blue and green
Issued:	1990 - 1993

Back Stamp	Price			
	U.S. $	Can. $	U.K. £	Aust. $
BK-5	175.00	250.00	100.00	250.00

DB83
SUSAN BUNNYKINS AS
QUEEN OF THE MAY™

Designer:	Graham Tongue
Modeller:	Martyn Alcock
Height:	4", 10.1 cm
Colour:	White polka-dot dress, blue and brown chair
Issued:	1990 - 1992

Back Stamp	Price			
	U.S. $	Can. $	U.K. £	Aust. $
BK-5	150.00	250.00	100.00	250.00

DB84
FISHERMAN BUNNYKINS™
Style One

Designer:	Graham Tongue
Modeller:	Warren Platt
Height:	4 ¼", 10.8 cm
Colour:	Maroon, yellow and grey
Issued:	1990 - 1993

Back Stamp	Price			
	U.S. $	Can. $	U.K. £	Aust. $
BK-5	150.00	200.00	100.00	225.00

DB85
COOK BUNNYKINS™

Designer:	Graham Tongue
Modeller:	Warren Platt
Height:	4 ¼", 10.8 cm
Colour:	White and green
Issued:	1990 - 1994

Back Stamp	Price			
	U.S. $	Can. $	U.K. £	Aust. $
BK-5	125.00	175.00	75.00	200.00

DB86
SOUSAPHONE BUNNYKINS™
Second Variation

Designer:	Harry Sales
Modeller:	David Lyttleton
Height:	3 ½", 8.9 cm
Colour:	Blue uniform and yellow sousaphone
Issued:	1990 in a limited edition of 250
Varieties:	DB23, DB105
Series:	Bunnykins Oompah Band

Back Stamp	Price			
	U.S. $	Can. $	U.K. £	Aust. $
BK-5	500.00	750.00	300.00	800.00
DB86 to 90 (5pcs.)	2,500.00	4,000.00	1,650.00	4,000.00

DB87
TRUMPETER BUNNYKINS™
Second Variation

Designer:	Harry Sales
Modeller:	David Lyttleton
Height:	3 ¾", 9.5 cm
Colour:	Blue uniform and yellow trumpet
Issued:	1990 in a limited edition of 250
Varieties:	DB24, DB106
Series:	Bunnykins Oompah Band

Back Stamp	U.S. $	Price Can. $	U.K. £	Aust. $
BK-5	500.00	750.00	300.00	800.00

DB88
CYMBALS BUNNYKINS™
Second Variation

Designer:	Harry Sales
Modeller:	David Lyttleton
Height:	3 ½", 8.9 cm
Colour:	Blue uniform and yellow cymbals
Issued:	1990 in a limited edition of 250
Varieties:	DB25, DB107
Series:	Bunnykins Oompah Band

Back Stamp	U.S. $	Price Can. $	U.K. £	Aust. $
BK-5	500.00	750.00	300.00	800.00

DB89
DRUMMER BUNNYKINS™
Style One, Third Variation

Designer:	Harry Sales
Modeller:	David Lyttleton
Height:	3 ¾", 9.5 cm
Colour:	Blue trousers and sleeves, yellow vest, cream and red drum
Issued:	1990 in a limited edition of 250
Varieties:	DB26B, DB108
Series:	Bunnykins Oompah Band

Back Stamp	U.S. $	Price Can. $	U.K. £	Aust. $
BK-5 Special	500.00	750.00	300.00	800.00

DB90
DRUM-MAJOR BUNNYKINS™
Second Variation

Designer:	Harry Sales
Modeller:	David Lyttleton
Height:	3 ¾", 9.5 cm
Colour:	Blue and yellow uniform
Issued:	1990 in a limited edition of 250
Varieties:	DB27, DB109
Series:	Bunnykins Oompah Band

Back Stamp	Price			
	U.S. $	Can. $	U.K. £	Aust. $
BK-5	500.00	750.00	300.00	800.00

DB91
KING JOHN™
Second Variation

Designer:	Harry Sales
Modeller:	David Lyttleton
Height:	4", 10.1 cm
Colour:	Purple, yellow and white
Issued:	1990 in a limited edition of 250
Varieties:	DB45
Series:	Bunnykins Royal Family

Back Stamp	Price			
	U.S. $	Can. $	U.K. £	Aust. $
BK-5 Special	500.00	750.00	300.00	800.00
Set DB91 - 95 (5 pcs.)	2,500.00	4,000.00	1,650.00	4,000.00

DB92
QUEEN SOPHIE™
Second Variation

Designer:	Harry Sales
Modeller:	David Lyttleton
Height:	4 ½", 11.9 cm
Colour:	Pink and purple
Issued:	1990 in a limited edition of 250
Varieties:	DB46
Series:	Bunnykins Royal Family

Back Stamp	Price			
	U.S. $	Can. $	U.K. £	Aust. $
BK-5	500.00	750.00	300.00	800.00

DB93
PRINCESS BEATRICE™
Second Variation

Designer:	Harry Sales
Modeller:	David Lyttleton
Height:	3 ½", 8.9 cm
Colour:	Yellow and gold
Issued:	1990 in a limited edition of 250
Varieties:	DB47
Series:	Bunnykins Royal Family

Back Stamp	Price			
	U.S. $	Can. $	U.K. £	Aust. $
BK-5a	500.00	750.00	300.00	800.00

DB94
PRINCE FREDERICK™
Second Variation

Designer:	Harry Sales
Modeller:	David Lyttleton
Height:	3 ½", 8.9 cm
Colour:	Red, blue and yellow
Issued:	1990 in a limited edition of 250
Varieties:	DB48
Series:	Bunnykins Royal Family

Back Stamp	Price			
	U.S. $	Can. $	U.K. £	Aust. $
BK-5a	500.00	750.00	300.00	800.00

DB95
HARRY THE HERALD™
Second Variation

Designer:	Harry Sales
Modeller:	David Lyttleton
Height:	3 ½", 8.9 cm
Colour:	Blue, red and yellow
Issued:	1990 in a limited edition of 250
Varieties:	DB49, DB115
Series:	Bunnykins Royal Family

Back Stamp	Price			
	U.S. $	Can. $	U.K. £	Aust. $
BK-5a	500.00	750.00	300.00	800.00

DB96
TOUCHDOWN BUNNYKINS™
Third Variation (Ohio State University)

Designer:	Harry Sales
Modeller:	David Lyttleton
Height:	3 ¼", 8.3 cm
Colour:	Grey and orange
Issued:	1990 in a limited edition of 200
Varieties:	DB29A, DB29B, DB97, DB98, DB99, DB100

Back Stamp	Price U.S. $	Can. $	U.K. £	Aust. $
BK-5	600.00	900.00	400.00	1,000.00
Set DB96-100 (5 pcs.)	3,000.00	4,500.00	2,000.00	5,000.00

DB97
TOUCHDOWN BUNNYKINS™
Fourth Variation (University of Michigan)

Designer:	Harry Sales
Modeller:	David Lyttleton
Height:	3 ¼", 8.3 cm
Colour:	Yellow and blue
Issued:	1990 in a limited edition of 200
Varieties:	DB29A, DB29B, DB96, DB98, DB99, DB100

Back Stamp	Price U.S. $	Can. $	U.K. £	Aust. $
BK-5	600.00	900.00	400.00	1,000.00

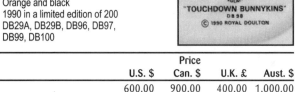

DB98
TOUCHDOWN BUNNYKINS™
Fifth Variation (Cincinnati Bengals)

Designer:	Harry Sales
Modeller:	David Lyttleton
Height:	3 ½", 8.9 cm
Colour:	Orange and black
Issued:	1990 in a limited edition of 200
Varieties:	DB29A, DB29B, DB96, DB97, DB99, DB100

Back Stamp	Price U.S. $	Can. $	U.K. £	Aust. $
BK-5	600.00	900.00	400.00	1,000.00

DB99
TOUCHDOWN BUNNYKINS™
Sixth Variation (Notre Dame College)

Designer:	Harry Sales
Modeller:	David Lyttleton
Height:	3 ½", 8.9 cm
Colour:	Green and yellow
Issued:	1990 in a limited edition of 200
Varieties:	DB29A, DB29B, DB96, DB97, DB98, DB100

Back Stamp	Price			
	U.S. $	Can. $	U.K. £	Aust. $
BK-5	600.00	900.00	400.00	1,000.00

DB100
TOUCHDOWN BUNNYKINS™
Seventh Variation (University of Indiana)

Designer:	Harry Sales
Modeller:	David Lyttleton
Height:	3 ½", 8.9 cm
Colour:	White and red
Issued:	1990 in a limited edition of 200
Varieties:	DB29A, DB29B, DB96, DB97, DB98, DB99

Back Stamp	Price			
	U.S. $	Can. $	U.K. £	Aust. $
BK-5	600.00	900.00	400.00	1,000.00

DB101
BRIDE BUNNYKINS™

Designer:	Graham Tongue
Modeller:	Amanda Hughes-Lubeck
Height:	4", 10.1 cm
Colour:	Cream dress, grey, blue and white train
Issued:	1991 - 2001

Back Stamp	Price			
	U.S. $	Can. $	U.K. £	Aust. $
BK-5	55.00	75.00	35.00	75.00

DB102
GROOM BUNNYKINS™

Designer:	Graham Tongue
Modeller:	Martyn Alcock
Height:	4 ½", 11.9 cm
Colour:	Grey and burgundy
Issued:	1991 - 2001

Back Stamp	Price U.S. $	Can. $	U.K. £	Aust. $
BK-5a	55.00	75.00	35.00	75.00

DB103
BEDTIME BUNNYKINS™
Fourth Variation

Designer:	Graham Tongue
Modeller:	David Lyttleton
Height:	3 ¼", 8.3 cm
Colour:	Yellow and green striped pyjamas, brown teddy bear
Issued:	1991 - 1991
Varieties:	DB55, DB63, DB79
Series:	Special Events Tour 1991

Back Stamp	Colour	Price U.S. $	Can. $	U.K. £	Aust. $
BK-5a Special	Pale yellow	225.00	325.00	150.00	400.00
BK-5a Special	Daffodil yellow	225.00	325.00	150.00	400.00

DB104
CAROL SINGER BUNNYKINS™

Designer:	Harry Sales
Modeller:	David Lyttleton
Height:	4", 10.1 cm
Colour:	Dark green, red, yellow and white
Issued:	1991 in a special edition of 1,000

Back Stamp	Price U.S. $	Can. $	U.K. £	Aust. $
BK-5a, UK Backstamp - 700	300.00	450.00	200.00	550.00
BK-5a, USA Backstamp - 300	450.00	650.00	300.00	700.00

DB105
SOUSAPHONE BUNNYKINS™
Third Variation

Designer:	Harry Sales
Modeller:	David Lyttleton
Height:	4", 10.1 cm
Colour:	Dark green, red and yellow
Issued:	1991 in a special edition of 250
Varieties:	DB23, DB86
Series:	Bunnykins Oompah Band

SOUSAPHONE BUNNYKIN
FROM THE OOMPAH BAND
DB 105
© 1991 ROYAL DOULTON

Back Stamp	Price			
	U.S. $	Can. $	U.K. £	Aust. $
BK-5	550.00	850.00	350.00	900.00
Set DB105 to 109 (5 pcs.)	2,750.00	4,250.00	1,750.00	4,500.00

DB106
TRUMPETER BUNNYKINS™
Third Variation

Designer:	Harry Sales
Modeller:	David Lyttleton
Height:	3 ¾", 9.5 cm
Colour:	Dark green, red and yellow
Issued:	1991 in a special edition of 250
Varieties:	DB24, DB87
Series:	Bunnykins Oompah Band

TRUMPETER BUNNYKINS
FROM THE OOMPAH BAND
DB 106
© 1991 ROYAL DOULTON

Back Stamp	Price			
	U.S. $	Can. $	U.K. £	Aust. $
BK-5	550.00	850.00	350.00	900.00

DB107
CYMBALS BUNNYKINS™
Third Variation

Designer:	Harry Sales
Modeller:	David Lyttleton
Height:	4", 10.1 cm
Colour:	Dark green, red and yellow
Issued:	1991 in a special edition of 250
Varieties:	DB25, DB88
Series:	Bunnykins Oompah Band

"CYMBAL BUNNYKINS"
FROM THE OOMPAH BAND
DB 107
© 1991 ROYAL DOULTON

Back Stamp	Price			
	U.S. $	Can. $	U.K. £	Aust. $
BK-5	550.00	850.00	350.00	900.00

DB108
DRUMMER BUNNYKINS™
Style One, Fourth Variation

Designer:	Harry Sales
Modeller:	David Lyttleton
Height:	3 ½", 8.9 cm
Colour:	Dark green, red and white
Issued:	1991 in a special edition of 250
Varieties:	DB26B, DB89
Series:	Bunnykins Oompah Band

Back Stamp	Price			
	U.S. $	Can. $	U.K. £	Aust. $
BK-5 Special	550.00.	850.00	350.00	900.00

DB109
DRUM-MAJOR BUNNYKINS™
Third Variation

Designer:	Harry Sales
Modeller:	David Lyttleton
Height:	3 ½", 8.9 cm
Colour:	Dark green, red and yellow
Issued:	1991 in a special edition of 250
Varieties:	DB27, DB90
Series:	Bunnykins Oompah Band

Back Stamp	Price			
	U.S. $	Can. $	U.K. £	Aust. $
BK-5	550.00	850.00	350.00	900.00

DB110 TO DB114 NOT ALLOCATED

DB115
HARRY THE HERALD™
Third Variation

Designer:	Harry Sales
Modeller:	David Lyttleton
Height:	3 ½", 8.9 cm
Colour:	Yellow and dark green
Issued:	1991 in a special edition of 300
Varieties:	DB49, DB95
Series:	Bunnykins Royal Family

Back Stamp	Price			
	U.S. $	Can. $	U.K. £	Aust. $
BK-5a Special	950.00	1,400.00	600.00	1,600.00

DB116
GOALKEEPER BUNNYKINS™
First Variation

Designer:	Denise Andrews
Modeller:	Warren Platt
Height:	4 ½", 11.9 cm
Colour:	Green and black
Issued:	1991 in a special edition of 250
Varieties:	DB118, DB120, DB122
Series:	Footballers

Back Stamp	Price			
	U.S. $	Can. $	U.K. £	Aust. $
BK-5a Special	500.00	800.00	350.00	900.00

DB117
FOOTBALLER BUNNYKINS™
First Variation

Designer:	Denise Andrews
Modeller:	Warren Platt
Height:	4 ½", 11.9 cm
Colour:	Green and white
Issued:	1991 in a special edition of 250
Varieties:	DB119, DB121; also called Soccer Player, DB123
Series:	Footballers

Back Stamp	Price			
	U.S. $	Can. $	U.K. £	Aust. $
BK-5a Special	500.00	800.00	350.00	900.00

DB118
GOALKEEPER BUNNYKINS™
Second Variation

Designer:	Denise Andrews
Modeller:	Warren Platt
Height:	4 ½", 11.9 cm
Colour:	Red and black
Issued:	1991 in a special edition of 250
Varieties:	DB116, DB120, DB122
Series:	Footballers

Back Stamp	Price			
	U.S. $	Can. $	U.K. £	Aust. $
BK-5a Special	500.00	800.00	350.00	900.00

DB119
FOOTBALLER BUNNYKINS™
Second Variation

Designer:	Denise Andrews
Modeller:	Warren Platt
Height:	4 ½", 11.9 cm
Colour:	Red
Issued:	1991 in a special edition of 250
Varieties:	DB117, DB121; also called Soccer Player, DB123
Series:	Footballers

Back Stamp	Price			
	U.S. $	Can. $	U.K. £	Aust. $
BK-5a Special	500.00	800.00	350.00	900.00

DB120
GOALKEEPER BUNNYKINS™
Third Variation

Designer:	Denise Andrews
Modeller:	Warren Platt
Height:	4 ½", 11.9 cm
Colour:	Yellow and black
Issued:	1991 in a special edition of 250
Varieties:	DB116, DB118, DB122
Series:	Footballers

Back Stamp	Price			
	U.S. $	Can. $	U.K. £	Aust. $
BK-5a Special	500.00	800.00	350.00	900.00

DB121
FOOTBALLER BUNNYKINS™
Third Variation

Designer:	Denise Andrews
Modeller:	Warren Platt
Height:	4 ½", 11.9 cm
Colour:	White and blue
Issued:	1991 in a special edition of 250
Varieties:	DB117, DB119; also called Soccer Player, DB123
Series:	Footballers

Back Stamp	Price			
	U.S. $	Can. $	U.K. £	Aust. $
BK-5a Special	500.00	800.00	350.00	900.00

DB122
GOALKEEPER BUNNYKINS™
Fourth Variation

Designer:	Denise Andrews
Modeller:	Warren Platt
Height:	4 ½", 11.9 cm
Colour:	Yellow and black
Issued:	1991 in a special edition of 250
Varieties:	DB116, DB118, DB120
Series:	Footballers

Back Stamp	Price			
	U.S. $	Can. $	U.K. £	Aust. $
BK-5a Special	500.00	800.00	350.00	900.00

DB123
SOCCER PLAYER BUNNYKINS™

Designer:	Denise Andrews
Modeller:	Warren Platt
Height:	4 ½", 11.9 cm
Colour:	Dark blue and white
Issued:	1991 in a special edition of 250
Varieties:	Also called Footballer Bunnykins, DB117, DB119, DB121
Series:	Footballers

Back Stamp	Price			
	U.S. $	Can. $	U.K. £	Aust. $
BK-5a Special	500.00	800.00	350.00	900.00

DB124
ROCK AND ROLL BUNNYKINS™

Designer:	Harry Sales
Modeller:	David Lyttleton
Height:	4 ½", 11.9 cm
Colour:	White, blue and red
Issued:	1991 in a limited edition of 1,000
Varieties:	Also called Mr. Bunnybeat Strumming, DB16

Back Stamp	Price			
	U.S. $	Can. $	U.K. £	Aust. $
BK-5a Special	450.00	675.00	300.00	750.00

DB125
MILKMAN BUNNYKINS™

Designer:	Graham Tongue
Modeller:	Amanda Hughes-Lubeck
Height:	4 ½", 11.9 cm
Colour:	White, green and grey
Issued:	1992 in a special edition of 1,000

Back Stamp	Price			
	U.S. $	Can. $	U.K. £	Aust. $
BK-5a Special	500.00	750.00	325.00	800.00

DB126
MAGICIAN BUNNYKINS™
First Variation

Designer:	Graham Tongue
Modeller:	Warren Platt
Height:	4 ½", 11.9 cm
Colour:	Black suit, yellow shirt, yellow table cloth with deeper yellow border
Issued:	1992 in a limited edition of 1,000
Varieties:	DB159

Back Stamp	Price			
	U.S. $	Can. $	U.K. £	Aust. $
BK-5	250.00	350.00	150.00	400.00

DB127
GUARDSMAN BUNNYKINS™

Designer:	Denise Andrews
Modeller:	Warren Platt
Height:	4 ½", 11.9 cm
Colour:	Scarlet jacket, black trousers and bearskin hat
Issued:	1992 in a special edition of 1,000

Back Stamp	Price			
	U.S. $	Can. $	U.K. £	Aust. $
BK-5a Special	475.00	600.00	300.00	600.00

DB128
CLOWN BUNNYKINS™
First Variation

Designer:	Denise Andrews
Modeller:	Warren Platt
Height:	4 ¼", 10.8 cm
Colour:	White costume with black stars and pompons, red square on trousers and red ruff at neck
Issued:	1992 in a special edition of 750
Varieties:	DB129

Back Stamp	Price			
	U.S. $	Can. $	U.K. £	Aust. $
BK-5a Special	500.00	750.00	350.00	850.00

DB129
CLOWN BUNNYKINS™
Second Variation

Designer:	Denise Andrews
Modeller:	Warren Platt
Height:	4 ¼", 10.8 cm
Colour:	White costume with red stars and black pompons, black ruff around neck
Issued:	1992 in a special edition of 250
Varieties:	DB128

Back Stamp	Price			
	U.S. $	Can. $	U.K. £	Aust. $
BK-5a Special	1,100.00	1,500.00	700.00	1,600.00

DB130
SWEETHEART BUNNYKINS™
First Variation

Designer:	Graham Tongue
Modeller:	Warren Platt
Height:	3 ¾", 9.5 cm
Colour:	Yellow sweater, blue trousers, red heart
Issued:	1992 - 1997
Varieties:	DB174

Back Stamp	Price			
	U.S. $	Can. $	U.K. £	Aust. $
BK-5	70.00	90.00	45.00	90.00

DB131
MASTER POTTER BUNNYKINS™

Designer:	Graham Tongue
Modeller:	Warren Platt
Height:	3 ¾", 9.5 cm
Colour:	Blue white, green and brown
Issued:	1992 - 1993
Series:	ICC Members Exclusive

Back Stamp	Price			
	U.S. $	Can. $	U.K. £	Aust. $
BK-5 Special	250.00	325.00	150.00	350.00

DB132
HALLOWEEN BUNNYKINS™

Designer:	Graham Tongue
Modeller:	Martyn Alcock
Height:	3 ¼", 8.3 cm
Colour:	Orange and yellow pumpkin
Issued:	1993 - 1997

Back Stamp	Price			
	U.S. $	Can. $	U.K. £	Aust. $
BK-5a	70.00	90.00	45.00	95.00

DB133
AUSSIE SURFER BUNNYKINS™

Designer:	Graham Tongue
Modeller:	Martyn Alcock
Height:	4", 10.1 cm
Colour:	Gold and green outfit, white and blue base
Issued:	1994 - 1997

Back Stamp	Price			
	U.S. $	Can. $	U.K. £	Aust. $
BK-5 Special	125.00	200.00	85.00	200.00

DB134
JOHN BULL BUNNYKINS™

Designer:	Denise Andrews
Modeller:	Amanda Hughes-Lubeck
Height:	4 ½", 11.9 cm
Colour:	Grey, yellow, red white and blue Union Jack waistcoat
Issued:	1993 in a special edition of 1,000

Back Stamp	Price			
	U.S. $	Can. $	U.K. £	Aust. $
BK-5a Special	450.00	600.00	275.00	650.00

DB135
MOUNTIE BUNNYKINS™

Designer:	Graham Tongue
Modeller:	Warren Platt
Height:	4", 10.1 cm
Colour:	Red jacket, dark blue trousers and brown hat
Issued:	1993 in a special edition of 750
Varieties:	DB136

Back Stamp	Price			
	U.S. $	Can. $	U.K. £	Aust. $
Bk-5a Special	600.00	850.00	375.00	1,100.00

DB136
SERGEANT MOUNTIE BUNNYKINS™

Designer:	Graham Tongue
Modeller:	Warren Platt
Height:	4", 10.1 cm
Colour:	Red jacket, yellow stripes on sleeve, dark blue trousers, brown hat
Issued:	1993 in a special edition of 250
Varieties:	DB135

Back Stamp	Price			
	U.S. $	Can. $	U.K. £	Aust. $
Bk-5a Special	950.00	1,300.00	625.00	1,850.00

DB137
60th ANNIVERSARY BUNNYKINS™

Designer:	Graham Tongue
Modeller:	Martyn Alcock
Height:	4 ½", 11.9 cm
Colour:	Lemon, yellow and white
Issued:	1994 - 1994

Back Stamp	Price			
	U.S. $	Can. $	U.K. £	Aust. $
BK-5a	75.00	100.00	50.00	100.00

DB138 TO DB141 NOT ALLOCATED.

DB142
CHEERLEADER BUNNYKINS™
First Variation

Designer:	Denise Andrews
Modeller:	Warren Platt
Height:	4 ½", 11.9 cm
Colour:	Red, white, yellow and black
Issued:	1994 in a special edition of 1,000
Varieties:	DB143

Back Stamp	Price			
	U.S. $	Can. $	U.K. £	Aust. $
BK-5a Special	250.00	350.00	175.00	400.00

DB143
CHEERLEADER BUNNYKINS™
Second Variation

Designer:	Denise Andrews
Modeller:	Warren Platt
Height:	4 ½", 11.9 cm
Colour:	Yellow, white and black
Issued:	1994 in a special edition of 1,000
Varieties:	DB142

Back Stamp	Price			
	U.S. $	Can. $	U.K. £	Aust. $
BK-5a Special	250.00	350.00	175.00	375.00

DB144
BATSMAN BUNNYKINS™

Designer:	Denise Andrews
Modeller:	Amanda Hughes-Lubeck
Height:	4", 10.1 cm
Colour:	White, beige and black
Issued:	1994 in a special edition of 1,000
Series:	Cricket

Back Stamp	Price			
	U.S. $	Can. $	U.K. £	Aust. $
BK-5a Special	350.00	500.00	225.00	550.00

DB145
BOWLER BUNNYKINS™

Designer:	Denise Andrews
Modeller:	Warren Platt
Height:	4", 10.1 cm
Colour:	White, beige and black
Issued:	1994 in a special edition of 1,000
Series:	Cricket

Back Stamp	Price			
	U.S. $	Can. $	U.K. £	Aust. $
BK-5a Special	350.00	500.00	225.00	550.00

DB146
CHRISTMAS SURPRISE BUNNYKINS™

Designer:	Graham Tongue
Modeller:	Warren Platt
Height:	3 ½", 8.9 cm
Colour:	Cream and red
Issued:	1994 - 2000
Varieties:	Also called Santa's Helper Bunnykins, DB192

Back Stamp	Price			
	U.S. $	Can. $	U.K. £	Aust. $
BK-5 to BK-9	50.00	65.00	30.00	75.00

Note: A colourway variation exists see DB192 for details.

DB147
RAINY DAY BUNNYKINS™

Designer:	Graham Tongue
Modeller:	Warren Platt
Height:	4", 10.1 cm
Colour:	Yellow coat and hat, blue trousers, black boots
Issued:	1994 - 1997

RAINY DAY
BUNNYKINS
DB 147
© 1994 ROYAL DOULTON

Back		Price		
Stamp	U.S. $	Can. $	U.K. £	Aust. $
BK-5a	50.00	65.00	30.00	75.00

DB148
BATHTIME BUNNYKINS™

Designer:	Graham Tongue
Modeller:	Warren Platt
Height:	4", 10.1 cm
Colour:	White bathrobe with grey trim, yellow towel and duck
Issued:	1994 - 1997

BATHTIME BUNNYKINS
DB 148
© 1994 ROYAL DOULTON

MADE IN ENGLAND
ROYAL DOULTON

Back		Price		
Stamp	U.S. $	Can. $	U.K. £	Aust. $
BK-5a	50.00	65.00	30.00	70.00

DB149
EASTER GREETINGS BUNNYKINS™

Designer:	Graham Tongue
Modeller:	Warren Platt
Height:	4 ½", 11.9 cm
Colour:	Yellow, white and green
Issued:	1995 - 1999
Varieties:	Also called Easter Surprise Bunnykins, DB225

EASTER GREETINGS
BUNNYKINS
DB 149
© 1994 ROYAL DOULTON

Back		Price		
Stamp	U.S. $	Can. $	U.K. £	Aust. $
BK-5 to BK-7	50.00	65.00	30.00	70.00

DB150
WICKETKEEPER BUNNYKINS™

Designer:	Denise Andrews
Modeller:	Amanda Hughes-Lubeck
Height:	3 ½", 8.9 cm
Colour:	White, beige and black
Issued:	1995 in a special edition of 1,000
Series:	Cricket

Back Stamp	Price			
	U.S. $	Can. $	U.K. £	Aust. $
BK-5a Special	350.00	500.00	225.00	550.00

DB151
PARTNERS IN COLLECTING™

Designer:	Walter Hayward
Modeller:	Albert Hallam
Height:	3", 7.6 cm
Colour:	Red, white and blue
Issued:	1995 - 1995
Varieties:	Also called Storytime Bunnykins, DB9, DB59
Series:	ICC Members Exclusive (15th Anniversary of ICC)

Back Stamp	Price			
	U.S. $	Can. $	U.K. £	Aust. $
BK-5 Special	125.00	175.00	70.00	200.00

DB152
BOY SKATER BUNNYKINS™
First Variation

Designer:	Graham Tongue
Modeller:	Martyn Alcock
Height:	4 ¼", 10.8 cm
Colour:	Blue coat, brown pants, yellow hat, green boots and black skates
Issued:	1995 - 1998
Varieties:	DB187

Back Stamp	Price			
	U.S. $	Can. $	U.K. £	Aust. $
BK-5 to BK-6	65.00	85.00	40.00	90.00

DB153
GIRL SKATER BUNNYKINS™

Designer:	Graham Tongue
Modeller:	Martyn Alcock
Height:	3 ½", 8.9 cm
Colour:	Green coat, with white trim, pink dress, blue books, yellow skates
Issued:	1995 - 1997

Back Stamp	Price			
	U.S. $	Can. $	U.K. £	Aust. $
BK-5	60.00	80.00	40.00	85.00

DB154
FATHER BUNNYKINS™
Style One

Designer:	Martyn Alcock
Modeller:	Martyn Alcock
Height:	4", 10.1 cm
Colour:	Red and white stripped blazer, creamy yellow trousers
Issued:	1996 - 1996
Series:	1. Bunnykins of the Year
	2. Holiday Outing

Back Stamp	Price			
	U.S. $	Can. $	U.K. £	Aust. $
BK-5 Special	60.00	80.00	40.00	85.00

DB155
MOTHER'S DAY BUNNYKINS™

Designer:	Graham Tongue
Modeller:	Shane Ridge
Height:	3 ½", 8.9 cm
Colour:	Brown and blue
Issued:	1995 - 2000

Back Stamp	Price			
	U.S. $	Can. $	U.K. £	Aust. $
BK-5 to BK-9	55.00	70.00	35.00	75.00

DB156
GARDENER BUNNYKINS™

Designer: Warren Platt
Modeller: Warren Platt
Height: 4 ¼", 10.8 cm
Colour: Brown jacket, white shirt, grey
trousers, light green wheelbarrow
Issued: 1996 - 1998

Back Stamp	Price			
	U.S. $	Can. $	U.K. £	Aust. $
BK-5 to BK-6	55.00	70.00	35.00	75.00

DB157
GOODNIGHT BUNNYKINS™

Designer: Graham Tongue
Modeller: Shane Ridge
Height: 3 ¾", 9.5 cm
Colour: Pink nightgown, reddish brown
teddy, blue and white base
Issued: 1995 - 1999

Back Stamp	Price			
	U.S. $	Can. $	U.K. £	Aust. $
BK-5 to BK-7	55.00	70.00	35.00	75.00

DB158
NEW BABY BUNNYKINS™

Designer: Graham Tongue
Modeller: Graham Tongue
Height: 3 ¾", 9.5 cm
Colour: Blue dress with white trim,
white cradle, pink pillow,
yellow blanket
Issued: 1995 - 1999

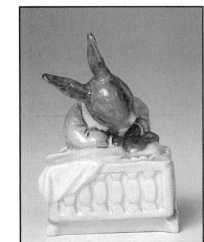

Back Stamp	Price			
	U.S. $	Can. $	U.K. £	Aust. $
BK-5 to BK-7	55.00	70.00	35.00	75.00

DB159
MAGICIAN BUNNYKINS™
Second Variation

Designer:	Graham Tongue
Modeller:	Warren Platt
Height:	4 ½", 11.9 cm
Colour:	Black suit, yellow shirt, yellow table cloth with red border
Issued:	1998 in a special edition of 1,500
Varieties:	DB126

Back Stamp	Price			
	U.S. $	Can. $	U.K. £	Aust. $
BK-5 Special	275.00	400.00	175.00	475.00

DB160
OUT FOR A DUCK BUNNYKINS™

Designer:	Denise Andrews
Modeller:	Amanda Hughes-Lubeck
Height:	4", 10.1 cm
Colour:	White, beige and green
Issued:	1995 in a special edition of 1,250
Series:	Cricket

Back Stamp	Price			
	U.S. $	Can. $	U.K. £	Aust. $
BK-5 Special	350.00	500.00	225.00	550.00

DB161
JESTER BUNNYKINS™

Designer:	Denise Andrews
Modeller:	Shane Ridge
Height:	4 ½", 11.9 cm
Colour:	Red, green and yellow
Issued:	1995 in a special edition of 1,500

Back Stamp	Price			
	U.S. $	Can. $	U.K. £	Aust. $
BK-5 Special	375.00	500.00	225.00	600.00

DB162
TRICK OR TREAT BUNNYKINS™

Designer:	Denise Andrews
Modeller:	Amanda Hughes-Lubeck
Height:	4 ½", 11.9 cm
Colour:	Red dress, black hat, shoes and cloak, white moons and stars
Issued:	1995 in a special edition of 1,500

TRICK OR TREAT BUNNYKINS
DB 162
PRODUCED EXCLUSIVELY
FOR U.K.I. CERAMICS LTD.
IN A SPECIAL EDITION OF 1,500
© 1995 ROYAL DOULTON

Back Stamp	Price			
	U.S. $	Can. $	U.K. £	Aust. $
BK-5 Special	550.00	800.00	350.00	875.00

DB163
BEEFEATER BUNNYKINS™

Designer:	Denise Andrews
Modeller:	Amanda Hughes-Lubeck
Height:	4 ½", 11.9 cm
Colour:	Red, gold, black and white livery, black hat with red, blue and white band
Issued:	1996 in a special edition of 1,500

BEEFEATER BUNNYKINS
DB 163
PRODUCED EXCLUSIVELY
FOR U.K.I. CERAMICS LTD.
IN A SPECIAL EDITION OF 1,500
© 1996 ROYAL DOULTON

Back Stamp	Price			
	U.S. $	Can. $	U.K. £	Aust. $
BK-5a Special	325.00	450.00	200.00	500.00

DB164
JUGGLER BUNNYKINS™

Designer:	Denise Andrews
Modeller:	Warren Platt
Height:	4 ½", 11.9 cm
Colour:	Blue suit, black pompons, white ruff
Issued:	1996 in a special edition of 1,500

JUGGLER BUNNYKINS
DB 164
PRODUCED EXCLUSIVELY
FOR U.K.I. CERAMICS LTD.
IN A SPECIAL EDITION OF 1,500
© 1995 ROYAL DOULTON

Back Stamp	Price			
	U.S. $	Can. $	U.K. £	Aust. $
BK-5 Special	275.00	400.00	175.00	425.00

DB165
RINGMASTER BUNNYKINS™

Designer: Denise Andrews
Modeller: Warren Platt
Height: 4 ½", 11.9 cm
Colour: Black hat and trousers,
red jacket, white waistcoat
and shirt, black bowtie
Issued: 1996 in a special edition of 1,500

| Back | Price | | | |
Stamp	U.S. $	Can. $	U.K. £	Aust. $
BK-5 Special	250.00	350.00	150.00	350.00

DB166
SAILOR BUNNYINS™

Designer: Graham Tongue
Modeller: Shane Ridge
Height: 2 ½", 6.4 cm
Colour: White and blue
Issued: 1997 - 1997
Series: 1. Bunnykins of the Year
2. Holiday Outing

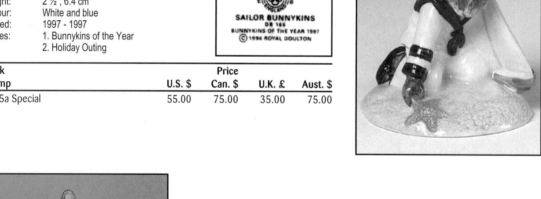

| Back | Price | | | |
Stamp	U.S. $	Can. $	U.K. £	Aust. $
BK-5a Special	55.00	75.00	35.00	75.00

DB167
MOTHER AND BABY BUNNYKINS™
Style One

Designer: Shane Ridge
Modeller: Shane Ridge
Height: 4 ½", 11.9 cm
Colour: Brown, light pink dress,
red shoes, yellow blanket
Issued: 1997 - 2001

| Back | Price | | | |
Stamp	U.S. $	Can. $	U.K. £	Aust. $
BK-5 to BK-11	55.00	75.00	35.00	75.00

DB168
WIZARD BUNNYKINS™

Designer:	Denise Andrews
Modeller:	Shane Ridge
Height:	5", 12.7 cm
Colour:	Brown rabbit, purple robe and hat
Issued:	1997 in a special edition of 2,000

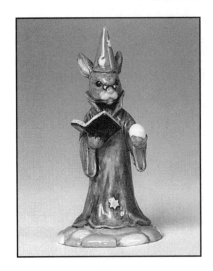

Back Stamp	Price			
	U.S. $	Can. $	U.K. £	Aust. $
BK-5 Special	400.00	525.00	250.00	550.00

DB169
JOCKEY BUNNYKINS™

Designer:	Denise Andrews
Modeller:	Martyn Alcock
Height:	4 ½", 11.9 cm
Colour:	Green, white and yellow jockey suit, black shoes
Issued:	1997 in a special edition of 2,000

Back Stamp	Price			
	U.S. $	Can. $	U.K. £	Aust. $
BK-5a Special	275.00	350.00	150.00	350.00

DB170
FISHERMAN BUNNYKINS™
Style Two

Designer:	Graham Tongue
Modeller:	Shane Ridge
Height:	4", 10.1 cm
Colour:	Blue hat and trousers, light yellow sweater, black wellingtons
Issued:	1997 - 2000

Back Stamp	Price			
	U.S. $	Can. $	U.K. £	Aust. $
BK-5 to BK-9	55.00	70.00	35.00	75.00

DB171
JOKER BUNNYKINS™

Designer:	Denise Andrews
Modeller:	Martyn Alcock
Height:	5", 12.7 cm
Colour:	Yellow jacket, orange and white trousers, black hat
Issued:	1997 in a special edition of 2,500

Back Stamp	Price			
	U.S. $	Can. $	U.K. £	Aust. $
BK-5 Special	150.00	225.00	85.00	250.00

Note: Models exist with different coloured trousers.

DB172
WELSHLADY BUNNYKINS™

Designer:	Denise Andrews
Modeller:	Warren Platt
Height:	5", 12.7 cm
Colour:	Light pink and yellow dress, black hat, maroon shawl
Issued:	1997 in a special edition of 2,500

Back Stamp	Price			
	U.S. $	Can. $	U.K. £	Aust. $
BK-5 Special	250.00	350.00	150.00	350.00

Note: A colourway model exists with a white shawl and is 4" high.

DB173
BRIDESMAID BUNNYKINS™

Designer:	Graham Tongue
Modeller:	Amanda Hughes-Lubeck
Height:	3 ¾", 9.5 cm
Colour:	Light yellow dress, darker yellow flowers
Issued:	1997 - 1999

Back Stamp	Price			
	U.S. $	Can. $	U.K. £	Aust. $
BK-5a to BK-7a	55.00	75.00	35.00	75.00

DB174
SWEETHEART BUNNYKINS™
Second Variation - I Love Bunnykins

Designer:	Graham Tongue
Modeller:	Warren Platt
Height:	3 ¾", 9.5 cm
Colour:	White and blue, pink heart
Issued:	1997 in a special edition of 2,500
Varieties:	DB130

Back Stamp	Price			
	U.S. $	Can. $	U.K. £	Aust. $
BK-5 Special	175.00	250.00	100.00	275.00

DB175
UNCLE SAM BUNNYKINS™
Second Variation

Designer:	Harry Sales
Modeller:	David Lyttleton
Height:	4 ½", 11.9 cm
Colour:	Red jacket, yellow shirt, blue and white striped trousers, red white and blue hat, platinum bowtie
Issued:	1997 in a special edition of 1,500
Varieties:	DB50
Series:	American Heritage Collection

Back Stamp	Price			
	U.S. $	Can. $	U.K. £	Aust. $
BK-5a Special	250.00	325.00	150.00	325.00

DB176
BALLERINA BUNNYKINS™

Designer:	Graham Tongue
Modeller:	Graham Tongue
Height:	3 ½", 8.9 cm
Colour:	Pink dress, yellow footstool
Issued:	1998 - 2001

Back Stamp	Price			
	U.S. $	Can. $	U.K. £	Aust. $
BK-6a to BK-9a	50.00	65.00	30.00	70.00

DB177
SEASIDE BUNNYKINS™

Designer:	Martyn Alcock
Modeller:	Martyn Alcock
Height:	3", 7.6 cm
Colour:	Blue bathing costume, white and blue bathing cap, yellow sandy base
Issued:	1998 - 1998
Series:	1. Bunnykins of the Year
	2. Holiday Outing

Back Stamp	Price			
	U.S. $	Can. $	U.K. £	Aust. $
BK-6 Special	75.00	100.00	50.00	100.00

DB178
IRISHMAN BUNNYKINS™

Designer:	Denise Andrews
Modeller:	Martyn Alcock
Height:	5", 12.7 cm
Colour:	Green waistcoat with shamrocks, white shirt, tan hat and trousers, white socks and black shoes
Issued:	1998 in a special edition of 2,500

Back Stamp	Price			
	U.S. $	Can. $	U.K. £	Aust. $
BK-6a Special	200.00	250.00	125.00	275.00

DB179
CAVALIER BUNNYKINS™

Designer:	Graham Tongue
Modeller:	Graham Tongue
Height:	4 ½", 11.9 cm
Colour:	Red tunic, white collar, black trousers and hat, yellow cape, light brown boots
Issued:	1998 in a special edition of 2,500

Back Stamp	Price			
	U.S. $	Can. $	U.K. £	Aust. $
BK-6a Special	250.00	350.00	150.00	375.00

DB180
SCOTSMAN BUNNYKINS™

Designer:	Denise Andrews
Modeller:	Graham Tongue
Height:	5", 12.7 cm
Colour:	Dark blue jacket and hat, red-yellow kilt, white shirt, sporran and socks, black shoes
Issued:	1998 in a special edition of 2,500

Back Stamp	Price			
	U.S. $	Can. $	U.K. £	Aust. $
BK-6a Special	150.00	225.00	100.00	250.00

DB181
DOCTOR BUNNYKINS™

Designer:	Martyn Alcock
Modeller:	Martyn Alcock
Height:	4 ¼", 10.8 cm
Colour:	White lab coat and shirt, dark blue trousers, black shoes, white and blue striped tie
Issued:	1998 - 2000

Back Stamp	Price			
	U.S. $	Can. $	U.K. £	Aust. $
BK-6	65.00	85.00	40.00	95.00

DB182
BANJO PLAYER BUNNYKINS™

Designer:	Kimberley Curtis
Modeller:	Shane Ridge
Height:	5", 12.7 cm
Colour:	White and red striped blazer, black trousers, yellow straw hat
Issued:	1999 in a special edition of 2,500
Series:	Jazz Band Collection

Back Stamp	Price			
	U.S. $	Can. $	U.K. £	Aust. $
BK-6a Special	175.00	250.00	100.00	275.00

DB183
FIREMAN BUNNYKINS™
Second Variation

Designer:	Graham Tongue
Modeller:	Martyn Alcock
Height:	4 ¼", 10.8 cm
Colour:	Red jacket and helmet, black, trousers, yellow boots
Issued:	1998 in a special edition of 3,500
Varieties:	DB75; Also called American Firefighter Bunnykins, DB268

Back Stamp	Price			
	U.S. $	Can. $	U.K. £	Aust. $
BK-6a Special	125.00	175.00	75.00	200.00

DB184
CLARINET PLAYER BUNNYKINS™

Designer:	Kimberley Curtis
Modeller:	Shane Ridge
Height:	5", 12.7 cm
Colour:	Blue and white striped jacket, grey trousers, yellow straw hat
Issued:	1999 in a special edition of 2,500
Series:	Jazz Band Collection

Back Stamp	Price			
	U.S. $	Can. $	U.K. £	Aust. $
BK-6a Special	175.00	250.00	100.00	275.00

DB185
DOUBLE BASS PLAYER BUNNYKINS™

Designer:	Kimberley Curtis
Modeller:	Shane Ridge
Height:	5", 12.7 cm
Colour:	Green and yellow striped jacket, green trousers, yellow straw hat
Issued:	1999 in a special edition of 2,500
Series:	Jazz Band Collection

Back Stamp	Price			
	U.S. $	Can. $	U.K. £	Aust. $
BK-6a Special	175.00	250.00	100.00	275.00

DB186
SAXOPHONE PLAYER BUNNYKINS™

Designer:	Kimberley Curtis
Modeller:	Shane Ridge
Height:	5", 12.7 cm
Colour:	Navy and white striped shirt, blue vest, black trousers
Issued:	1999 in a special edition of 2,500
Series:	Jazz Band Collection

Back Stamp	Price			
	U.S. $	Can. $	U.K. £	Aust. $
BK-6 Special	175.00	250.00	100.00	275.00

DB187
BOY SKATER BUNNYKINS™
Second Variation

Designer:	Graham Tongue
Modeller:	Martyn Alcock
Height:	4 ¼", 10.8 cm
Colour:	Blue jacket, white trousers, red boots
Issued:	1998 in a special edition of 2,500
Varieties:	DB152

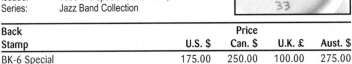

Back Stamp	Price			
	U.S. $	Can. $	U.K. £	Aust. $
BK-6a Special	150.00	200.00	100.00	225.00

DB188
JUDGE BUNNYKINS™

Designer:	Caroline Dadd
Modeller:	Shane Ridge
Height:	4 ¼", 10.8 cm
Colour:	Red and white
Issued:	1999 - 1999
Series:	ICC Membership Gift

Back Stamp	Price			
	U.S. $	Can. $	U.K. £	Aust. $
BK-6 Special	65.00	85.00	40.00	95.00

Note: White unfinished models exist on which the final red glaze was not applied.

DB189
MOTHER BUNNYKINS™

Designer:	Caroline Dadd
Modeller:	Martyn Alcock
Height:	4", 10.1 cm
Colour:	Blue, white and red
Issued:	1999 - 1999
Series:	1. Bunnykins of the Year
	2. Holiday Outing

Back Stamp	Price			
	U.S. $	Can. $	U.K. £	Aust. $
BK-6 Special	50.00	65.00	30.00	65.00

DB190
TOURIST BUNNYKINS™

Designer:	Caroline Dadd
Modeller:	Martyn Alcock
Height:	5", 12.7 cm
Colour:	Blue, yellow, ICC on hat
Issued:	1999 in a limited time offer.
Series:	1. Holiday Outing
	2. ICC Members Exclusive

Back Stamp	Price			
	U.S. $	Can. $	U.K. £	Aust. $
BK-7 Special	95.00	125.00	60.00	125.00

DB191
PIPER BUNNYKINS™

Designer:	Martyn Alcock
Modeller:	Martyn Alcock
Height:	4 ¼", 10.8 cm
Colour:	Green, brown and black
Issued:	1999 in a special edition of 3,000

Back Stamp	Price			
	U.S. $	Can. $	U.K. £	Aust. $
BK-6a Special	150.00	200.00	100.00	200.00

DB192
SANTA'S HELPER BUNNYKINS™

Designer:	Graham Tongue
Modeller:	Warren Platt
Height:	3 ½", 8.9 cm
Colour:	Brown, green, red and yellow
Issued:	1999 in a special edition of 2,500
Varieties:	Also called Christmas Surprise Bunnykins, DB146

Back Stamp	U.S. $	Can. $	U.K. £	Aust. $
		Price		
BK-7a Special	125.00	175.00	75.00	200.00

Note: A colourway variation exists with a white box, suite and hat.

DB193
DETECTIVE BUNNYKINS™

Designer:	Kimberley Curtis
Modeller:	Warren Platt
Height:	4 ¾", 12.1 cm
Colour:	Brown, green, white and tan
Issued:	1999 in a special edition of 2,500

Back Stamp	U.S. $	Can. $	U.K. £	Aust. $
		Price		
BK-7 Special	150.00	200.00	100.00	225.00

DB194
MERRY CHRISTMAS BUNNYKINS TABLEAU™

Designer:	Caroline Dadd
Modeller:	Shane Ridge
Height:	7 ¼" x 5 ½", 18.4 x 14.0 cm
Colour:	Brown, green, red, white and black
Issued:	1999 in a limited edition of 2,000
Series:	Tableau

Back Stamp	U.S. $	Can. $	U.K. £	Aust. $
		Price		
BK-7 Special	400.00	525.00	250.00	600.00

DB195
SYDNEY BUNNYKINS™

Designer:	Dalglish, Bryant, Bartholomeucz
Modeller:	Amanda Hughes-Lubeck
Height:	5", 12.7 cm
Colour:	Blue, white, black and brown
Issued:	1999 in a special numbered edition of 2,500
Series:	Australian Heritage

Back Stamp	Price			
	U.S. $	Can. $	U.K. £	Aust. $
BK-7a Special	175.00	250.00	100.00	275.00

DB196
ANGEL BUNNYKINS™

Designer:	Caroline Dadd
Modeller:	Martyn Alcock
Height:	4", 10.1 cm
Colour:	Brown, yellow and white
Issued:	1999 - 2001

Back Stamp	Price			
	U.S. $	Can. $	U.K. £	Aust. $
BK-7 to BK-9	50.00	65.00	30.00	70.00

DB197
MYSTIC BUNNYKINS™

Designer:	Martyn Alcock
Modeller:	Martyn Alcock
Height:	4 ¾", 12.1 cm
Colour:	Brown, yellow, green and purple
Issued:	July to December 1999

Back Stamp	Price			
	U.S. $	Can. $	U.K. £	Aust. $
BK-8a	65.00	85.00	40.00	95.00

Note: This backstamp incorporates the Top Hat cypher of 1999 and the Millenium stamp.

DB198
STATUE OF LIBERTY BUNNYKINS™

Designer:	Caroline Dadd
Modeller:	Amanda Hughes-Lubeck
Height:	5", 12.7 cm
Colour:	Red, white and blue
Issued:	1999 in a special edition of 3,000
Series:	American Heritage

Back Stamp	Price U.S. $	Can. $	U.K. £	Aust. $
BK-7a Special	165.00	225.00	100.00	250.00

DB199
AIRMAN BUNNYKINS™

Designer:	Caroline Dadd
Modeller:	Shane Ridge
Height:	4 ¼", 10.8 cm
Colour:	Brown, black and yellow
Issued:	1999 in a numbered limited edition of 5,000

Back Stamp	Price U.S. $	Can. $	U.K. £	Aust. $
BK-7 Special	80.00	125.00	50.00	150.00

DB200
HAPPY MILLENNIUM BUNNYKINS™
TABLEAU

Designer:	Caroline Dadd
Modeller:	Shane Ridge
Height:	Unknown
Colour:	Blue, pink, red and black
Issued:	2000

Backstamp not
available
at press time

Back Stamp	Price U.S. $	Can. $	U.K. £	Aust. $
BK- Not known		See below		

Note: Only two produced. One sold at the Bunnykins Millennium Exhibition
Auction for £9,800.00, $15,000.00 U.S. with the proceeds going to charity.
The other is held in the Royal Doulton Archives.

DB201
COWBOY BUNNYKINS™

Designer:	Kimberley Curtis
Modeller:	Martyn Alcock
Height:	4 ½", 11.9 cm
Colour:	Brown, red and cream
Issued:	1999 in a special edition of 2,500

Back Stamp	Price			
	U.S. $	Can. $	U.K. £	Aust. $
BK-7 Special	175.00	275.00	100.00	300.00

DB202
INDIAN BUNNYKINS™

Designer:	Kimberley Curtis
Modeller:	Martyn Alcock
Height:	4 ½", 11.9 cm
Colour:	Brown, cream, red, white and blue
Issued:	1999 in a special edition of 2,500

Back Stamp	Price			
	U.S. $	Can. $	U.K. £	Aust. $
BK-7a Special	175.00	275.00	100.00	300.00

DB203
BUSINESSMAN BUNNYKINS™

Designer:	Caroline Dadd
Modeller:	Martyn Alcock
Height:	4 ¾", 12.1 cm
Colour:	Brown, grey, black and red
Issued:	1999 in a numbered limited edition of 5,000

Back Stamp	Price			
	U.S. $	Can. $	U.K. £	Aust. $
BK-7 Special	80.00	125.00	50.00	150.00

DB204
MORRIS DANCER BUNNYKINS™

Designer:	Caroline Dadd
Modeller:	Shane Ridge
Height:	4 ½", 11.9 cm
Colour:	Brown, cream, black, red and green
Issued:	2000 - 2000
Series:	1. Dancers of the World
	2. Special Events

Back Stamp	Price U.S. $	Can. $	U.K. £	Aust. $
BK-9a Special	70.00	95.00	45.00	100.00

DB205
RUNNER BUNNYKINS™

Designer:	Romanda Groom
Modeller:	Shane Ridge
Height:	4", 10.1 cm
Colour:	Brown, black, white, red and yellow
Issued:	1999 in a limited edition of 2,500
Series:	Bunnykins Games

Back Stamp	Price U.S. $	Can. $	U.K. £	Aust. $
BK-7 Special	100.00	150.00	65.00	150.00
DB205 - 209; 5 pce set	475.00	750.00	300.00	800.00

Note: The Bunnykins Games set was issued with a wooden display stand and certificate.

DB206
SWIMMER BUNNYKINS™

Designer:	Romanda Groom
Modeller:	Shane Ridge
Height:	3", 7.6 cm
Colour:	Brown, blue, green, yellow and black
Issued:	1999 in a limited edition of 2,500
Series:	Bunnykins Games

Back Stamp	Price U.S. $	Can. $	U.K. £	Aust. $
BK-7a Special	100.00	150.00	65.00	150.00

Note: There is only one individually numbered certificate for the complete set of Bunnykins Games.

DB207
GYMNAST BUNNYKINS™

Designer:	Romanda Groom
Modeller:	Shane Ridge
Height:	4", 10.1 cm
Colour:	Brown, red and yellow
Issued:	1999 in a limited edition of 2,500
Series:	Bunnykins Games

Back Stamp	Price			
	U.S. $	Can. $	U.K. £	Aust. $
BK-7 Special	100.00	150.00	65.00	150.00

DB208
BASKETBALL BUNNYKINS™
Style One

Designer:	Romanda Groom
Modeller:	Shane Ridge
Height:	5", 12.7 cm
Colour:	Brown, blue, red and white
Issued:	1999 in a limited edition of 2,500
Series:	Bunnykins Games

Back Stamp	Price			
	U.S. $	Can. $	U.K. £	Aust. $
BK-7a Special	100.00	150.00	65.00	150.00

DB209
SOCCER BUNNYKINS™

Designer:	Romanda Groom
Modeller:	Shane Ridge
Height:	4", 10.1 cm
Colour:	Brown, blue, white, green black and red
Issued:	1999 in a limited edition of 2,500
Series:	Bunnykins Games

Back Stamp	Price			
	U.S. $	Can. $	U.K. £	Aust. $
BK-7 Special	100.00	150.00	65.00	150.00

DB210
TRUMPET PLAYER BUNNYKINS™

Designer: Kimberley Curtis
Modeller: Shane Ridge
Height: 5", 12.7 cm
Colour: Light blue and white striped jacket
black trousers, yellow straw hat
Issued: 2000 in a limited edition of 2,500
Series: Jazz Band Collection

Back Stamp	Price			
	U.S. $	Can. $	U.K. £	Aust. $
BK-8a to BK-9a Special	175.00	250.00	100.00	275.00

DB211
MINSTREL BUNNYKINS™

Designer: Kimberley Curtis
Modeller: Martyn Alcock
Height: 4 ½", 11.9 cm
Colour: Green, red yellow and brown
Issued: 1999 in a numbered limited edition
of 2,500

Back Stamp	Price			
	U.S. $	Can. $	U.K. £	Aust. $
BK-7 Special	175.00	250.00	115.00	250.00

DB212
PILGRIM BUNNYKINS™

Designer: Caroline Dadd
Modeller: Amanda Hughes-Lubeck
Height: 4 ½", 11.9 cm
Colour: Dark green, brown, white,
black and pale blue
Issued: 1999 in a special numbered edition
of 2,500
Series: American Heritage

Back Stamp	Price			
	U.S. $	Can. $	U.K. £	Aust. $
BK-7 Special	200.00	275.00	125.00	300.00

DB213
SUNDIAL BUNNYKINS™

Designer:	Martyn Alcock
Modeller:	Martyn Alcock
Height:	4 ½", 11.9 cm
Colour:	Pale blue, white and brown
Issued:	2000 - 2000
Series:	1. Bunnykins of the Year
	2. Time

Back Stamp	Price			
	U.S. $	Can. $	U.K. £	Aust. $
BK-7 Special to BK-9 Special	55.00	75.00	35.00	85.00

DB214
LAWYER BUNNYKINS™

Designer:	Martyn Alcock
Modeller:	Martyn Alcock
Height:	4", 10.1 cm
Colour:	Brown, black, grey and white
Issued:	2000 - 2000
Series:	ICC Membership Gift

Back Stamp	Price			
	U.S. $	Can. $	U.K. £	Aust. $
BK-7 Special to BK-9 Special	55.00	75.00	35.00	85.00

DB215
SIGHTSEER BUNNYKINS™

Designer:	Caroline Dadd
Modeller:	Martyn Alcock
Height:	4 ½", 11.9 cm
Colour:	Pink, light and dark brown
Issued:	From January to April, 2000
Series:	ICC Members Exclusive

Back Stamp	Price			
	U.S. $	Can. $	U.K. £	Aust. $
BK-9 Special	80.00	100.00	50.00	100.00

DB216A
ENGLAND ATHLETE BUNNYKINS SYDNEY 2000™
First Variation

Changed early in production to DB216B.

Designer: Kimberley Curtis
Modeller: Shane Ridge
Height: 5 ½", 14.0 cm
Colour: White, blue and red
Issued: 2000 (quantity unknown)
Varieties: DB216B

Back		Price		
Stamp	U.S. $	Can. $	U.K. £	Aust. $
BK-9a Special	1,000.00	1,350.00	650.00	1,500.00

DB216B
ENGLAND ATHLETE BUNNYKINS SYDNEY 2000™
Second Variation

Designer: Kimberley Curtis
Modeller: Shane Ridge
Height: 5 ½", 14.0 cm
Colour: White, blue and red
Issued: 2000 in a numbered limited edition
             of 2,500
Varieties: DB216A

Back		Price		
Stamp	U.S. $	Can. $	U.K. £	Aust. $
BK-9a Special	150.00	225.00	100.00	250.00

DB217
OLD BALLOON SELLER BUNNYKINS™

Designer: From a design by Leslie Harradine
Modeller: Amanda Hughes-Lubeck
Height: 4", 10.1 om
Colour: Brown, black shawl and skirt,
             white apron, pink shirt,
             multicoloured balloons
Issued: 2000 in a special numbered edition
             of 2,000

Back		Price		
Stamp	U.S. $	Can. $	U.K. £	Aust. $
BK-Exc	225.00	300.00	150.00	350.00

DB218
FORTUNE TELLER BUNNYKINS™

Designer: Warren Platt
Modeller: Warren Platt
Height: 4 ½", 11.9 cm
Colour: Brown, pink, yellow and dark green
Issued: April to September 2000

Back Stamp	Price			
	U.S. $	Can. $	U.K. £	Aust. $
Bk-8a	55.00	75.00	35.00	75.00

DB219
BRITANNIA BUNNYKINS™

Designer: Kimberley Curtis
Modeller: Amanda Hughes-Lubeck
Height: 4 ¼", 10.8 cm
Colour: Brown, white, yellow, red and blue
Issued: 2000 in a numbered limited edition of 2,500

Back Stamp	Price			
	U.S. $	Can. $	U.K. £	Aust. $
BK-9 Special	135.00	200.00	85.00	250.00

DB220
LITTLE BO PEEP BUNNYKINS™

Designer: Martyn Alcock
Modeller: Martyn Alcock
Height: 4 ¼", 10.8 cm
Colour: Brown, white and yellow
Issued: 2000 to the present
Series: Nursery Rhyme Collection

Back Stamp	Price			
	U.S. $	Can. $	U.K. £	Aust. $
BK-9a to BK-15a	75.00	95.00	45.00	100.00

DB221
LITTLE JACK HORNER BUNNYKINS™

Designer:	Martyn Alcock
Modeller:	Martyn Alcock
Height:	4 ¼", 10.8 cm
Colour:	Brown, red suit and hat, black shoes
Issued:	2000 to the present
Series:	Nursery Rhyme Collection

Back Stamp	Price			
	U.S. $	Can. $	U.K. £	Aust. $
BK-9a to BK-14a	65.00	90.00	40.00	100.00

DB222
JACK AND JILL BUNNYKINS™

Designer:	Martyn Alcock
Modeller:	Martyn Alcock
Height:	4 ¼", 10.8 cm
Colour:	Brown, white, black and yellow
Issued:	2000 to the present
Series:	Nursery Rhyme Collection

Back Stamp	Price			
	U.S. $	Can. $	U.K. £	Aust. $
BK-9a to BK-14a	95.00	150.00	60.00	175.00

DB223
CHOIR SINGER BUNNYKINS™

Designer:	Martyn Alcock
Modeller:	Martyn Alcock
Height:	4", 10.5 cm
Colour:	Black, beige, red and white
Issued:	2001 - 2001
Series:	ICC Members Exclusive

Back Stamp	Price			
	U.S. $	Can. $	U.K. £	Aust. $
BK-10a Special	65.00	85.00	40.00	95.00

DB224
FEDERATION BUNNYKINS™

Designer:	Brian Dalglish and Bill Bryant
Modeller:	Shane Ridge
Height:	5", 12.7 cm
Colour:	Brown, blue, red and white
Issued:	2000 in a special edition of 2,500
Series:	Australian Heritage

Back Stamp	U.S. $	Can. $	U.K. £	Aust. $
BK-9a Special	175.00	250.00	110.00	250.00

DB225
EASTER SURPRISE BUNNYKINS™

Designer:	Graham Tongue
Modeller:	Warren Platt
Height:	4 ½", 11.9 cm
Colour:	Purple, yellow and black
Issued:	2000 in a special edition of 2,500
Varieties:	Also called Easter Greetings Bunnykins, DB149

Back Stamp	U.S. $	Can. $	U.K. £	Aust. $
BK-9a Special	100.00	135.00	60.00	150.00

DB226
MOTHER AND BABY BUNNYKINS™
Style Two (Large Size)

Designer:	Amanda Hughes-Lubeck
Modeller:	Amanda Hughes-Lubeck
Height:	6 ¼", 15.9 cm
Colour:	Blue, white and yellow
Issued:	2000 in a limited edition of 2,000
Series:	The Bunnykins Family

Back Stamp	U.S. $	Can. $	U.K. £	Aust. $
BK-11 Special	80.00	125.00	50.00	150.00

Note: A colourway variation exists with a dark blue dress, pink and maroon apron, and dark yellow baby's shawl.

DB227
FATHER BUNNYKINS™
Style Two (Large size)

Designer:	Amanda Hughes-Lubeck
Modeller:	Amanda Hughes-Lubeck
Height:	6 ¾", 17.1 cm
Colour:	Cream, red, tan and yellow
Issued:	2000 in a limited edition of 2,000
Series:	The Bunnykins Family

Back Stamp	Price			
	U.S. $	Can. $	U.K. £	Aust. $
BK-11 Special	80.00	125.00	50.00	150.00

Note: A colourway variation exists with dark maroon braces, grey-blue shirt, maroon and yellow tie.

DB228
SANDCASTLE MONEY BOX™

Designer:	Warren Platt
Modeller:	Warren Platt
Height:	4 ¼", 10.8 cm
Colour:	Blue, green, pink, red, white and yellow
Issued:	2001-2002 in a limited edition of 2,002
Series:	Tableau

Back Stamp	Price			
	U.S. $	Can. $	U.K. £	Aust. $
BK-13a Special	200.00	275.00	120.00	300.00

DB229
SANDS OF TIME BUNNYKINS™

Designer:	Martyn Alcock
Modeller:	Martyn Alcock
Height:	3 ½", 9 cm
Colour:	Yellow robe with suns and moons
Issued:	2001 - 2001
Series:	1. Bunnykins of the Year
	2. Time

Back Stamp	Price			
	U.S. $	Can. $	U.K. £	Aust. $
BK-10a Special	65.00	85.00	40.00	85.00

DB230
LITTLE RED RIDING HOOD BUNNYKINS™

Designer:	Martyn Alcock
Modeller:	Martyn Alcock
Height:	4 ¼", 10.5 cm
Colour:	Black, dark blue, green, red tan and white
Issued:	2001 in a limited edition of 2000
Series:	1. Fairy Tales
	2. Special Events

Back Stamp	Price			
	U.S. $	Can. $	U.K. £	Aust. $
BK-12a Special	135.00	200.00	90.00	250.00

DB231
CINDERELLA BUNNYKINS™

Designer:	Unknown
Modeller:	Martyn Alcock
Height:	4 ¼", 10.8 cm
Colour:	Pink and yellow
Issued:	2002 - 2002
Series:	1. Fairy Tales
	2. ICC Members Exclusive

Back Stamp	Price			
	U.S. $	Can. $	U.K. £	Aust. $
BK-13a Special	60.00	85.00	35.00	100.00

Note: DB232 May Queen was not issued.

DB233
SHOPPER BUNNYKINS™

Designer:	Warren Platt
Modeller:	Warren Platt
Height:	4 ½", 11.5 cm
Colour:	Blue dress, beige coat, pink scarf, brown and white bag
Issued:	2001 to the present

Back Stamp	Price			
	U.S. $	Can. $	U.K. £	Aust. $
BK-12 to BK-14	50.00	75.00	30.00	85.00

DB234
MR. PUNCH BUNNYKINS™

Designer:	Kimberley Curtis
Modeller:	Martyn Alcock
Height:	4 ¾", 12 cm
Colour:	Blue, brown, orange, red and white
Issued:	2001 in a limited edition of 2,500
Series:	Punch and Judy Collection

Back Stamp	Price			
	U.S. $	Can. $	U.K. £	Aust. $
BK-11a Special	135.00	200.00	85.00	250.00

DB235
JUDY BUNNYKINS™

Designer:	Kimberley Curtis
Modeller:	Martyn Alcock
Height:	4¼", 11 cm
Colour:	Blue, brown and yellow
Issued:	2001 in a limited edition of 2,500
Series:	Punch and Judy Collection

Back Stamp	Price			
	U.S. $	Can. $	U.K. £	Aust. $
BK-11a Special	135.00	200.00	85.00	250.00

DB236
WALTZING MATILDA BUNNYKINS™

Designer:	Wendy Boyce-Davies
Modeller:	Martyn Alcock
Height:	4", 10.1 cm
Colour:	Brown, blue, lemon, pink, white and yellow
Issued:	2001 in a limited edition of 2001
Series:	Australian Heritage

Back Stamp	Price			
	U.S. $	Can. $	U.K. £	Aust. $
BK-11 Special	135.00	200.00	85.00	250.00

DB237
FATHER CHRISTMAS BUNNYKINS™

Designer:	Warren Platt
Modeller:	Warren Platt
Height:	5", 12.7 cm
Colour:	Red, white, black, grey and silver
Issued:	2000 in a special edition of 2,500

Back Stamp	Price			
	U.S. $	Can. $	U.K. £	Aust. $
BK-10 Special	100.00	150.00	65.00	200.00

DB238
ON LINE BUNNYKINS™

Designer:	Shane Ridge
Modeller:	Shane Ridge
Height:	2 ¾", 7.0 cm
Colour:	Brown, light blue trousers, blue and white shirt, red vest
Issued:	2001 in a special edition of 2,500

Back Stamp	Price			
	U.S. $	Can. $	U.K. £	Aust. $
BK-12 Special	175.00	250.00	100.00	300.00

DB239
LITTLE BOY BLUE BUNNYKINS™

Designer:	Caroline Dadd
Modeller:	Shane Ridge
Height:	3 ¾", 9.5 cm
Colour:	Pale blue and white
Issued:	2002 to the present
Series:	Nursery Rhyme Collection

Back Stamp	Price			
	U.S. $	Can. $	U.K. £	Aust. $
BK-11 to BK-14	60.00	110.00	35.00	120.00

DB240
LITTLE MISS MUFFET BUNNYKINS™

Designer:	Caroline Dadd
Modeller:	Warren Platt
Height:	3 ½", 8.9 cm
Colour:	Pale blue, white and green
Issued:	2002 to the present
Series:	Nursery Rhyme Collection

Back Stamp	Price			
	U.S. $	Can. $	U.K. £	Aust. $
BK-11 Special	65.00	95.00	40.00	100.00

DB241
BATH NIGHT BUNNYKINS™

Designer:	After a design by Barbara Vernon
Modeller:	Martyn Alcock
Height:	4 ¼", 10.8 cm
Colour:	Beige, blue, red and white
Issued:	2001 in a limited edition of 5,000
Series:	Tableau

Back Stamp	Price			
	U.S. $	Can. $	U.K. £	Aust. $
BK-11 Special	135.00	175.00	85.00	225.00

DB242
TYROLEAN DANCER BUNNYKINS™

Designer:	Shane Ridge
Modeller:	Shane Ridge
Height:	4", 10.1 cm
Colour:	White, black and grey
Issued:	2001 - 2001
Series:	1. Dancers of the World
	2. Special Events

Back Stamp	Price			
	U.S. $	Can. $	U.K. £	Aust. $
BK-11 Special	75.00	100.00	45.00	100.00

DB243
LITTLE JOHN BUNNYKINS™

Designer:	Martyn Alcock
Modeller:	Martyn Alcock
Height:	5", 12.5 cm
Colour:	Light and dark brown, red and white
Issued:	2001 to the present
Series:	Robin Hood Collection

Back Stamp	Price			
	U.S. $	Can. $	U.K. £	Aust. $
BK-10a Special	60.00	110.00	30.00	95.00

Note: A castle-like stand is available for the eight Bunnykins of the Robin Hood Collection, see page 318.

DB244
ROBIN HOOD BUNNYKINS™

Designer:	Martyn Alcock
Modeller:	Martyn Alcock
Height:	4 ½", 11.9 cm
Colour:	Beige, brown, forest green, red and yellow
Issued:	2001 to the present
Series:	Robin Hood Collection

Back Stamp	Price			
	U.S. $	Can. $	U.K. £	Aust. $
BK-10a Special	60.00	110.00	30.00	95.00

DB245
MAID MARION BUNNYKINS™

Designer:	Martyn Alcock
Modeller:	Martyn Alcock
Height:	4 ¼", 10.8 cm
Colour:	Pink, purple, yellow, green and gold
Issued:	2001 to the present
Series:	Robin Hood Collection

Back Stamp	Price			
	U.S. $	Can. $	U.K. £	Aust. $
BK-10a Special	60.00	110.00	30.00	100.00

DB246
FRIAR TUCK BUNNYKINS™

Designer:	Martyn Alcock
Modeller:	Martyn Alcock
Height:	4 ½", 11.9 cm
Colour:	Brown, green, yellow and grey
Issued:	2001 to the present
Series:	Robin Hood Collection

Back Stamp	Price			
	U.S. $	Can. $	U.K. £	Aust. $
BK-11a Special	60.00	110.00	30.00	95.00

DB247
MARY MARY QUITE CONTRARY BUNNYKINS™

Designer:	Caroline Dadd
Modeller:	Shane Ridge
Height:	4 ¼", 10.8 cm
Colour:	Pink and white
Issued:	2002 to the present
Series:	Nursery Rhyme Collection

Back Stamp	Price			
	U.S. $	Can. $	U.K. £	Aust. $
BK-11a Special to BK-14a Special	60.00	90.00	40.00	100.00

DB248
DIGGER BUNNYKINS™

Designer:	Dalglish, Bryant, Bartholmeucz
Modeller:	Warren Platt
Height:	5 ½", 14 cm
Colour:	Khaki, beige, brown, silver and navy blue
Issued:	2001 in a special edition of 2,500
Series:	Australian Heritage

Back Stamp	Price			
	U.S. $	Can. $	U.K. £	Aust. $
BK-11a Special	165.00	250.00	100.00	275.00

DB249
DODGEM BUNNYKINS™

Designer:	After a design by Barbara Vernon
Modeller:	Martyn Alcock
Height:	3" x 4", 7.6 x 10 cm
Colour:	Black, red, white and yellow
Issued:	2001 in a limited edition of 2,500
Series:	Travel Bunykins

Back Stamp	U.S. $	Price Can. $	U.K. £	Aust. $
BK-11 Special	165.00	250.00	100.00	275.00

DB250
DRUMMER BUNNYKINS™
Style Two

Designer:	Kimberley Curtis
Modeller:	Shane Ridge
Height:	4 ¼", 10.8 cm
Colour:	Black, white, pink and blue
Issued:	2002 in a limited edition of 2,500
Series:	Jazz Band Collection

Back Stamp	U.S. $	Price Can. $	U.K. £	Aust. $
BK-11a Special	125.00	175.00	75.00	225.00

DB251
CAPTAIN COOK BUNNYKINS™

Designer:	Wendy Boyce-Davies
Modeller:	Warren Platt
Height:	4 ¼", 10.8 cm
Colour:	Blue coat, yellow trousers, blue and yellow hat
Issued:	2002 in a limited edition of 2,500
Series:	Australian Heritage

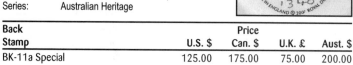

Back Stamp	U.S. $	Price Can. $	U.K. £	Aust. $
BK-11a Special	125.00	175.00	75.00	200.00

DB252
MANDARIN BUNNYKINS™

Designer:	Caroline Dadd
Modeller:	Martyn Alcock
Height:	4 ¼", 10.8 cm
Colour:	Yellow robe; grey dragon; purple
Issued:	2001 in a limited edition of 2,500
Series:	Bunnykins of the World (1 of 15)

Back Stamp	Price			
	U.S. $	Can. $	U.K. £	Aust. $
BK-11 Special	135.00	200.00	80.00	250.00

DB253
STOP WATCH BUNNYKINS™

Designer:	Martyn Alcock
Modeller:	Martyn Alcock
Height:	4 ¼", 10.8 cm
Colour:	Green, yellow and black
Issued:	2002 - 2002
Series:	1. Bunnykins of the Year
	2. Time

Back Stamp	Price			
	U.S. $	Can. $	U.K. £	Aust. $
BK-11a Special	60.00	95.00	35.00	100.00

DB254
VICAR BUNNYKINS™

Designer:	Shane Ridge
Modeller:	Shane Ridge
Height:	4 ¼", 10.8 cm
Colour:	Black, white and purple
Issued:	2002 - 2002
Series:	ICC Membership Gift

Back Stamp	Price			
	U.S. $	Can. $	U.K. £	Aust. $
BK-11a Special	70.00	95.00	45.00	100.00

DB255
GOLFER BUNNYKINS™

Designer:	Shane Ridge
Modeller:	Shane Ridge
Height:	5 ¼", 13.3 cm
Colour:	Black, burgundy and grey, white and yellow
Issued:	2001 - 2002

Back Stamp	Price			
	U.S. $	Can. $	U.K. £	Aust. $
BK-11	60.00	95.00	35.00	100.00

Note: Issued in the UK August 2001, in Australia March 2002 and Worldwide December 2002. Figure was exclusive to Royal Doulton outlets worldwide.

DB256
FLAMENCO BUNNYKINS™

Designer:	Shane Ridge
Modeller:	Shane Ridge
Height:	4 ½", 11.9 cm
Colour:	Dark blue with yellow ruffles
Issued:	2002 - 2002
Series:	1. Dancers of the World
	2. Special Events

Back Stamp	Price			
	U.S. $	Can. $	U.K. £	Aust. $
BK-12 Special	60.00	95.00	35.00	100.00

DB257
LIBERTY BELL BUNNYKINS™

Designer:	Shane Ridge
Modeller:	Shane Ridge
Height:	5", 12.7 cm
Colour:	Black, blue, beige, grey and white
Issued:	2001 in a limited edition of 2,000
Series:	American Heritage

Back Stamp	Price			
	U.S. $	Can. $	U.K. £	Aust. $
BK-11 Special	135.00	200.00	90.00	225.00

DB258
KING RICHARD BUNNYKINS™

Designer:	Martyn Alcock
Modeller:	Martyn Alcock
Height:	4 ¼", 11.0 cm
Colour:	Blue, grey, white and red
Issued:	2002 to the present
Series:	Robin Hood Collection

Back Stamp	Price			
	U.S. $	Can. $	U.K. £	Aust. $
BK-12a Special to BK-14a Special	60.00	110.00	32.00	95.00

DB259
TOWN CRIER BUNNYKINS™

Designer:	Caroline Dadd
Modeller:	Martyn Alcock
Height:	4 ½", 11.9 cm
Colour:	Black, red, yellow and grey
Issued:	2002 in a limited edition of 2,500

Back Stamp	Price			
	U.S. $	Can. $	U.K. £	Aust. $
BK-12 Special	125.00	175.00	75.00	225.00

DB260
DAY TRIP BUNNYKINS™

Designer:	Caroline Dadd
Modeller:	Martyn Alcock
Height:	3 ½", 9.0 cm
Colour:	Green, blue, red, yellow and white
Issued:	2002 in a limited edition of 2,500
Series:	Travel Bunnykins

Back Stamp	Price			
	U.S. $	Can. $	U.K. £	Aust. $
BK-12a Special	165.00	225.00	100.00	250.00

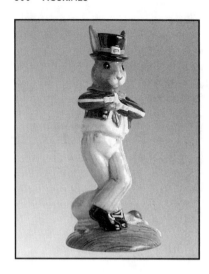

DB261
HORNPIPER BUNNYKINS™

Modeller:	Warren Platt
Height:	4 ¼", 10.8 cm
Colour:	Dark and light blue, white, black and pink
Issued:	2003 - 2003
Series:	Special Events

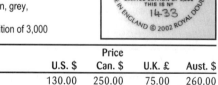

Back Stamp	Price			
	U.S. $	Can. $	U.K. £	Aust. $
BK-14 Special	45.00	80.00	30.00	80.00

DB262
BASKETBALL BUNNYKINS™
Style Two

Modeller:	Shane Ridge
Height:	5", 12.7 cm
Colour:	Yellow, blue and brown
Issued:	2002 in a limited edition of 2,000

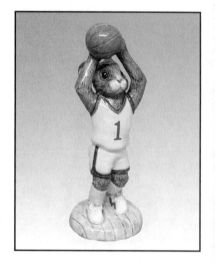

Back Stamp	Price			
	U.S. $	Can. $	U.K. £	Aust. $
BK-12a Special	100.00	150.00	65.00	175.00

DB263
MERMAID BUNNYKINS™

Modeller:	Shane Ridge
Height:	3 ¾", 9.5 cm
Colour:	Yellow, green, brown, grey, red and gold
Issued:	2003 in a limited edition of 3,000

Back Stamp	Price			
	U.S. $	Can. $	U.K. £	Aust. $
BK-11 Special	130.00	250.00	75.00	260.00

DB264
WILL SCARLETT BUNNYKINS™

Modeller:	Martyn Alcock
Height:	4", 10.1 cm
Colour:	Light and dark green, red, yellow and brown
Issued:	2002 to the present
Series:	Robin Hood Collection

Back Stamp	Price			
	U.S. $	Can. $	U.K. £	Aust. $
BK-12a to BK-13a	60.00	110.00	32.00	95.00

DB265
SHERIFF OF NOTTINGHAM BUNNYKINS™

Modeller:	Martyn Alcock
Height:	4 ½", 11.5 cm
Colour:	Brown, grey, black, dark yellow
Issued:	2002 to the present
Series:	Robin Hood Collection

Back Stamp	Price			
	U.S. $	Can. $	U.K. £	Aust. $
BK-12a to BK-13a	60.00	110.00	32.00	95.00

DB266
PRINCE JOHN BUNNYKINS™

Modeller:	Martyn Alcock
Height:	4 ½", 11.5 cm
Colour:	Dark green, red, yellow and peach
Issued:	2002 to the present
Series:	Robin Hood Collection

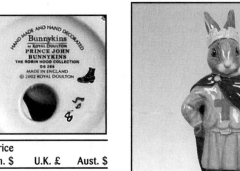

Back Stamp	Price			
	U.S. $	Can. $	U.K. £	Aust. $
BK-12a to BK-13a	60.00	110.00	32.00	95.00

DB267
CHOCS AWAY BUNNYKINS™

Modeller:	Martyn Alcock
Height:	4 ¼" x 5 ¼", 11.0 x 13.0 cm
Colour:	Yellow, red, blue, brown and black
Issued:	2003 in a limited edition of 2,000
Series:	Travel Bunnykins

Back Stamp	Price U.S. $	Can. $	U.K. £	Aust. $
BK-12a Special	150.00	250.00	95.00	300.00

DB268
AMERICAN FIREFIGHTER BUNNYKINS™

Designer:	Graham Tongue
Modeller:	Martyn Alcock
Height:	4 ¼", 10.5 cm
Colour:	Tan, black, light brown, yellow, grey and red
Issued:	2002 in a limited edition of 2,001
Varieties:	Also called Fireman Bunnykins, DB75, DB183
Series:	American Heritage

Back Stamp	Price U.S. $	Can. $	U.K. £	Aust. $
BK-12a Special	95.00	135.00	60.00	150.00

DB269
WITH LOVE BUNNYKINS™

Modeller:	Shane Ridge
Height:	4", 10.1 cm
Colour:	Pale yellow, yellow, white, pink, and green
Issued:	2002 to the present

Back Stamp	Price U.S. $	Can. $	U.K. £	Aust. $
BK-12a to BK-14a	70.00	125.00	45.00	125.00

Note: Issued with a brass plaque on the base for engraving.

DB270
WEE WILLIE WINKIE BUNNYKINS™

Modeller:	Shane Ridge
Height:	4 ½", 11.5 cm
Colour:	White, yellow, brown and grey
Issues:	2002 to the present
Series:	Nursery Rhyme Collection

Back Stamp	Price			
	U.S. $	Can. $	U.K. £	Aust. $
BK-12 Special to BK-14 Special	70.00	100.00	45.00	110.00

DB271
CADDIE BUNYKINS™

Modeller:	Shane Ridge
Height:	5", 12.7 cm
Colour:	Yellow jumper, tan trousers, red cap, green golf bag
Issued:	2002 to the present

Back Stamp	Price			
	U.S. $	Can. $	U.K. £	Aust. $
BK-12 Special to BK-14 SpeciaL	70.00	100.00	45.00	110.00

DB272
TEST CENTURY BUNNYKINS™

Modeller:	Martyn Alcock
Height:	4 ½", 11.5 cm
Colour:	White and hunter green
Issued:	2003 in a limited edition of 2,000
Series:	Cricket

Backstamp not
available
at press time

Back Stamp	Price			
	U.S. $	Can. $	U.K. £	Aust. $
BK- Not known	150.00	200.00	95.00	200.00

DB273
DEEP SEA DIVER BUNNYKINS™

Modeller:	Shane Ridge
Height:	4 ¾", 12.0 cm
Colour:	White, yellow, black, grey and blue
Issued:	2003 in a limited edition of 3,000

Back Stamp	Price U.S. $	Can. $	U.K. £	Aust. $
BK-12 Special	130.00	250.00	75.00	260.00

DB274
DUTCH BUNNYKINS™

Modeller:	Martyn Alcock
Height:	4 ½", 11.5 cm
Colour:	Brown, white, yellow, blue, orange and green
Issued:	2003 in a limited edition of 2,000

Back Stamp	Price U.S. $	Can. $	U.K. £	Aust. $
BK-12a Special	130.00	250.00	75.00	275.00

DB275
ESKIMO BUNNYKINS™

Modeller:	Shane Ridge
Height:	4 ¾", 12.1 cm
Colour:	Light brown, cream, red and black
Issued:	2003 - 2003
Series:	Bunnykins of the Year

Back Stamp	Price U.S. $	Can. $	U.K. £	Aust. $
BK-14 Special	43.00	75.00	25.00	80.00

DB276
SWEET DREAMS BABY BUNNY™

Modeller:	Martyn Alcock
Height:	3 ½", 8.9 cm
Colour:	Green, pink, yellow and white
Issued:	2002 to the present

Back	Price			
Stamp	U.S. $	Can. $	U.K. £	Aust. $
BK-12	60.00	115.00	35.00	120.00

DB277
STRAWBERRIES BUNNYKINS™

Modeller:	Warren Platt
Height:	3 ¼", 8.3 cm
Colour:	Pink, white and red
Issued:	2002 in a limited edition of 3,000

Back	Price			
Stamp	U.S. $	Can. $	U.K. £	Aust. $
BK-12 Special	87.50	175.00	50.00	175.00

Note: Sold only as a pair with DB278

DB278
TENNIS BUNNYKINS™

Modeller:	Warren Platt
Height:	3 ¾", 9.5 cm
Colour:	Pink white, tan and grey
Issued:	2002 in a limited edition of 3,000

Back	Price			
Stamp	U.S. $	Can. $	U.K. £	Aust. $
BK-12 Special	87.50	175.00	50.00	175.00

Note: Sold only as a pair with DB277. U.K. price for the pair is £98.99.

DB279
SHIP AHOY BUNNYKINS™

Modeller:	Shane Ridge
Height:	4 ¼", 11.0 cm
Colour:	Dark and light blue, white, orange, tan, gold accents
Issued:	2004 in a limited edition of 2,000
Series:	Travel Bunnykins

Backstamp not
available
at press time

Back Stamp	Price U.S. $	Can. $	U.K. £	Aust. $
BK - Not known	Prices not established at press time			

DB280
SAMURAI BUNNYKINS™

Modeller:	Shane Ridge
Height:	4 ¾", 12.0 cm
Colour:	Cream, orange, yellow and green
Issued:	2003 in a limited edition of 2,000

Back Stamp	Price U.S. $	Can. $	U.K. £	Aust. $
BK-13a Special	125.00	175.00	70.00	185.00

DB281
MATADOR BUNNYKINS™

Modeller:	Shane Ridge
Height:	4 ½", 11.5 cm
Colour:	Dark blue, red, gold and black
Issued:	2003 in a limited edition of 2,000

Back Stamp	Price U.S. $	Can. $	U.K. £	Aust. $
BK-13a Special	125.00	175.00	70.00	185.00

DB282
ICE HOCKEY BUNNYKINS™

Modeller:	Shane Ridge
Height:	4 ¾", 12.1 cm
Colour:	Yellow, green and black
Issued:	2003 in a limited edition of 1,500
Series:	Special Events

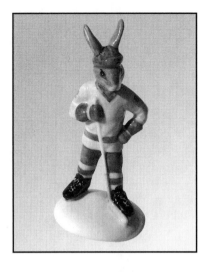

Back Stamp	Price U.S. $	Can. $	U.K. £	Aust. $
BK-13a Special	125.00	175.00	65.00	185.00

DB283
JULIET BUNNYKINS™

Modeller:	Shane Ridge
Height:	4 ¼", 11.0 cm
Colour:	Yellow and peach dress with red accents
Issued:	2003 - 2003
Series:	I.C.C. Membership Gift

Back Stamp	Price U.S. $	Can. $	U.K. £	Aust. $
BK-14a Special	54.75	75.00	30.00	99.95

DB284
ROMEO BUNNYKINS™

Modeller:	Martyn Alcock
Height:	3 ¾". 9.5 cm
Colour:	Green, red, white, black and brown
Issued:	2003 2003
Series:	I.C.C. Members Exclusive

Back Stamp	Price U.S. $	Can. $	U.K. £	Aust. $
BK-14a Special	41.25	75.00	25.00	79.95

DB285
CHRISTMAS MORNING BUNNYKINS™

Modeller:	Shane Ridge
Height:	4 ¾", 12.1 cm
Colour:	Pink, red, green, white and blue
Issued:	2003 to the present
Series:	The Occasions Collection

Back	Price			
Stamp	U.S. $	Can. $	U.K. £	Aust. $
BK-14	41.25	75.00	25.00	79.95

DB286
GRADUATION DAY BUNNYKINS™

Modeller:	Shane Ridge
Height:	4 ¾", 12.1 cm
Colour:	Black, yellow, green, grey and white
Issued:	2003 to the present
Series:	The Occasions Collection

Back	Price			
Stamp	U.S. $	Can. $	U.K. £	Aust. $
BK-14	41.25	75.00	25.00	79.95

DB287
WEDDING DAY BUNNYKINS™

Modeller:	Martyn Alcock
Height:	4 ¾", 12.1 cm
Colour:	White, black, yellow, red and green, grey base
Issued:	2003 to the present
Series:	The Occasions Collection

Back	Price			
Stamp	U.S. $	Can. $	U.K. £	Aust. $
BK-14	41.25	75.00	25.00	79.95

BUNNYKINS

DB288 – Love Heart Bunnykins

DB289 – Easter Treat Bunnykins

DB290 – Birthday Girl Bunnykins

DB291 – Congratulations
Bunnykins

DB292 – Easter Parade
Bunnykins

DB293 – Witches Cauldron
Bunnykins

DB294 – Centurion
Bunnykins

DB295 – Ankhesenamun
Bunnykins

DB296 – Tutankhamun
Bunnykins

DB297 – Winter Lapland
Bunnykins

DB298 – Summer Lapland
Bunnykins

DB299 – Sir Galahad
Bunnykins

BUNNYKINS

DB300 – Sir Gawain
Bunnykins

DB301 – Sir Lancelot
Bunnykins

DB302 – Queen Guinevere
Bunnykins

DB303 – Merlin
Bunnykins

DB304 – King Arthur
Bunnykins

DB305 – Henry VIII
Bunnykins

DB306 – Catherine of Aragon
Bunnykins

DB307 – Anne Boleyn
Bunnykins

DB308 – Jane Seymour
Bunnykins

DB309 – Anne of Cleves
Bunnykins

DB310 – Kathryn Howard
Bunnykins

BUNNYKINS

DB311 – Catherine Parr
Bunnykins

DB312 – Emperor Bunnykins

DB313 – Betsy Ross Bunnykins

Extravaganza 2003 – Prototypes

Mayday Bunnykins (Blue)

Summer Holiday Bunnykins

Sleepytime Bunnykins

Mayday Bunnykins (Pink)

Toby Jugs

D7157 – Fortune Teller
Bunnykins

D7160 – Party Time
Bunnykins

D7166 – Witching Time
Bunnykins

D7185 – Toy Soldier
Bunnykins

COUNTRY MANOR TEASET

DBD1 – Lord of the Manor
Coffee Pot

DBD2 – Lady of the Manor
Teapot

DBD4 – Miss of the Manor
Cup and Saucer

DBD3 – Master of the Manor
Cup and Saucer

DBD7 – Country Manor Chef
Candy Box

DBD5 – Country Manor Butler
Cream Jug

DBD6 – Country Manor Maid
Covered Sugar

EARTHENWARE
Beaker Covers

HW15R – Cycling

HW13R – Footballer

EC1 – Sleeping in a Rocking Chair

HW11R – Kissing under the Mistletoe
Second Version

HW12R – Leapfrog

Backstamp on
early Beaker Cover

Hot Water Bowls

SF11 – Game of Golf
by Casa Gessel of Argentina

LF15 – Family Photograph
by Broqua Scholberg of Uruguay

CHINA
Egg Boxes

Large – Daisy Chains
HW25

Medium – Afternoon Tea
HW116

Small – Skipping Game
HW 139R

WHITE CHINA
Beakers

HW6 – Netting a Cricket

HW14 – Pressing Trousers

HW2 – Pulling on Trousers

HW1R – Dunce

Beaker Covers

EC4 – Holding Hat and Coat

Backstamp

Shape Two
c. 1940

WHITE CHINA
5 inch plates

HW7 – Greetings

SF9 – Santa Claus

LFd – Wedding Day

HW1 – Artist

Rex Mugs

HW14 – Pressing Trousers

HW11 – Proposal

HW12 – Family at Breakfast

PATTERN CONDITION

Condition is an important factor when dealing with collectables and Bunnykins tableware is no different. Mint condition items will command the highest premium in the collectors market place.

Early tableware was bought to be used, therefore mint (new) is an anomaly in an item which began with this characteristic. Illustrated are two similar plates in order to demonstrate the differences in condition: mint vs used.

Mint:

The above plate has a complete, crisp, brilliant pattern. The outline of the bunny is shown in its entirety, as is the check pattern on the "pressed" trousers. The colours of the bunny's waistcoat and trousers are bright. There are no scratches or blemishes.

Used:

The plate on the right shows a deterioration in the pattern, the bunny's ears are fading, as is the check pattern on the "pressed" trousers. The colours of the bunny's waistcoat and trousers are faded and dull. There are visible scratches on the bunny's face and trousers.

This plate will command a price that is possibly half the value of the mint conditioned one.

DB288
LOVE HEART BUNNYKINS™

Modeller:	Shane Ridge
Height:	4 ¾", 12.1 cm
Colour:	Blue dress, red heart, green base
Issued:	2003 to the present
Series:	The Occasions Collection

Back Stamp	Price			
	U.S. $	Can. $	U.K. £	Aust. $
BK-14	41.25	75.00	25.00	79.95

DB289
EASTER TREAT BUNNYKINS™

Modeller:	Shane Ridge
Height:	3 ¾", 9.5 cm
Colour:	Blue, grey, orange, tan and yellow
Issued:	2003 to the present
Series:	The Occasions Collection

Back Stamp	Price			
	U.S. $	Can. $	U.K. £	Aust. $
BK-14	41.25	75.00	25.00	79.95

Note: A stand is available for the Occasions Collection, see page 318.

DB290
BIRTHDAY GIRL BUNNYKINS™

Modeller:	Shane Ridge
Height:	4 ¼", 11.0 cm
Colour:	Pink, yellow, green and beige
Issued:	2003 to the present
Series:	The Occasions Collection

Backstamp not available at press time

Back Stamp	Price			
	U.S. $	Can. $	U.K. £	Aust. $
BK-14	41.25	75.00	25.00	79.95

DB291
CONGRATULATIONS BUNNYKINS™

Modeller:	Martyn Alcock
Height:	4 ¼", 11.0 cm
Colour:	Light blue, green, yellow, red, white, beige and black
Issued:	2003 to the present
Series:	The Occasions Collection

Back Stamp	Price			
	U.S. $	Can. $	U.K. £	Aust. $
BK-14a	41.25	75.00	25.00	79.95

DB292
EASTER PARADE BUNNYKINS™

Modeller:	Shane Ridge
Height:	4 ¼", 11.0 cm
Colour:	Yellow, blue, red, green and brown
Issued:	2003 to the present
Series:	The Occasions Collection

Back Stamp	Price			
	U.S. $	Can. $	U.K. £	Aust. $
BK-14	41.25	75.00	25.00	79.95

Backstamp not available at press time

DB293
WITCHES CAULDRON BUNNYKINS™

Modeller:	Martyn Alcock
Height:	4 ¼", 11.0 cm
Colour:	Red, purple, dark green, brown, gold, green and black
Issued:	2004 in a limited edition of 1,500

Backstamp not available at press time

Back Stamp	Price			
	U.S. $	Can. $	U.K. £	Aust. $
Not known	Price not established at press time			

DB294
CENTURION BUNNYKINS™

Modeller:	Martyn Alcock
Height:	4 ½", 11.5 cm
Colour:	White, brown, peach, purple and yellow
Issued:	2004
Series:	Roman Empire Collection

Backstamp not available at press time

Back	Price			
Stamp	U.S. $	Can. $	U.K. £	Aust. $
Not known	Price not established at press time			

DB295
ANKHESENAMUN BUNNYKINS™

Modeller:	Unknown
Height:	4 ½", 11.5 cm
Colour:	Cream, orange, blue, green, brown and white
Issued:	2004 - 2004
Series:	I.C.C. Membership Gift

Backstamp not available at press time

Back	Price			
Stamp	U.S. $	Can. $	U.K. £	Aust. $
Not known	Price not established at press time			

DB296
TUTANKHAMUN BUNNYKINS™

Modeller:	Unknown
Height:	4 ½", 11.5 cm
Colour:	Cream, blue, red, yellow, brown and green
Issued:	2004 - 2004
Series:	I.C.C. Members Exclusive

Backstamp not available at press time

Back	Price			
Stamp	U.S. $	Can. $	U.K. £	Aust. $
Not known	Price not established at press time			

DB297
WINTER LAPLAND BUNNYKINS™

Modeller:	Unknown
Height:	4 ½", 11.5 cm
Colour:	Blue, red, dark yellow, green, dark and light brown; white base
Issued:	2004 - 2004
Series:	Bunnykins of the Year

Backstamp not
available
at press time

Back Stamp	Price			
	U.S. $	Can. $	U.K. £	Aust. $
Not known	Price not established at press time			

DB298
SUMMER LAPLAND BUNNYKINS™

Modeller:	Unknown
Height:	4 ½", 11.5 cm
Colour:	Red, white, blue, yellow, green, brown; white base
Issued:	2004 - 2004
Series:	Special Events

Backstamp not
available
at press time

Back Stamp	Price			
	U.S. $	Can. $	U.K. £	Aust. $
Not known	Price not established at press time			

DB299
SIR GALAHAD BUNNYKINS™

Modeller:	Unknown
Height:	4 ½", 11.5 cm
Colour:	Cream, red, white, purple, dark yellow, grey and brown
Issued:	2004
Series:	Athurian Legends Collection

Backstamp not
available
at press time

Back Stamp	Price			
	U.S. $	Can. $	U.K. £	Aust. $
Not known	Price not established at press time			

DB300
SIR GAWAIN BUNNYKINS™

Modeller:	Unknown
Height:	3 ½", 9.0 cm
Colour:	Light green, cream, red, purple, beige, grey and brown
Issued:	2004
Series:	Arthurian Legends Collection

Backstamp not available at press time

Back Stamp	Price			
	U.S. $	Can. $	U.K. £	Aust. $
Not known	Price not established at press time			

DB301
SIR LANCELOT BUNNYKINS™

Modeller:	Unknown
Height:	5 ¾", 14.5 cm
Colour:	Yellow, blue, red, light green, grey, orange, brown and dark green
Issued:	2004
Series:	Arthurian Legends Collection

Backstamp not available at press time

Back Stamp	Price			
	U.S. $	Can. $	U.K. £	Aust. $
Not known	Price not established at press time			

DB302
QUEEN GUINEVERE BUNNYKINS™

Modeller:	Unknown
Height:	4 ¼", 11.0 cm
Colour:	Royal blue, red, yellow, cream, grey and brown
Issued:	2004
Series:	Arthurian Legends Collection

Backstamp not available at press time

Back Stamp	Price			
	U.S. $	Can. $	U.K. £	Aust. $
Not known	Price not established at press time			

DB303
MERLIN BUNNYKINS™

Modeller:	Unknown
Height:	4 ¾", 12.0 cm
Colour:	Dark green, purple, yellow, grey and brown
Issued:	2004 - 2004
Series:	Arthurian Legends Collection

Backstamp not available at press time

Back Stamp	Price			
	U.S. $	Can. $	U.K. £	Aust. $
Not known	Price not established at press time			

DB304
KING ARTHUR BUNNYKINS™

Modeller:	Unknown
Height:	4 ¾", 12.0 cm
Colour:	Royal blue, black, maroon, grey, yellow, cream, red and brown
Issued:	2004
Series:	Arthurian Legends Collection

Backstamp not available at press time

Back Stamp	Price			
	U.S. $	Can. $	U.K. £	Aust. $
Not known	Price not established at press time			

DB305
HENRY VIII™

Modeller:	Martyn Alcock
Height:	4", 10.1 cm
Colour:	Green, yellow, orange, red and brown
Issued:	2003 to the present
Series:	Tudor Collection

HAND MADE AND HAND DECORATED
Bunnykins
by ROYAL DOULTON
THE TUDOR COLLECTION
HENRY VIII
DB 305
© 2003 ROYAL DOULTON

Back Stamp	Price			
	U.S. $	Can. $	U.K. £	Aust. $
BK-14	41.25	75.00	25.00	79.95

Note: A scenic base is available for the seven Bunnykins of the Tudor Collection. The base is designed so collectors can chose how to arrange the queens, see page 318.

DB306
CATHERINE OF ARAGON™

Modeller:	Martyn Alcock
Height:	4 ¼", 11.0 cm
Colour:	Red, coral, yellow, purple, gold and white
Issued:	2003 to the present
Series:	Tudor Collection

Back Stamp	Price			
	U.S. $	Can. $	U.K. £	Aust. $
BK-14	41.25	75.00	25.00	79.95

DB307
ANNE BOLEYN™

Modeller:	Martyn Alcock
Height:	4 ¼", 11.0 cm
Colour:	Purple, yellow, gold and brown
Issued:	2003 to the present
Series:	Tudor Collection

Back Stamp	Price			
	U.S. $	Can. $	U.K. £	Aust. $
BK-14	41.25	75.00	25.00	79.95

DB308
JANE SEYMOUR™

Modeller:	Martyn Alcock
Height:	4 ¼", 11.0 cm
Colour:	Light and dark green, red and gold
Issued:	2003 to the present
Series:	Tudor Collection

Back Stamp	Price			
	U.S. $	Can. $	U.K. £	Aust. $
BK-14	41.25	75.00	25.00	79.95

DB309
ANNE OF CLEVES™

Modeller:	Martyn Alcock
Height:	4 ¼", 11.0 cm
Colour:	Orange, black, yellow, red and gold
Issued:	2003 to the present
Series:	Tudor Collection

Back Stamp	Price			
	U.S. $	Can. $	U.K. £	Aust. $
BK-14	41.25	75.00	25.00	79.95

DB310
KATHRYN HOWARD™

Modeller:	Martyn Alcock
Height:	4 ¼", 11.0 cm
Colour:	Blue, black, yellow, red, white and gold
Issued:	2003 to the present
Series:	Tudor Collection

Back Stamp	Price			
	U.S. $	Can. $	U.K. £	Aust. $
BK-14	41.25	75.00	25.00	79.95

DB311
CATHERINE PARR™

Modeller:	Martyn Alcock
Height:	4 ¼", 11.0 cm
Colour:	Green, orange, white and black
Issued:	2003 to the present
Series:	Tudor Collection

Back Stamp	Price			
	U.S. $	Can. $	U.K. £	Aust. $
BK-14	41.25	75.00	25.00	79.95

DB312
EMPEROR BUNNYKINS™

Modeller:	Unknown
Height:	4 ¾", 12.0 cm
Colour:	Brown, purple, grey, cream, yellow, gold, white and green
Issued:	2004
Series:	Roman Empire Collection

Backstamp not
available
at press time

Back Stamp	Price			
	U.S. $	Can. $	U.K. £	Aust. $
BK- Not known	Price not established at press time			

DB313
BETSY ROSS BUNNYKINS™

Modeller:	Unknown
Height:	4 ¼", 10.5 cm
Colour:	Pale blue and white dress; red, white and blue flag; beige scarf, hat, basket and base
Issued:	2003 in a limited edition of 2,000
Series:	American Heritage Collection

Backstamp not
available
at press time

Back Stamp	Price			
	U.S. $	Can. $	U.K. £	Aust. $
BK- Not known	66.00	90.00	42.00	100.00

BUNNYKINS FIGURINE BASES

THE ROBIN HOOD COLLECTION BASE

Modeller: Martyn Alcock
Size: 3 ¼" x 14", 8.3 x 35.5 cm
Colour: Grey, green and brown
Issued: 2002 to the present

Description	U.S. $	Can. $	U.K. £	Aust. $
Robin Hood base, 7 figures	60.00	80.00	35.00	85.00

THE TUDOR COLLECTION SCENIC BASE

Modeller: Martyn Alcock
Size: 6 ¾" x 15 ¾", 17.2 x 40.0 cm
Colour: Red, brown and purple
Issued: 2003 to the present

Description	U.S. $	Can. $	U.K. £	Aust. $
Tudor base, 7 figures	70.00	95.00	39.00	100.00

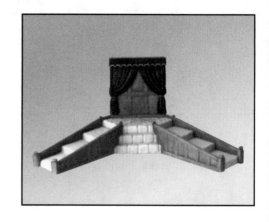

THE OCCASIONS COLLECTION SCENIC BASE

Modeller: Shane Ridge
Size: 3" x 15 ¼", 7.6 x 38.7 cm
Colour: Cream and red
Issued: 2003 to the present

Description	U.S. $	Can. $	U.K. £	Aust. $
Occasions base, 8 figures	60.00	80.00	35.00	85.00

RESIN ISSUES

1996-1997

DBR1
HARRY BUNNYKINS
A LITTLE BUNNY AT PLAY™

Designer:	Unknown
Modeller:	Unknown
Height:	1 ¾", 4.5 cm
Colour:	Pale blue pyjamas, red and dark blue toys
Issued:	1996 - 1997

Doulton Number	Price			
	U.S. $	Can. $	U.K. £	Aust. $
DBR1	25.00	35.00	15.00	40.00

DBR2
HARRY BUNNYKINS
PLAYTIME™

Designer:	Unknown
Modeller:	Unknown
Height:	2", 5.0 cm
Colour:	Pale blue pyjamas, yellow toys, pink, yellow and green pillow
Issued:	1996 - 1997

Doulton Number	Price			
	U.S. $	Can. $	U.K. £	Aust. $
DBR2	25.00	35.00	15.00	40.00

DBR3
REGINALD RATLEY
UP TO NO GOOD™

Designer:	Unknown
Modeller:	Unknown
Height:	2 ¼", 5,7 cm
Colour:	Black jacket, hat and shoes, yellow shirt, red tie
Issued:	1996 - 1997

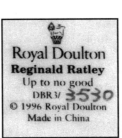

Doulton Number	Price			
	U.S. $	Can. $	U.K. £	Aust. $
DBR3	50.00	65.00	30.00	70.00

DBR4
SUSAN BUNNYKINS
THE HELPER™

Designer:	Unknown
Modeller:	Unknown
Height:	3", 7.6 cm
Colour:	White and blue dress
Issued:	1996 - 1997

Photograph not
available
at press time

Doulton Number		Price		
	U.S. $	Can. $	U.K. £	Aust. $
DBR4	40.00	55.00	25.00	60.00

DBR5
WILLIAM BUNNYKINS
ASLEEP IN THE SUN™

Designer:	Unknown
Modeller:	Unknown
Height:	2 ¼", 5.7 cm
Colour:	White shirt, red jacket, brown trousers
Issued:	1996 - 1997

Doulton Number		Price		
	U.S. $	Can. $	U.K. £	Aust. $
DBR5	40.00	55.00	25.00	60.00

DBR6
LADY RATLEY
HER LADYSHIP EXPLAINS™

Designer:	Unknown
Modeller:	Unknown
Height:	3 ¼", 8.3 cm
Colour:	Light and dark purple dress black shoes and handbag
Issued:	1996 - 1997

Doulton Number		Price		
	U.S. $	Can. $	U.K. £	Aust. $
DBR6	40.00	55.00	25.00	60.00

DBR7
MRS. BUNNYKINS
A BUSY MORNING SHOPPING™

Designer:	Unknown
Modeller:	Unknown
Height:	3 ½", 8.9 cm
Colour:	White dress with blue flowers, pale yellow apron and hat, brown basket
Issued:	1996 - 1997

Doulton Number	Price			
	U.S. $	Can. $	U.K. £	Aust. $
DBR7	35.00	45.00	20.00	50.00

Royal Doulton
Mrs Bunnykins
A busy morning
shopping
DBR7/ *186*
© 1996 Royal Doulton
Made in China

DBR8
FATHER BUNNYKINS
HOME FROM WORK™

Designer:	Unknown
Modeller:	Unknown
Height:	3 ¾", 9.5 cm
Colour:	Crean trousers, green jacket and black shoes
Issued:	1996 - 1997

Doulton Number	Price			
	U.S. $	Can. $	U.K. £	Aust. $
DBR8	35.00	45.00	20.00	50.00

Royal Doulton
Father Bunnykins
Home from work
DBR8/ *1036*
© 1996 Royal Doulton
Made in China

DBR9
WILLIAM BUNNYKINS
A BUNNY IN A HURRY™

Designer:	Unknown
Modeller:	Unknown
Height:	2 ¼", 5.7 cm
Colour:	Brown trousers, white shirt and red jacket
Issued:	1996 - 1997

Doulton Number	Price			
	U.S. $	Can. $	U.K. £	Aust. $
DBR9	35.00	45.00	20.00	50.00

Royal Doulton
Susan Bunnykins
Wildlife spotting
DBR10/ *3548*
© 1996 Royal Doulton
Made in China

DBR10
SUSAN BUNNYKINS
WILDLIFE SPOTTING™

Designer:	Unknown
Modeller:	Unknown
Height:	2 ¾", 7.0 cm
Colour:	White dress with blue flowers, brown basket
Issued:	1996 - 1997

Doulton	Price			
Number	U.S. $	Can. $	U.K. £	Aust. $
DBR10	25.00	35.00	15.00	35.00

DBR11
SUSAN AND HARRY BUNNYKINS
MINDING THE BABY BROTHER™

Designer:	Unknown
Modeller:	Unknown
Height:	2 ½", 6.4 cm
Colour:	Susan - white dress with blue flowers
	Harry - pale blue pyjamas, multicoloured toys
Issued:	1996 - 1997

Doulton	Price			
Number	U.S. $	Can. $	U.K. £	Aust. $
DBR11	35.00	45.00	20.00	50.00

DBR12
FATHER BUNNYKINS AND HARRY
DECORATING THE TREE™

Designer:	Unknown
Modeller:	Unknown
Height:	4", 10.1 cm
Colour:	Father - blue trousers, white shirt and red pullover
	Harry - white pyjamas, green tree
Issued:	1996 - 1997

Doulton	Price			
Number	U.S. $	Can. $	U.K. £	Aust. $
DBR12	50.00	65.00	30.00	70.00

DBR13
MRS. BUNNYKINS AND WILLIAM
THE BIRTHDAY CAKE™

Designer:	Unknown
Modeller:	Unknown
Height:	3 ¼", 8.3 cm
Colour:	White dress with blue flowers, light yellow apron, red jacket, white shirt and brown trousers
Issued:	1996 - 1997

Doulton	Price			
Number	U.S. $	Can. $	U.K. £	Aust. $
DBR13	35.00	45.00	20.00	45.00

DBR14
HAPPY CHRISTMAS FROM THE
BUNNYKINS FAMILY™

Designer:	Unknown
Modeller:	Unknown
Height:	6", 15.0 cm
Colour:	Multi-coloured
Issued:	1996 - 1997
Series:	Music Box

Doulton	Price			
Number	U.S. $	Can. $	U.K. £	Aust. $
DBR14	150.00	200.00	95.00	200.00

DBR15
PICNIC TIME WITH THE
BUNNYKINS FAMILY™

Designer:	Unknown
Modeller:	Unknown
Height:	5", 12.7 cm
Colour:	Multi-coloured
Issued:	1996 - 1997
Series:	Music Box

Doulton	Price			
Number	U.S. $	Can. $	U.K. £	Aust. $
DBR15	150.00	200.00	95.00	200.00

DBR16
BIRTHDAY GIRL™

Designer:	Unknown
Modeller:	Unknown
Height:	1 ½", 4 cm
Colour:	Pink and white dress
Issued:	1997 - 1997

Doulton		Price		
Number	U.S.$	Can. $	U.K. £	Aust. $
DBR16	25.00	35.00	15.00	35.00

DBR17
BIRTHDAY BOY™

Designer:	Unknown
Modeller:	Unknown
Height:	1 ½", 4 cm
Colour:	Blue pyjamas, white bib
Issued:	1997 - 1997

Doulton		Price		
Number	U.S.$	Can. $	U.K. £	Aust. $
DBR17	25.00	35.00	15.00	35.00

DBR18
THE NEW BABY™

Designer:	Unknown
Modeller:	Unknown
Height:	3 ½", 8.9 cm
Colour:	Mother - white, lilac and rose
	Baby - light blue
Issued:	1997 - 1997

Doulton		Price		
Number	U.S. $	Can. $	U.K. £	Aust. $
DBR18	35.00	45.00	20.00	50.00

DBR19
THE ROCKING HORSE™

Designer:	Unknown
Modeller:	Unknown
Height:	2 ¾", 7.0 cm
Colour:	Brown bunny, red and white dress, white horse
Issued:	1997 - 1997

Doulton		Price		
Number	U.S. $	Can. $	U.K. £	Aust. $
DBR19	35.00	45.00	20.00	45.00

INDICES

ALPHABETICAL INDEX TO BUNNYKINS TABLEWARE

NUMERICAL INDEX TO BUNNYKINS TABLEWARE

ALPHABETICAL INDEX TO
BUNNYKINS EARTHENWARE FIGURINES

NUMERICAL INDEX TO BUNNYKINS
EARTHENWARE FIGURINES

ALPHABETICAL INDEX TO BUNNYKINS RESIN FIGURINES

342

Royal Doulton Shops

ROYAL DOULTON SHOPS – CANADA

Calgary
Market Mall
C2 - 3625 Shaganappi Trail
NW, Calgary, AB
T3A 0E2

Cookstown
Cookstown Manufactures
Outlet, RR1, Cookstown,
ON L0L 1L0

Dartmouth
Micmac Mall, 21 Micmac
Dartmouth, NS B3A 4K7

Edmonton
West Edmonton Mall
8882 - 170th Street
Edmonton, AB T5T 3J7

Fredericton
Regent Mall
1381 Regent Street,
Fredericton, NB E3C 1A2

London
White Oaks Mall
1105 Wellington Road
London, ON N6E 1V4

Markham
Markville Shopping Centre
5000 Highway #7
Markham, ON
L3R 4M9

Pickering
Pickering Town Centre
1355 Kingston Road
Pickering, ON L1V 1B8

Surrey
Guildford Town Centre
Surrey, BC V3R 7C1

Toronto
Fairview Mall
1800 Sheppard Avenue East
Willowdale, ON M2J 5A7

Waterloo
St. Jacobs Factory Outlet
Mall, 25 Benjamin Road
Waterloo, ON N2V 2G8

Winnipeg
Polo Park Shopping Centre
1485 Portage Ave.
Winnipeg, MA R3G 0W4

ROYAL DOULTON SHOPS – UNITED STATES

Birch Run
Prime Outlets - Birch Run
12240 S. Beyer Rd., Suite E80
Birch Run, MI 48415

Burlington
Prime Outlets – Burlington
288 Fashion Way, Store #5
Burlington, WA 98233

Cabazon
Dester Hills Premium Outlets
48650 Seminole Dr.
Building C, Suite 152
Cabazon, CA 92230

Calhoun
Prime Outlets - Colhoun
455 Belwood Rd., Suite 20
Calhoun, GA 30701

Camarillo
Camarillo Premium Outlets
740 Ventura Blvd., Suite 530
Camarillo, CA 93010

Central Valley
Woodbury Common
Premium Outlets
161 Marigold Court
Central Valley, NY 10917

Conroe
Prime Outlets – Conroe
1111 League Line Rd.
Suite 112
Conroe, TX 77303

Dawsonville
North Georgia
Premium Outlets
800 Highway 400
Suite 250
Dawsonville, GA 30534

Ellenton
Gulf Coast Factory Stores
5501 Factory Shops Blvd.
Ellenton Fl 34222

Estero
Miromar Outlets
10801 Corkscrew Rd.
Suite 366, Estero, Fl
33928

Flemington
Liberty Village
Premium Outlets
34 Liberty Village
Flemington, NJ
08822

Gilroy
Premium Outlets – Gilroy
681 Leavesley Road
Suite B290, Gilroy CA 95020

Grove City
Prime Outlets at Grove City
1911 Leesburg-Grove City Rd.
Suite 210, P.O. Box 1014
Grove City, PA 16127

Jeffersonville
Ohio Factory Shops
8150 Factory Shops Blvd.
Jeffersonville, OH 43128

Kittery
Kittery Outlet Center
Route 1
Kittery, ME 03904-2505

Las Vegas
Belz Factory Outlet World
7400 Las Vegas Blvd. South
Suite 244
Las Vegas, NV 89123

Pigeon Forge
Belz Factory Outlet
2655 Teaster Lane, Suite 26
Pigeon Forge, TN 37683

Prince William
Potomac Mills
2700 Potomac Mills Circle
Suite 976
Prince William, VA
22192

San Marcos
Tanger Factory Outlet Centre
4015 Interstate 35 South
Suite 402
San Marcos, TX
78666

St. Augustine
Belz Factory Outlet World
500 Belz Outlet Blvd
Suite 80
St. Augustine, Fl 32084

Tannersville
The Crossings Outlet Center
1000 Rte 611, Suite A-23
Tannersville, PA 18372

Vacaville
Factory Stores at Vacaville
336 Nut Tree Rd.
Vacaville CA
95687

Visit our website at:
www.royaldoulton.com

Royal Doulton Shops

FACTORY SHOPS AND OUTLETS IN UK

Bridgend
Factory Outlet, Unit 66
Welsh Designer Outlet Village
Bridgend Shropshire
CF32 9SU

Burslem
Factory Shop, Nile Street
Burslem, Stoke-on-Trent
Staffordshire, ST6 2AJ

Colne
Factory Outlet
Boundary Mill Stores
Burnley Road
Colne, Lancashire
BB8 8LS

Dover
Factory Outlet, De Bradelei Wharf
Cambridge Road, Dover, Kent
CT17 9BY

Ellesmere Port
Factory Outlet, Unit 106
Cheshire Oaks, Kinsey Road
Ellesmere Port, Cheshire
L65 9LA

Fenton
Factory Shop
Distribution Centre
Victoria Road, Fenton
Stoke-on-Trent, Staffordshire
ST4 2PJ

Longton
Factory Shop, Regent Works
Lawley Street, Longton
Stoke-on-Trent, Staffordshire
ST3 1LZ

Stoke
Doulton & Company Outlet
Forge Lane, Etruria
Stoke-on-Trent, Staffordshire
ST1 5NN

Stourbridge
Factory Shop, Crystal Glass Centre
Churton House, Audnam
Stourbridge, West Midlands
DY8 4AJ

STORES IN UK

Blackpool
Lawleys, Unit 37
Houndshill Shopping Centre
Fylde, Blackpool, Lancashire
FY1 4HU

Carlisle
Lawleys
63 Castle Street, Carlisle
Cumbria, CA3 8SL

Chelmsford
Lawleys, 42 High Chelmer
Chelmsford, Essex
CM1 1XU

Derby
Lawleys
Edwards, 71 St. Peters Street
Derby, Derbyshire, DE1 2AB

Dudley
Doulton & Company, Unit 52
Merry Hill, Brierley Hill, Dudley
West Midlands, DY5 1SR

Eastbourne
Lawleys
220 Terminus Road
Eastbourne, East Sussex
BN21 3DF

Hereford
Lawleys, 19-21 Maylords Street
Maylord Shopping Centre
Hereford, Herefordshire
HR1 2DS

Peterborough
Lawleys, 7 Bridge Street
Peterborough, Cambridgeshire
PE1 1HJ

Reading
Lawleys
21 Queen Victoria Street
Reading, Berkshire, RG1 1SY